THIS BOOK, WHICH IS THE PROPERTY OF THE PROTESTANT SCHOOL BOARD
OF GREATER MONTREAL AND IS NOW ON LOAN TO THE PUPIL LAST NAMED
BELOW, MUST BE KEPT CLEAN AND FREE FROM ANY MARKS OR NOTATIONS.
IF LOST OR DAMAGED, A PENALTY WILL BE IMPOSED.

DATE	PUPIL'S NAME	ROOM NUMBER	CONDITION OF BOOK
74/75	Janet Humes	302	A
75-76	Gill Boone	105	A
76-77	Sandy Howey	304	A
77-78	MJN	306	B
78/79	Ken Stephen	306	B+
79/80	Bonnie McCunn	306	C

DORVAL HIGH SCHOOL
82-83 David Desjardins   306   D

Short Stories

An Anthology
for Secondary Schools

by
Edwin H. Sauer

and
Howard Mumford Jones

Holt, Rinehart and Winston, Inc.   New York

Cover photograph by Grunzweig of Photo Researchers, Inc.

The authors wish to thank the following authors, publishers, and other holders of copyright for permission to use copyrighted materials.

The Bodley Head Ltd. and The Viking Press for "Sredni Vashtar" from *The Complete Short Stories of Saki* by H. H. Munro (Saki).

Mary Deasy for "The High Hill" by Mary Deasy.

Farrar, Straus and Cudahy, Inc. for "After You, My Dear Alphonse" from *The Lottery* by Shirley Jackson, Copyright 1943, 1949, by Shirley Jackson.

Harcourt, Brace and World, Inc. for "A Visit of Charity" from *A Curtain of Green and Other Stories* by Eudora Welty, Copyright 1941 by Eudora Welty. Also for "He" from *Flowering Judas and Other Stories* by Katherine Ann Porter, Copyright 1930, 1935, Copyright 1958, by Katherine Ann Porter.

Alfred A. Knopf, Inc. for "The Open Boat" by Stephen Crane. Reprinted from *Stephen Crane: An Omnibus* by Robert Wooster Stallman, Copyright 1952, by Alfred A. Knopf, Inc.

J. B. Lippincott Company for "Madam Le Gimp" from *Guys and Dolls* by Damon Runyon, Copyright 1930, Copyright 1957, by Damon Runyon Jr. and Mary Runyon McCann.

Harold Matson Company for "Footfalls" by Wilbur Daniel Steele, Copyright 1929, by Wilbur Daniel Steele.

Harold Ober Associates, Inc. for "I'm a Fool" from *Horses and Men* by Sherwood Anderson, published by B. W. Huebsch 1934. Copyright 1924, 1952, by Eleanor Anderson.

Random House, Inc. for "Two Soldiers" from *Collected Stories of William Faulkner,* Copyright 1942, by Curtis Publishing Company. Also for "The Portable Phonograph" from *The Watchful Gods and Other Short Stories* by Walter Van Tilburg Clark, Copyright 1941, by Walter Van Tilburg Clark.

iv

INTRODUCTION

The idea behind the preparation of this book was to collect thirty short stories which, though not written with young readers exclusively in mind, could nevertheless be read, understood, and enjoyed by them. In other words, these stories are serious adult literature which will appeal to high school readers.

Not all the stories will appeal to all readers equally, of course. Some are stories of action and suspense, some of character, some of humor, some of fantasy, and some of ideas, that is, stories which invite the reader to think out a problem. A few stories are a combination of these different types. Some are short and others are long; and, for their full meaning, some require more than merely one reading. Many of the stories are written in the third person, and many are written in the first, as if the author were talking directly to the reader. Some stories are about the past and some about events which could happen today. A few are stories in which time does not matter at all.

If there are so many varieties of the short story, how can one possibly say what a short story is? How can the form be defined in any way which will apply to all of the stories of this collection?

Possibly it cannot. Once when he was asked to define a short story, Robert Penn Warren, a modern author who has written some excellent short stories of his own, said, "A short story is a story that is shorter than another story." He was not trying to be amusing; he wanted to show the great range of fiction, and he wanted also to give some notion of how often the form has changed in its history.

A number of writers have, to be sure, attempted to say from time to time what a short story is—or, in their opinion, ought to be. Some, like Edgar Allan Poe, for example, have had elaborate theories about the form. But they were not able to convince many other writers; and, even while they were stating their ideas, other authors of equal or superior reputation were constructing excellent stories of an entirely different nature.

Generally speaking, one can say that because a story is short, it limits itself to a short period of time or covers a rather limited number of events or deals with only a few characters. Yet there are short stories which cover long periods of time, are crowded with action, and contain a large number of characters. In this collection an example of the former kind of story would be "Clay" by James Joyce; of the latter, "The Story of Bras-Coupé" by George Washington Cable.

A question the reader should attempt to answer is: what is the author trying to do or what does he want me to take from the story? This is not always an easy question to answer, as a few of the stories in this collection will probably demonstrate. Chiefly, of course, the writer wants us to consider some variety of human experience which has interested him. He may choose to do this in a number of ways, through—as has already been mentioned— action, humor, fantasy, character, or idea. As he considers the nature of the experience, he comes to a conclusion about how best to present it to his reader. The nature of his theme begins to determine the number of words. The story has to be just as long as an adequate treatment of his material will demand.

Some teachers of writing, in describing the construction of a short story, have suggested that the students think of the short story as one which has one dramatic *incident*. The novel or novelette, on the other hand, contains a series of dramatic incidents which build into a dramatic situation. The distinction is helpful to readers, but, again, there are exceptions to the two kinds.

The careful reader wants to know, first of all, what the story is saying to him—how true it is to what he knows about life or how greatly it extends his range of knowledge; whether or not it moves him and why; what he can say about it in bringing it to the attention of others so that they too, can share his pleasure. He may or may not want to know something about the author. But certainly, if he has greatly enjoyed a story, he will want to know about the author's other work. All these decisions are ones which the individual reader will make, depending on how greatly the story has affected him. To give sustained thought to the author's purpose, however, is generally not only to enjoy the story more but also to understand the art of it better.

All the stories in this collection were written by British or American writers—there are no stories by Continental or Asiatic authors. This is not because Continental or Asiatic stories are inferior; authors like Maupassant, Chekhov and Mann have been among the greatest writers of the short story in modern literature. The reason for avoiding the Continental and Asiatic stories was simply that of avoiding the many problems of translation. The translated story often becomes something quite different from the original.

The arrangement of the stories aims at nothing more than variety. The effort was to put together something for everybody—for both boys and girls; for readers who want "deep" literature and for those who want something "light"; for the reader of science fiction and the reader of mysteries. No attempt has been made to arrange the stories chronologically or according to nationality or according to the themes of the stories. Readers should rejoice in the variety, their first interest being the many ways in which the short story can present and interpret life. The short story can range from the profound seriousness of a story like "The Portable Phonograph" by Walter Van Tilburg Clark to the zany humor of "The Night the Ghost Got

In" by James Thurber, and the reader can take different kinds of delight from both.

There is a bias, however, to this collection, namely the belief that something is supposed to happen in a short story—or, to put the matter differently, that the story is supposed to get somewhere, to a point entirely observable to the reader, though it may do so quietly and unobtrusively. In many of the stories being written at the present time, one can notice a kind of aimlessness on the part of the author. If the story has a definite point to make, it is hidden under such a gauze of symbols, unexpressed feelings, and complicated dialogue that the reader is mystified and frustrated.

These short stories have been plotted—that is, their structure has been thought out. The shape of the story was not something effortless and casual: a lot of hard work had to be done. If the author is really successful, the reader may not be at all conscious of the labor which went into the story. The art of the story conceals its art. The reader who takes a deep impression from a short story, however, remembers that a human intelligence, through creative energy and careful judgment, made his enjoyment possible.

E. H. S.
H. M. J.

Cambridge, Massachusetts
December 1961

CONTENTS

CLAY

JAMES JOYCE

James Joyce is one of the most controversial figures in modern literature, mainly because his two long novels, *Ulysses* and *Finnegans Wake*, are very difficult. Joyce liked to use the "stream of consciousness" technique; the reader is taken inside the mind of a character, and the thoughts and sensations of the character are presented just as they would occur, that is, with no logic or coherence. Then, too, in *Ulysses* Joyce attempts to establish in his story of three people in Dublin, Ireland, in 1914 exact parallels with the events of *The Odyssey*. The reader has to be both informed and alert.

In his short stories, published under the title *Dubliners*, Joyce demonstrates a theory of the short story which has been much in practice in modern literature. At first glance nothing seems to happen. When the reader is finished, he feels cheated. There is no moment of strong dramatic action, or sharp, bold crisis. "Clay" is a very quiet story, indeed. What really does take place?

Joyce believed that a short story should work toward what he called a moment of "epiphany." He took this word from the Christian feast which celebrates the showing of the Christ child to the three wise men.

1

The term refers to a day of human condition [handwritten marginal notes]

The word means "a revelation" or a "showing forth." In Joyce's stories we arrive eventually at a moment when the central character, or a character related importantly to the central character, sees the real truth of his life. Usually he sees that reality is not at all what he imagined it was, and from that moment on he is a somewhat different person. This moment of epiphany is built up to through a series of events, usually presented in symbolic objects. In other words, from the beginning of the story we are being prepared for the revelation—in Joyce's use of light and shadow, in the objects of nature and everyday life, and especially in music, which Joyce loved.

"Clay" is a touching story about a plain, physically unattractive spinster who has worked hard all her life and takes her only moments of pleasure from visiting her brother and his family on holiday occasions, in this case, Hallowe'en. Joyce uses a game played in Ireland on this night (and probably at other times as well) to show us not only the drabness of Maria's life but also her brother's sudden awareness of it. What is the epiphany and when does it occur? What is the significance of Joyce's title? How are the game, the song, Maria's work, the occurrence with the "gentleman" on the tram, all woven together tightly to give us a moment of illumination? Contrary to first impression, this is a story in which a great deal takes place.

The matron had given her leave to go out as soon as the women's tea was over and Maria looked forward to her evening out. The kitchen was spick and span: the cook said you could see yourself in the big copper boilers. The fire was nice and bright and on one of the side-tables were four very big barmbracks[1]. These barmbracks seemed uncut; but if you went closer you would see that they had been cut into long thick even slices and were ready to be handed round at tea. Maria had cut them herself.

Maria was a very, very small person indeed but she had a very long nose and a very long chin. She talked a little through her nose, always soothingly: *"Yes, my dear,"* and *"No, my dear."* She was always sent for when the women quarreled over their tubs and always succeeded in making peace. One day the matron had said to her:

"Maria, you are a veritable peace-maker!"

And the sub-matron and two of the Board ladies had heard the compliment. And Ginger Mooney was always saying what she wouldn't do to the

[1]Barmbracks. Pastry, similar to coffee cake.

dummy who had charge of the irons if it wasn't for Maria. Everyone was
so fond of Maria.

The women would have their tea at six o'clock and she would be able
to get away before seven. From Ballsbridge to the Pillar, twenty minutes;
from the Pillar to Drumcondra, twenty minutes; and twenty minutes to buy
the things. She would be there before eight. She took out her purse with
the silver clasps and read again the words *A Present from Belfast.* She was
very fond of that purse because Joe had brought it to her five years before
when he and Alphy had gone to Belfast on a Whit-Monday[2] trip. In
the purse were two half-crowns and some coppers. She would have five
shillings clear after paying tram fare. What a nice evening they would have,
all the children singing! Only she hoped that Joe wouldn't come in drunk.
He was so different when he took any drink.

Often he had wanted her to go and live with them; but she would have
felt herself in the way (though Joe's wife was ever so nice with her) and
she had become accustomed to the life of the laundry. Joe was a good
fellow. She had nursed him and Alphy too; and Joe used often to say:

"Mamma is mamma but Maria is my proper mother."

After the break-up at home the boys had got her that position in the
Dublin by Lamplight laundry, and she liked it. She used to have such a bad
opinion of Protestants but now she thought they were very nice people, a
little quiet and serious, but still very nice people to live with. Then she had
her plants in the conservatory and she liked looking after them. She had
lovely ferns and wax-plants and, whenever anyone came to visit her, she
always gave the visitor one or two slips from her conservatory. There was one
thing she didn't like and that was the tracts[3] on the walks; but the matron
was such a nice person to deal with, so genteel.

When the cook told her everything was ready she went into the
women's room and began to pull the big bell. In a few minutes the women
began to come in by twos and threes, wiping their steaming hands in their
petticoats and pulling down the sleeves of their blouses over their red
steaming arms. They settled down before their huge mugs which the cook
and the dummy filled up with hot tea, already mixed with milk and sugar
in huge tin cans. Maria superintended the distribution of the barmbrack
and saw that every woman got her four slices. There was a great deal of
laughing and joking during the meal. Lizzie Fleming said Maria was sure

[2] Whit-Monday. A religious holiday, the fifteenth day after Easter, celebrated in Ireland.

[3] Tracts. Religious advice. In this case, of Protestant origin, and therefore upsetting to
Maria.

to get the ring and, though Fleming had said that for so many Hallow Eves[4], Maria had to laugh and say she didn't want any ring or man either; and when she laughed her grey-green eyes sparkled with disappointed shyness and the tip of her nose nearly met the tip of her chin. Then Ginger Mooney lifted her mug of tea and proposed Maria's health while all the other women clattered with their mugs on the table, and said she was sorry she hadn't a sup of porter[5] to drink it in. And Maria laughed again till the tip of her nose nearly met the tip of her chin and till her minute body nearly shook itself asunder because she knew that Mooney meant well though, of course, she had the notions of a common woman.

But wasn't Maria glad when the women had finished their tea and the cook and the dummy had begun to clear away the tea-things! She went into her little bedroom and, remembering that the next morning was a mass morning[6], changed the hand of the alarm from seven to six. Then she took off her working skirt and her house-boots and laid her best skirt out on the bed and her tiny dress-boots beside the foot of the bed. She changed her blouse too and, as she stood before the mirror, she thought of how she used to dress for mass on Sunday morning when she was a young girl; and she looked with quaint affection at the diminutive body which she had so often adorned. In spite of its years she found it a nice tidy little body.

When she got outside the streets were shining with rain and she was glad of her old brown waterproof. The tram was full and she had to sit on the little stool at the end of the car, facing all the people, with her toes barely touching the floor. She arranged in her mind all she was going to do and thought how much better it was to be independent and to have your own money in your pocket. She hoped they would have a nice evening. She was sure they would but she could not help thinking what a pity it was Alphy and Joe were not speaking. They were always falling out now but when they were boys together they used to be the best of friends: but such was life.

She got out of her tram at the Pillar and ferreted her way quickly among the crowds. She went into Downes's cake-shop but the shop was so full of people that it was a long time before she could get herself attended to. She bought a dozen of mixed penny cakes, and at last came out of the shop laden with a big bag. Then she thought what else would she buy: she wanted to buy something really nice. They would be sure to have plenty

---

[4] Hallow Eves. Hallowe'en, in America.

[5] Porter. A thick dark beer.

[6] Mass morning. The first of November is the Feast of All Saints, when the faithful must attend mass.

of apples and nuts. It was hard to know what to buy and all she could think of was cake. She decided to buy some plumcake but Downes's plumcake had not enough almond icing on top of it so she went over to a shop in Henry Street. Here she was a long time in suiting herself and the stylish young lady behind the counter, who was evidently a little annoyed by her, asked her was it wedding-cake she wanted to buy. That made Maria blush and smile at the young lady; but the young lady took it all very seriously and finally cut a thick slice of plumcake, parcelled it up and said:

"Two-and-four, please."

She thought she would have to stand in the Drumcondra tram because none of the young men seemed to notice her but an elderly gentleman made room for her. He was a stout gentleman and he wore a brown hard hat; he had a square red face and a greyish moustache. Maria thought he was a colonel-looking gentleman and she reflected how much more polite he was than the young men who simply stared straight before them. The gentleman began to chat with her about Hallow Eve and the rainy weather. He supposed the bag was full of good things for the little ones and said it was only right that the youngsters should enjoy themselves while they were young. Maria agreed with him and favoured him with demure nods and hems. He was very nice with her, and when she was getting out at the Canal Bridge she thanked him and bowed, and he bowed to her and raised his hat and smiled agreeably; and while she was going up along the terrace, bending her tiny head under the rain, she thought how easy it was to know a gentleman even when he has a drop taken.

Everybody said: "*O, here's Maria!*" when she came to Joe's house. Joe was there, having come home from business, and all the children had their Sunday dresses on. There were two big girls in from next door and games were going on. Maria gave the bag of cakes to the eldest boy, Alphy, to divide and Mrs. Donnelly said it was too good of her to bring such a big bag of cakes and made all the children say:

"Thanks, Maria."

But Maria said she had brought something special for papa and mamma, something they would be sure to like, and she began to look for her plumcake. She tried in Downes's bag and then in the pockets of her waterproof and then on the hallstand but nowhere could she find it. Then she asked all the children had any of them eaten it—by mistake, of course— but the children all said no and looked as if they did not like to eat cakes if they were to be accused of stealing. Everybody had a solution for the mystery and Mrs. Donnelly said it was plain that Maria had left it behind on the tram. Maria, remembering how confused the gentleman with the greyish moustache had made her, coloured with shame and vexation and disappointment. At the thought of the failure of her little surprise and of the two and fourpence she had thrown away for nothing she nearly cried outright.

But Joe said it didn't matter and made her sit down by the fire. He was very nice with her. He told her all that went on in his office, repeating for her a smart answer which he had made to the manager. Maria did not understand why Joe laughed so much over the answer he had made but she said that the manager must have been a very overbearing person to deal with. Joe said he wasn't so bad when you knew how to take him, that he was a decent sort so long as you didn't rub him the wrong way. Mrs. Donnelly played the piano for the children and they danced and sang. Then the two next-door girls handed round the nuts. Nobody could find the nutcrackers and Joe was nearly getting cross over it and asked how did they expect Maria to crack nuts without a nutcracker. But Maria said she didn't like nuts and that they weren't to bother about her. Then Joe asked would she take a bottle of stout[7] and Mrs. Donnelly said there was port wine too in the house if she would prefer that. Maria said she would rather they didn't ask her to take anything: but Joe insisted.

So Maria let him have his way and they sat by the fire talking over old times and Maria thought she would put in a good word for Alphy. But Joe cried that God might strike him stone dead if ever he spoke a word to his brother again and Maria said she was sorry she had mentioned the matter. Mrs. Donnelly told her husband it was a great shame for him to speak that way of his own flesh and blood but Joe said that Alphy was no brother of his and there was nearly being a row on the head of it. But Joe said he would not lose his temper on account of the night it was and asked his wife to open some more stout. The two next-door girls had arranged some Hallow Eve games and soon everything was merry again. Maria was delighted to see the children so merry and Joe and his wife in such good spirits. The next-door girls put some saucers on the table and then led the children up to the table, blindfold. One got the prayer-book and the other three got the water; and when one of the next-door girls got the ring Mrs. Donnelly shook her finger at the blushing girl as much as to say: *O, I know all about it!* They insisted then on blindfolding Maria and leading her up to the table to see what she would get; and, while they were putting on the bandage, Maria laughed and laughed again till the tip of her nose nearly met the tip of her chin.

They led her up to the table amid laughing and joking and she put her hand out in the air as she was told to do. She moved her hand about

7 Stout. Another dark beer.

here and there in the air and descended on one of the saucers. She felt a soft wet substance with her fingers and was surprised that nobody spoke or took off her bandage. There was a pause for a few seconds; and then a great deal of scuffling and whispering. Somebody said something about the garden, and at last Mrs. Donnelly said something very cross to one of the next-door girls and told her to throw it out at once: that was no play. Maria understood that it was wrong that time and so she had to do it over again: and this time she got the prayer-book.

After that Mrs. Donnelly played Miss McCloud's Reel for the children and Joe made Maria take a glass of wine. Soon they were all quite merry again and Mrs. Donnelly said Maria would enter a convent before the year was out because she had got the prayer-book. Maria had never seen Joe so nice to her as he was that night, so full of pleasant talk and reminiscences. She said they were all very good to her.

At last the children grew tired and sleepy and Joe asked Maria would she not sing some little song before she went, one of the old songs. Mrs. Donnelly said "*Do, please, Maria!*" and so Maria had to get up and stand beside the piano. Mrs. Donnelly bade the children be quiet and listen to Maria's song. Then she played the prelude and said "*Now, Maria!*" and Maria, blushing very much, began to sing in a tiny quavering voice. She sang *I Dreamt that I Dwelt,* and when she came to the second verse she sang again:

> *I dreamt that I dwelt in marble halls*
> *With vassals and serfs at my side,*
> *And of all who assembled within those walls*
> *That I was the hope and the pride.*
>
> *I had riches too great to count; could boast*
> *Of a high ancestral name,*
> *But I also dreamt, which pleased me most,*
> *That you loved me still the same*[8].

[8] Joyce does not quote the first stanza quite correctly. The second stanza is the point:

> I dream'd that suitors besought my hand,
>   That Knights upon bended knee
> And with vows no maiden heart could withstand,
>   That they pledg'd their faith to me.
> And I dream'd that one of this noble host
>   Came forth my hand to claim;
> Yet I also dream'd which charm'd me most
>   That you lov'd me still the same.

The words were written by Alfred Bunn.

But no one tried to show her her mistake; and when she had ended her song Joe was very much moved. He said that there was no time like the long ago and no music for him like poor old Balfe, whatever other people might say; and his eyes filled up so much with tears that he could not find what he was looking for and in the end he had to ask his wife to tell him where the corkscrew was.

STUDY QUESTIONS

1. Maria's position in life is a very lowly one, and yet she has managed to turn it into one of some dignity. How has she done this? What is the nature of her relationship to the other women who work in the laundry?

2. Find evidence in the story of these three themes: marriage, family relationships, good manners.

3. What is important about the fact that the plate of clay was placed in front of Maria by one of the neighbor girls?

4. What is the significance of the fact that Maria does not sing the second verse of "I Dreamt I Dwelt in Marble Halls?"

5. Why does Joe cry?

6. Do you think the evening's experience has made any deep impression on Maria, that is, do you think it will affect her life in any way? Why or why not?

7. Will Maria be quite as eager to visit her brother and his family on a later holiday occasion, say, Christmas? Why or why not?

THE OPEN BOAT

A tale intended to be after the fact. Being the experience of four men from the sunk steamer "Commodore."

STEPHEN CRANE

Stephen Crane wrote both fiction and poetry. He is probably best known for his novel *The Red Badge of Courage*, a story of the experiences of a young soldier in the Civil War. Crane was not born until 1871, six years after the Civil War ended, but his novel is considered realistically accurate. In *The Red Badge of Courage* war is an ugly, terrifying business, without the glamor and romance which earlier writers had given it.

Crane lived a very short life. He died of tuberculosis when he was only twenty-eight years old. He was born in Newark, New Jersey, and briefly attended Lafayette College and Syracuse University, but there is probably little relation between his formal schooling and his writing. Like many other modern authors, he was a newspaper reporter, and he was sent at various times to cover events in the West, in Cuba, and in Greece. He read constantly and was particularly impressed by the novels of the Russian writer, Tolstoy.

"The Open Boat," like other stories of Crane, presents a sharp, ironic contrast. Four men in an open boat are in danger of losing their lives, yet they are so near shore, where other people can see them clearly, that rescue would seem a very easy matter. Crane's point is that moments of acute crisis often occur in the routine of everyday life, when no one is aware that anything out of the ordinary is going on. So it is also in *The Red Badge of Courage*. War gets to be tedious and humdrum, and what passes for courage and bravery are merely accidental occurrences.

The four characters of "The Open Boat" are quite different people, and Crane shows us the various ways they react to danger. The story is based on a real event, of which Crane actually wrote a newspaper account. "The Open Boat," however, is more than journalism. What did Crane add to lift it above mere newspaper reporting? How does he involve the reader in a more active way than a newspaper story would do? "The Open Boat" has been called a "nearly perfect story." Upon what qualities of the story would this judgment seem to be based?

I

None of them knew the color of the sky. Their eyes glanced level, and were fastened upon the waves that swept toward them. These waves were of the hue of slate, save for the tops, which were of foaming white, and all of the men knew the colors of the sea. The horizon narrowed and widened, and dipped and rose, and at all times its edge was jagged with waves that seemed thrust up in points like rocks. Many a man ought to have a bathtub larger than the boat which here rode upon the sea. These waves were most wrongfully and barbarously abrupt and tall, and each froth-top was a problem in small-boat navigation.

The cook squatted in the bottom and looked with both eyes at the six inches of gunwale which separated him from the ocean. His sleeves were rolled over his fat forearms, and the two flaps of his unbuttoned vest dangled as he bent to bail out the boat. Often he said: "Gawd! That was a narrow clip." As he remarked it he invariably gazed eastward over the broken sea.

The oiler, steering with one of the two oars in the boat, sometimes raised himself suddenly to keep clear of water that swirled in over the stern. It was a thin little oar and it seemed often ready to snap.

The correspondent, pulling at the other oar, watched the waves and wondered why he was there.

The injured captain, lying in the bow, was at this time buried in that profound dejection and indifference which comes, temporarily at least, to even the bravest and most enduring when, willy nilly, the firm fails, the army loses, the ship goes down. The mind of the master of a vessel is rooted deep in the timbers of her, though he commands for a day or a decade, and this captain had on him the stern impression of a scene in the greys of dawn of seven turned faces, and later a stump of a top-mast with a white ball on it that slashed to and fro at the waves, went low and lower, and down. Thereafter there was something strange in his voice. Although steady, it was deep with mourning, and of a quality beyond oration or tears.

"Keep 'er a little more south, Billie," said he.

" 'A little more south,' sir" said the oiler in the stern.

A seat in this boat was not unlike a seat upon a bucking broncho, and by the same token, a broncho is not much smaller. The craft pranced and reared, and plunged like an animal. As each wave came, and she rose for it, she seemed like a horse making at a fence outrageously high. The manner of her scramble over these walls of water is a mystic thing, and, moreover, at the top of them were ordinarily these problems in white water, the foam racing down from the summit of each wave, requiring a new leap, and a leap from the air. Then, after scornfully bumping a crest, she would slide, and race, and splash down a long incline, and arrive bobbing and nodding in front of the next menace.

A singular disadvantage of the sea lies in the fact that after success-fully surmounting one wave you discover that there is another behind it just as important and just as nervously anxious to do something effective in the way of swamping boats. In a ten-foot dinghy one can get an idea of the resources of the sea in the line of waves that is not probable to the average experience, which is never at sea in a dinghy. As each slatey wall of water approached, it shut all else from the view of the men in the boat, and it was not difficult to imagine that this particular wave was the final outburst of the ocean, the last effort of the grim water. There was a terrible grace in the move of the waves, and they came in silence, save for the snarling of the crests.

In the wan light, the faces of the men must have been grey. Their eyes must have glinted in strange ways as they gazed steadily astern. Viewed from a balcony, the whole thing would doubtless have been weirdly pictur-esque. But the men in the boat had no time to see it, and if they had had leisure there were other things to occupy their minds. The sun swung stead-ily up the sky, and they knew it was broad day because the color of the sea changed from slate to emerald-green, streaked with amber lights, and the foam was like tumbling snow. The process of the breaking day was unknown to them. They were aware only of this effect upon the color of the waves that rolled toward them.

In disjointed sentences the cook and the correspondent argued as to the difference between a life-saving station and a house of refuge. The cook had said: "There's a house of refuge just north of the Mosquito Inlet Light, and as soon as they see us, they'll come off in their boat and pick us up."

"As soon as who see us?" said the correspondent.

"The crew," said the cook.

"Houses of refuge don't have crews," said the correspondent. "As I understand them, they are only places where clothes and grub are stored for the benefit of shipwrecked people. They don't carry crews."

"Oh, yes, they do," said the cook.

"No, they don't," said the correspondent.

"Well, we're not there yet, anyhow," said the oiler, in the stern.

"Well," said the cook, "perhaps it's not a house of refuge that I'm thinking of as being near Mosquito Inlet Light. Perhaps it's a life-saving station."

"We're not there yet," said the oiler, in the stern.

II

As the boat bounced from the top of each wave, the wind tore through the hair of the hatless men, and as the craft plopped her stern down again the spray splashed past them. The crest of each of these waves was a hill, from the top of which the men surveyed, for a moment, a broad tumultuous expanse, shining and wind-riven. It was probably splendid. It was probably glorious, this play of the free sea, wild with lights of emerald and white and amber.

"Bully good thing it's an on-shore wind," said the cook. "If not, where would we be? Wouldn't have a show."

"That's right," said the correspondent.

The busy oiler nodded his assent.

Then the captain, in the bow, chuckled in a way that expressed humor, contempt, tragedy, all in one. "Do you think we've got much of a show now, boys?" said he.

Whereupon the three were silent, save for a trifle of hemming and hawing. To express any particular optimism at this time they felt to be childish and stupid, but they all doubtless possessed this sense of the situation in their minds. A young man thinks doggedly at such times. On the other hand, the ethics of their condition was decidedly against any open suggestion of hopelessness. So they were silent.

"Oh, well," said the captain, soothing his children, "we'll get ashore all right."

But there was that in his tone which made them think, so the oiler quoth: "Yes! If this wind holds!"

The cook was bailing: "Yes! If we don't catch hell in the surf."

Canton flannel gulls flew near and far. Sometimes they sat down on the sea, near patches of brown seaweed that rolled on the waves with a movement like carpets on a line in a gale. The birds sat comfortably in groups, and they were envied by some in the dinghy, for the wrath of the sea was no more to them than it was to a covey of prairie chickens a thousand miles inland. Often they came very close and stared at the men with black bead-like eyes. At these times they were uncanny and sinister in their unblinking scrutiny, and the men hooted angrily at them, telling them to be gone. One came, and evidently decided to alight on the top of the captain's head. The bird flew parallel to the boat and did not circle, but made short sidelong jumps in the air in chicken-fashion. His black eyes were wistfully fixed upon the captain's head. "Ugly brute," said the oiler to the bird. "You look as if you were made with a jack-knife." The cook and the correspondent swore darkly at the creature. The captain naturally wished to knock it away with the end of the heavy painter; but he did not dare do it, because anything resembling an emphatic gesture would have capsized this freighted boat, and so with his open hand, the captain gently and carefully waved the gull away. After it had been discouraged from the pursuit the captain breathed easier on account of his hair, and others breathed easier because the bird struck their minds at this time as being somehow gruesome and ominous. In the meantime the oiler and the correspondent rowed. And also they rowed.

They sat together in the same seat, and each rowed an oar. Then the oiler took both oars; then the correspondent took both oars; then the oiler; then the correspondent. They rowed and they rowed. The very ticklish part of the business was when the time came for the reclining one in the stern to take his turn at the oars. By the very last star of truth, it is easier to steal eggs from under a hen than it was to change seats in the dinghy. First the man in the stern slid his hand along the thwart and moved with care, as if he were of Sèvres. Then the man in the rowing seat slid his hand along the other thwart. It was all done with the most extraordinary care. As the two sidled past each other, the whole party kept watchful eyes on the coming wave, and the captain cried: "Look out now! Steady there!"

The brown mats of seaweed that appeared from time to time were like islands, bits of earth. They were traveling, apparently, neither one way nor the other. They were, to all intents, stationary. They informed the men in the boat that it was making progress slowly toward the land.

The captain, rearing cautiously in the bow, after the dinghy soared on a great swell, said that he had seen the lighthouse at Mosquito Inlet. Presently the cook remarked that he had seen it. The correspondent was at the oars then, and for some reason he too wished to look at the lighthouse, but his back was toward the far shore and the waves were important, and for some time he could not seize an opportunity to turn his head. But at last there came a wave more gentle than the others, and when at the crest of it he swiftly scoured the western horizon.

"See it?" said the captain.

"No," said the correspondent slowly, "I didn't see anything."

"Look again," said the captain. He pointed. "It's exactly in that direction."

At the top of another wave, the correspondent did as he was bid, and this time his eyes chanced on a small still thing on the edge of the swaying horizon. It was precisely like the point of a pin. It took an anxious eye to find a lighthouse so tiny.

"Think we'll make it, captain?"

"If this wind holds and the boat don't swamp, we can't do much else," said the captain.

The little boat, lifted by each towering sea, and splashed viciously by the crests, made progress that in the absence of seaweed was not apparent to those in her. She seemed just a wee thing wallowing, miraculously top-up, at the mercy of five oceans. Occasionally, a great spread of water, like white flames, swarmed into her.

"Bail her, cook," said the captain serenely.

"All right, captain," said the cheerful cook.

III

It would be difficult to describe the subtle brotherhood of men that was here established on the seas. No one said that it was so. No one mentioned it. But it dwelt in the boat, and each man felt it warm him. They were a captain, an oiler, a cook, and a correspondent, and they were friends, friends in a more curiously iron-bound degree than may be common. The hurt captain, lying against the water-jar in the bow, spoke always in a low voice and calmly, but he could never command a more ready and swiftly obedient crew than the motley three of the dinghy. It was more than a mere recognition of what was best for the common safety. There was surely in it a quality that was personal and heartfelt. And after this devotion to the commander of the boat there was this comradeship that the correspondent, for instance, who had been taught to be cynical of men, knew even at the time was the best experience of his life. But no one said that it was so. No one mentioned it.

"I wish we had a sail," remarked the captain. "We might try my overcoat on the end of an oar and give you two boys a chance to rest." So the cook and the correspondent held the mast and spread wide the overcoat. The oiler steered, and the little boat made good way with her new rig. Sometimes the oiler had to scull sharply to keep a sea from breaking into the boat, but otherwise sailing was a success.

Meanwhile the lighthouse had been growing slowly larger. It had now almost assumed color, and appeared like a little grey shadow on the sky. The man at the oars could not be prevented from turning his head rather often to try for a glimpse of this little grey shadow.

At last, from the top of each wave the men in the tossing boat could see land. Even as the lighthouse was an upright shadow on the sky, this land seemed but a long black shadow on the sea. It certainly was thinner than paper. "We must be about opposite New Smyrna," said the cook, who had coasted this shore often in schooners. "Captain, by the way, I believe they abandoned that life-saving station there about a year ago."

"Did they?" said the captain.

The wind slowly died away. The cook and the correspondent were not now obliged to slave in order to hold high the oar. But the waves continued their old impetuous swooping at the dinghy, and the little craft, no longer under way, struggled woundily over them. The oiler or the correspondent took the oars again.

Shipwrecks are à propos of nothing. If men could only train for them and have them occur when the men had reached pink condition, there would be less drowning at sea. Of the four in the dinghy none had slept any time worth mentioning for two days and two nights previous to embarking in the dinghy, and in the excitement of clambering about the deck of a foundering ship they had also forgotten to eat heartily.

For these reasons, and for others, neither the oiler nor the correspondent was fond of rowing at this time. The correspondent wondered ingenuously how in the name of all that was sane could there be people who thought it amusing to row a boat. It was not an amusement; it was a diabolical punishment, and even a genius of mental aberrations could never conclude that it was anything but a horror to the muscles and a crime against the back. He mentioned to the boat in general how the amusement of rowing struck him, and the weary-faced oiler smiled in full sympathy. Previously to the foundering, by the way, the oiler had worked double-watch in the engineroom of the ship.

"Take her easy, now, boys," said the captain. "Don't spend yourselves. If we have to run a surf you'll need all your strength, because we'll sure have to swim for it. Take your time."

Slowly the land arose from the sea. From a black line it became a line of black and a line of white, trees and sand. Finally, the captain said that he could make out a house on the shore. "That's the house of refuge, sure," said the cook. "They'll see us before long, and come out after us."

The distant lighthouse reared high. "The keeper ought to be able to make us out now, if he's looking through a glass," said the captain. "He'll notify the life-saving people."

"None of those other boats could have got ashore to give word of the wreck," said the oiler, in a low voice. "Else the lifeboat would be out hunting us."

Slowly and beautifully the land loomed out of the sea. The wind came again. It had veered from the north-east to the south-east. Finally, a new sound struck the ears of the men in the boat. It was the low thunder of the surf on the shore. "We'll never be able to make the lighthouse now," said the captain. "Swing her head a little more north, Billie," said he.

" 'A little more north,' sir," said the oiler.

Whereupon the little boat turned her nose once more down the wind, and all but the oarsman watched the shore grow. Under the influence of this expansion doubt and direful apprehension was leaving the minds of the men. The management of the boat was still most absorbing, but it could not prevent a quiet cheerfulness. In an hour, perhaps, they would be ashore.

Their backbones had become thoroughly used to balancing in the boat, and they now rode this wild colt of a dinghy like circus men. The correspondent thought that he had been drenched to the skin, but happening to feel in the top pocket of his coat, he found therein eight cigars. Four of them were soaked with sea-water; four were perfectly scathless. After a search, somebody produced three dry matches, and thereupon the four waifs rode impudently in their little boat, and with an assurance of an impending rescue shining in their eyes, puffed at the big cigars and judged well and ill of all men. Everybody took a drink of water.

IV

"Cook," remarked the captain, "there don't seem to be any signs of life about your house of refuge."

"No," replied the cook. "Funny they don't see us!"

A broad stretch of lowly coast lay before the eyes of the men. It was of dunes topped with dark vegetation. The roar of the surf was plain, and sometimes they could see the white lip of a wave as it spun up the beach. A tiny house was blocked out black upon the sky. Southward, the slim lighthouse lifted its little grey length.

Tide, wind, and waves were swinging the dinghy northward. "Funny they don't see us," said the men.

The surf's roar was here dulled, but its tone was, nevertheless, thunderous and mighty. As the boat swam over the great rollers, the men sat listening to this roar. "We'll swamp sure," said everybody.

It is fair to say here that there was not a life-saving station within twenty miles in either direction, but the men did not know this fact, and in consequence they made dark and opprobrious remarks concerning the eyesight of the nation's life-savers. Four scowling men sat in the dinghy and surpassed records in the invention of epithets.

"Funny they don't see us."

The lightheartedness of a former time had completely faded. To their sharpened minds it was easy to conjure pictures of all kinds of incompetency and blindness and, indeed, cowardice. There was the shore of the populous land, and it was bitter and bitter to them that from it came no sign.

"Well," said the captain, ultimately, "I suppose we'll have to make a try for ourselves. If we stay out here too long, we'll none of us have strength left to swim after the boat swamps."

And so the oiler, who was at the oars, turned the boat straight for the shore. There was a sudden tightening of muscle. There was some thinking.

"If we don't all get ashore—" said the captain. "If we don't all get ashore, I suppose you fellows know where to send news of my finish?"

They then briefly exchanged some addresses and admonitions. As for the reflections of the men, there was a great deal of rage in them. Perchance they might be formulated thus: "If I am going to be drowned—if I am going to be drowned—if I am going to be drowned, why in the name of the seven mad gods who rule the sea, was I allowed to come thus far and

contemplate sand and trees? Was I brought here merely to have my nose
dragged away as I was about to nibble the sacred cheese of life? It is preposterous. If this old ninny-woman, Fate, cannot do better than this,
she should be deprived of the management of men's fortunes. She is an old
hen who knows not her intention. If she has decided to drown me, why did
she not do it in the beginning and save me all this trouble? The whole affair
is absurd. . . . But no, she cannot mean to drown me. She dare not drown
me. She cannot drown me. Not after all this work." Afterward the man
might have had an impulse to shake his fist at the clouds: "Just you drown
me, now, and then hear what I call you!"

The billows that came at this time were more formidable. They seemed
always just about to break and roll over the little boat in a turmoil of foam.
There was a preparatory and long growl in the speech of them. No mind
unused to the sea would have concluded that the dinghy could ascend these
sheer heights in time. The shore was still afar. The oiler was a wily surf-
man. "Boys," he said swiftly, "she won't live three minutes more, and
we're too far out to swim. Shall I take her to sea again, captain?"

"Yes! Go ahead!" said the captain.

This oiler, by a series of quick miracles, and fast and steady oarsman-
ship, turned the boat in the middle of the surf and took her safely to sea
again.

There was a considerable silence as the boat bumped over the furrowed sea to deeper water. Then somebody in gloom spoke. "Well, anyhow,
they must have seen us from the shore by now."

The gulls went in slanting flight up the wind toward the grey desolate
east. A squall, marked by dingy clouds, and clouds brick-red, like smoke
from a burning building, appeared from the south-east.

"What do you think of those life-saving people? Ain't they peaches?"

"Funny they haven't seen us."

"Maybe they think we're out here for sport! Maybe they think we're
fishin'. Maybe they think we're damned fools."

It was a long afternoon. A changed tide tried to force them southward,
but the wind and wave said northward. Far ahead, where coast-line, sea,
and sky formed their mighty angle, there were little dots which seemed to
indicate a city on the shore.

"St. Augustine?"

The captain shook his head. "Too near Mosquito Inlet."

And the oiler rowed, and then the correspondent rowed. Then the
oiler rowed. It was a weary business. The human back can become the seat
of more aches and pains than are registered in books for the compos-

ite anatomy of a regiment. It is a limited area, but it can become the
theatre of innumerable muscular conflicts, tangles, wrenches, knots, and
other comforts.

"Did you ever like to row, Billie?" asked the correspondent.

"No," said the oiler. "Hang it!"

When one exchanged the rowing-seat for a place in the bottom of the
boat, he suffered a bodily depression that caused him to be careless of
everything save an obligation to wiggle one finger. There was cold sea-
water swashing to and fro in the boat, and he lay in it. His head, pillowed
on a thwart, was within an inch of the swirl of a wave crest, and sometimes
a particularly obstreperous sea came in-board and drenched him once more.
But these matters did not annoy him. It is almost certain that if the boat
had capsized he would have tumbled comfortably out upon the ocean as if
he felt sure that it was a great soft mattress.

"Look! There's a man on the shore!"

"Where?"

"There! See 'im? See 'im?"

"Yes, sure! He's walking along."

"Now he's stopped. Look! He's facing us!"

"He's waving at us!"

"So he is! By thunder!"

"Ah, now we're all right! Now we're all right! There'll be a boat out
here for us in half-in-hour."

"He's going on. He's running. He's going up to that house there."

The remote beach seemed lower than the sea, and it required a searching
glance to discern the little black figure. The captain saw a floating stick and
they rowed to it. A bath-towel was by some weird chance in the boat, and,
tying this on the stick, the captain waved it. The oarsman did not dare turn
his head, so he was obliged to ask questions.

"What's he doing now?"

"He's standing still again. He's looking, I think. . . . There he goes
again. Toward the house. . . . Now he's stopped again."

"Is he waving at us?"

"No, not now! He was, though."

"Look! There comes another man!"

"He's running."

"Look at him go, would you."

"Why, he's on a bicycle. Now he's met the other man. They're both
waving at us. Look!"

"There comes something up the beach."

"What the devil is that thing?"

"Why it looks like a boat."

"Why, certainly it's a boat."

"No, it's on wheels."

"Yes, so it is. Well, that must be the life-boat. They drag them along shore on a wagon."

"That's the life-boat, sure."

"No, by——, it's—it's an omnibus."

"I tell you it's a life-boat."

"It is not! It's an omnibus. I can see it plain. See? One of these big hotel omnibuses."

"By thunder, you're right. It's an omnibus, sure as fate. What do you suppose they are doing with an omnibus? Maybe they are going around collecting the life-crew, hey?"

"That's it, likely. Look! There's a fellow waving a little black flag. He's standing on the steps of the omnibus. There come those other two fellows. Now they're all talking together. Look at the fellow with the flag. Maybe he ain't waving it."

"That ain't a flag, is it? That's his coat. Why, certainly, that's his coat."

"So it is. It's his coat. He's taken it off and is waving it around his head. But would you look at him swing it."

"Oh, say, there isn't any life-saving station there. That's just a winter resort hotel omnibus that has brought over some of the boarders to see us drown."

"What's that idiot with the coat mean? What's he signaling, anyhow?"

"It looks as if he were trying to tell us to go north. There must be a life-saving station up there."

"No! He thinks we're fishing. Just giving us a merry hand. See? Ah, there, Willie!"

"Well, I wish I could make something out of those signals. What do you suppose he means?"

"He don't mean anything. He's just playing."

"Well, if he'd just signal us to try the surf again, or to go to sea and wait, or go north, or go south, or go to hell—there would be some reason in it. But look at him. He just stands there and keeps his coat revolving like a wheel. The ass!"

"There come more people."

"Now there's quite a mob. Look! Isn't that a boat?"

"Where? Oh, I see where you mean. No, that's no boat."

"That fellow is still waving his coat."

"He must think we like to see him do that. Why don't he quit it? It don't mean anything."

"I don't know. I think he is trying to make us go north. It must be that there's a life-saving station there somewhere."

"Say, he ain't tired yet. Look at 'im wave."

"Wonder how long he can keep that up. He's been revolving his coat ever since he caught sight of us. He's an idiot. Why aren't they getting men to bring a boat out? A fishing boat—one of those big yawls—could come out here all right. Why don't he do something?"

"Oh, it's all right, now."

"They'll have a boat out here for us in less than no time, now that they've seen us."

A faint yellow tone came into the sky over the low land. The shadows on the sea slowly deepened. The wind bore coldness with it, and the men began to shiver.

"Holy smoke!" said one, allowing his voice to express his impious mood, "if we keep on monkeying out here! If we've got to flounder out here all night!"

"Oh, we'll never have to stay here all night! Don't you worry. They've seen us now, and it won't be long before they'll come chasing out after us."

The shore grew dusky. The man waving a coat blended gradually into this gloom, and it swallowed in the same manner the omnibus and the group of people. The spray, when it dashed uproariously over the side, made the voyagers shrink and swear like men who were being branded.

"I'd like to catch the chump who waved the coat. I feel like soaking him one, just for luck."

"Why? What did he do?"

"Oh, nothing, but then he seemed so damned cheerful."

In the meantime the oiler rowed, and then the correspondent rowed, and then the oiler rowed. Grey-faced and bowed forward, they mechanically, turn by turn, plied the leader oars. The form of the lighthouse had vanished from the southern horizon, but finally a pale star appeared, just lifting from the sea. The streaked saffron in the west passed before the all-merging darkness, and the sea to the east was black. The land had vanished, and was expressed only by the low and drear thunder of the surf.

"If I am going to be drowned—if I am going to be drowned—if I am going to be drowned, why, in the name of the seven mad gods who rule the

sea, was I allowed to come thus far and contemplate sand and trees? Was I
brought here merely to have my nose dragged away as I was about to nibble
the sacred cheese of life?"

The patient captain, drooped over the water-jar, was sometimes obliged
to speak to the oarsman.

"Keep her head up! Keep her head up!"

" 'Keep her head up,' sir." The voices were weary and low.

This was surely a quiet evening. All save the oarsman lay heavily and
listlessly in the boat's bottom. As for him, his eyes were just capable of
noting the tall black waves that swept forward in a most sinister silence, save
for an occasional subdued growl of a crest.

The cook's head was on a thwart, and he looked without interest at the
water under his nose. He was deep in other scenes. Finally he spoke.
"Billie," he murmured, dreamfully, "what kind of pie do you like best?"

V

"Pie," said the oiler and the correspondent, agitatedly. "Don't talk about
those things, blast you!"

"Well," said the cook, "I was just thinking about ham sandwiches
and—"

A night on the sea in an open boat is a long night. As darkness
settled finally, the shine of the light, lifting from the sea in the south,
changed to full gold. On the northern horizon a new light appeared, a small
bluish gleam on the edge of the waters. These two lights were the furniture
of the world. Otherwise there was nothing but waves.

Two men huddled in the stern, and distances were so magnificent in the
dinghy that the rower was enabled to keep his feet partly warmed by
thrusting them under his companions. Their legs indeed extended far under
the rowing-seat until they touched the feet of the captain forward. Sometimes, despite the efforts of the tired oarsman, a wave came piling into the
boat, an icy wave of the night, and the chilling water soaked them anew.
They would twist their bodies for a moment and groan, and sleep the dead
sleep once more, while the water in the boat gurgled about them as the craft
rocked.

The plan of the oiler and the correspondent was for one to row until
he lost the ability, and then arouse the other from his sea-water couch in
the bottom of the boat.

The oiler plied the oars until his head drooped forward, and the overpowering sleep blinded him. And he rowed yet afterward. Then he touched

a man in the bottom of the boat, and called his name. "Will you spell me for a little while?" he said, meekly.

"Sure, Billie," said the correspondent, awakening and dragging himself to a sitting position. They exchanged places carefully, and the oiler, cuddling down in the sea-water at the cook's side, seemed to go to sleep instantly.

The particular violence of the sea had ceased. The waves came without snarling. The obligation of the man at the oars was to keep the boat headed so that the tilt of the rollers would not capsize her, and to preserve her from filling when the crests rushed past. The black waves were silent and hard to be seen in the darkness. Often one was almost upon the boat before the oarsman was aware.

In a low voice the correspondent addressed the captain. He was not sure that the captain was awake, although this iron man seemed to be always awake. "Captain, shall I keep her making for that light north, sir?"

The same steady voice answered him. "Yes. Keep it about two points off the port bow."

The cook had tied a life-belt around himself in order to get even the warmth which this clumsy cork contrivance could donate, and he seemed almost stove-like when a rower, whose teeth invariably chattered wildly as soon as he ceased his labor, dropped down to sleep.

The correspondent, as he rowed, looked down at the two men sleeping under-foot. The cook's arm was around the oiler's shoulders, and, with their fragmentary clothing and haggard faces, they were the babes of the sea, a grotesque rendering of the old babes in the wood.

Later he must have grown stupid at his work, for suddenly there was a growling of water, and a crest came with a roar and a swash into the boat, and it was a wonder that it did not set the cook afloat in his life-belt. The cook continued to sleep, but the oiler sat up, blinking his eyes and shaking with the new cold.

"Oh, I'm awful sorry, Billie," said the correspondent contritely.

"That's all right, old boy," said the oiler, and lay down again and was asleep.

Presently it seemed that even the captain dozed, and the correspondent thought that he was the one man afloat on all the oceans. The wind had a voice as it came over the waves, and it was sadder than the end.

There was a long, loud swishing astern of the boat, and a gleaming trail of phosphorescence, like blue flame, was furrowed on the black waters. It might have been made by a monstrous knife.

Then there came a stillness, while the correspondent breathed with the open mouth and looked at the sea.

Suddenly there was another swish and another long flash of bluish light, and this time it was alongside the boat, and might almost have been reached with an oar. The correspondent saw an enormous fin speed like a shadow through the water, hurling the crystalline spray and leaving the long glowing trail.

The correspondent looked over his shoulder at the captain. His face was hidden, and he seemed to be asleep. He looked at the babes of the sea. They certainly were asleep. So, being bereft of sympathy, he leaned a little way to one side and swore softly into the sea.

But the thing did not then leave the vicinity of the boat. Ahead or astern, on one side or the other, at intervals long or short, fled the long sparkling streak, and there was to be heard the *whirroo* of the dark fin. The speed and power of the thing was greatly to be admired. It cut the water like a gigantic and keen projectile.

The presence of this biding thing did not affect the man with the same horror that it would if he had been a picnicker. He simply looked at the sea dully and swore in an undertone.

Nevertheless, it is true that he did not wish to be alone. He wished one of his companions to awaken by chance and keep him company with it. But the captain hung motionless over the water-jar, and the oiler and the cook in the bottom of the boat were plunged in slumber.

VI

"If I am going to be drowned—if I am going to be drowned—if I am going to be drowned, why, in the name of the seven mad gods who rule the sea, was I allowed to come thus far and contemplate sand and trees?"

During this dismal night, it may be remarked that a man would conclude that it was really the intention of the seven mad gods to drown him, despite the abominable injustice of it. For it was certainly an abominable injustice to drown a man who had worked so hard, so hard. The man felt it would be a crime most unnatural. Other people had drowned at sea since galleys swarmed with painted sails, but still—

When it occurs to a man that nature does not regard him as important, and that she feels she would not maim the universe by disposing of him, he at first wishes to throw bricks at the temple, and he hates deeply the fact that there are no bricks and no temples. Any visible expression of nature would surely be pelleted with his jeers.

Then, if there be no tangible thing to hoot he feels, perhaps, the desire to confront a personification and indulge in pleas, bowed to one knee, and with hands supplicant, saying: "Yes, but I love myself."

A high cold star on a winter's night is the word he feels that she says to him. Thereafter he knows the pathos of his situation.

The men in the dinghy had not discussed these matters, but each had, no doubt, reflected upon them in silence and according to his mind. There was seldom any expression upon their faces save the general one of complete weariness. Speech was devoted to the business of the boat.

To chime the notes of his emotion, a verse mysteriously entered the correspondent's head. He had even forgotten that he had forgotten this verse, but it suddenly was in his mind.

"A soldier of the Legion lay dying in Algiers,
There was a lack of woman's nursing, there was dearth of woman's tears;
But a comrade stood beside him, and he took that comrade's hand,
And he said: 'I never more shall see my own, my native land.'"

In his childhood, the correspondent had been made acquainted with the fact that a soldier of the Legion lay dying in Algiers, but he had never regarded the fact as important. Myriads of his school-fellows had informed him of the soldier's plight, but the dinning had naturally ended by making him perfectly indifferent. He had never considered it his affair that a soldier of the Legion lay dying in Algiers, nor had it appeared to him as a matter for sorrow. It was less to him than the breaking of a pencil's point.

Now, however, it quaintly came to him as a human, living thing. It was no longer merely a picture of a few throes in the breast of a poet, meanwhile drinking tea and warming his feet at the grate; it was an actuality— stern, mournful, and fine.

The correspondent plainly saw the soldier. He lay on the sand with his feet out straight and still. While his pale left hand was upon his chest in an attempt to thwart the going of his life, the blood came between his fingers. In the far Algerian distance, a city of low square forms was set against a sky that was faint with the last sunset hues. The correspondent, plying the oars and dreaming of the slow and slower movements of the lips of the soldier, was moved by a profound and perfectly impersonal comprehension. He was sorry for the soldier of the Legion who lay dying in Algiers.

The thing which had followed the boat and waited had evidently grown bored at the delay. There was no longer to be heard the slash of the cut-water, and there was no longer the flame of the long trail. The light in the north still glimmered, but it was apparently no nearer to the boat. Sometimes the boom of the surf rang in the correspondent's ears, and he turned the craft seaward then and rowed harder. Southward, some one had evidently built a watch-fire on the beach. It was too low and too far to be seen, but it made a shimmering, roseate reflection upon the bluff back of it, and thus could be discerned from the boat. The wind came stronger, and sometimes a wave suddenly raged out like a mountain-cat, and there was to be seen the sheen and sparkle of a broken crest.

The captain, in the bow, moved on his water-jar and sat erect. "Pretty long night," he observed to the correspondent. He looked at the shore. "Those life-saving people take their time."

"Did you see that shark playing around?"

"Yes, I saw him. He was a big fellow, all right."

"Wish I had known you were awake."

Later the correspondent spoke into the bottom of the boat.

"Billie!" There was a slow and gradual disentanglement. "Billie, will you spell me?" "Sure," said the oiler.

As soon as the correspondent touched the cold comfortable sea-water in the bottom of the boat, and had huddled close to the cook's life-belt he was deep in sleep, despite the fact that his teeth played all the popular airs. This sleep was so good to him that it was but a moment before he heard a voice call his name in a tone that demonstrated the last stages of exhaustion. "Will you spell me?"

"Sure Billie."

The light in the north had mysteriously vanished, but the correspondent took his course from the wide-awake captain.

Later in the night they took the boat farther out to sea, and the captain directed the cook to take one oar at the stern and keep the boat facing the seas. He was to call out if he should hear the thunder of the surf. This plan enabled the oiler and the correspondent to get respite together. "We'll give those boys a chance to get into shape again," said the captain. They curled down and, after a few preliminary chatterings and trembles, slept once more the dead sleep. Neither knew they had bequeathed to the cook the company of another shark, or perhaps the same shark.

As the boat caroused on the waves, spray occasionally bumped over the side and gave them a fresh soaking, but this had no power to break their repose. The ominous slash of the wind and the water affected them as it would have affected mummies.

"Boys," said the cook, with the notes of every reluctance in his voice, "she's drifted in pretty close. I guess one of you had better take her to sea again." The correspondent, aroused, heard the crash of the toppled crests.

As he was rowing, the captain gave him some whisky-and-water, and this steadied the chills out of him. "If I ever get ashore and anybody shows me even a photograph of an oar—"

At last there was a short conversation.

"Billie. . . . Billie, will you spell me?"

"Sure," said the oiler.

When the correspondent again opened his eyes, the sea and the sky were each of the grey hue of the dawning. Later, carmine and gold was painted upon the waters. The morning appeared finally, in its splendor, with a sky of pure blue, and the sunlight flamed on the tips of the waves.

On the distant dunes were set many little black cottages, and a tall white windmill reared above them. No man, nor dog, nor bicycle appeared on the beach. The cottages might have formed a deserted village.

The voyagers scanned the shore. A conference was held in the boat. "Well," said the captain, "if no help is coming we might better try a run through the surf right away. If we stay out here much longer we will be too weak to do anything for ourselves at all." The others silently acquiesced in this reasoning. The boat was headed for the beach. The correspondent wondered if none ever ascended the tall wind-tower, and if then they never looked seaward. This tower was a giant, standing with its back to the plight of the ants. It represented in a degree, to the correspondent, the serenity of nature amid the struggles of the individual—nature in the wind, and nature in the vision of men. She did not seem cruel to him then, nor beneficent, nor treacherous, nor wise. But she was indifferent, flatly indifferent. It is, perhaps, plausible that a man in this situation, impressed with the uncern of the universe, should see the innumerable flaws of his life, and have them taste wickedly in his mind and wish for another chance. A distinction between right and wrong seems absurdly clear to him, then, in this new ignorance of the grave-edge, and he understands that if he were given another opportunity he would mend his conduct and his words, and be better and brighter during an introduction or at a tea.

"Now, boys," said the captain, "she is going to swamp, sure. All we can do is to work her in as far as possible, and then when she swamps, pile out and scramble for the beach. Keep cool now, and don't jump until she swamps sure."

The oiler took the oars. Over his shoulders he scanned the surf. "Captain," he said, "I think I'd better bring her about, and keep her head-on to the seas and back her in."

"All right, Billie," said the captain. "Back her in." The oiler swung the boat then and, seated in the stern, the cook and the correspondent were obliged to look over their shoulders to contemplate the lonely and indifferent shore.

The monstrous in-shore rollers heaved the boat high until the men were again enabled to see the white sheets of water scudding up the slanted beach. "We won't get in very close," said the captain. Each time a man could wrest his attention from the rollers, he turned his glance toward the shore, and in the expression of the eyes during this contemplation there was a singular quality. The correspondent, observing the others, knew that they were not afraid, but the full meaning of their glances was shrouded.

As for himself, he was too tired to grapple fundamentally with the fact. He tried to coerce his mind into thinking of it, but the mind was dominated at this time by the muscles, and the muscles said they did not care. It merely occurred to him that if he should drown it would be a shame.

There were no hurried words, no pallor, no plain agitation. The men simply looked at the shore. "Now, remember to get well clear of the boat when you jump," said the captain.

Seaward the crest of a roller suddenly fell with a thunderous crash, and the long white comber came roaring down upon the boat.

"Steady now," said the captain. The men were silent. They turned their eyes from the shore to the comber and waited. The boat slid up the incline, leaped at the furious top, bounced over it, and swung down the long back of the wave. Some water had been shipped and the cook bailed it out.

But the next crest crashed also. The tumbling, boiling flood of white water caught the boat and whirled it almost perpendicular. Water swarmed in from all sides. The correspondent had his hands on the gunwale at this time, and when the water entered at that place he swiftly withdrew his fingers, as if he objected to wetting them.

The little boat, drunken with this weight of water, reeled and snuggled deeper into the sea.

"Bail her out, cook! Bail her out," said the captain.

"All right, captain," said the cook.

"Now, boys, the next one will do for us, sure," said the oiler. "Mind to jump clear of the boat."

The third wave moved forward, huge, furious, implacable. It fairly swallowed the dinghy, and almost simultaneously the men tumbled into the

sea. A piece of lifebelt had lain in the bottom of the boat, and as the correspondent went overboard he held this to his chest with his left hand.

The January water was icy, and he reflected immediately that it was
colder than he had expected to find it on the coast of Florida. This appeared to
his dazed mind as a fact important enough to be noted at the time. The coldness of the water was sad; it was tragic. This fact was somehow so mixed
and confused with his opinion of his own situation that it seemed almost a
proper reason for tears. The water was cold.

When he came to the surface he was conscious of little but the noisy
water. Afterward he saw his companions in the sea. The oiler was ahead in
the race. He was swimming strongly and rapidly. Off to the correspondent's
left, the cook's great white and corked back bulged out of the water, and in
the rear the captain was hanging with his one good hand to the keel of the
overturned dinghy.

There is a certain immovable quality to a shore, and the correspondent
wondered at it amid the confusion of the sea.

It seemed also very attractive, but the correspondent knew that it was
a long journey, and he paddled leisurely. The piece of life-preserver
lay under him, and sometimes he whirled down the incline of a wave as if
he were on a hand-sled.

But finally he arrived at a place in the sea where travel was beset with
difficulty. He did not pause swimming to inquire what manner of current
had caught him, but there his progress ceased. The shore was set before him
like a bit of scenery on a stage, and he looked at it and understood with his
eyes each detail of it.

As the cook passed, much farther to the left, the captain was calling to
him, "Turn over on your back, cook! Turn over on your back and use
the oar."

"All right, sir." The cook turned on his back, and, paddling with an
oar, went ahead as if he were a canoe.

Presently the boat also passed to the left of the correspondent with the
captain clinging with one hand to the keel. He would have appeared like a
man raising himself to look over a board fence, if it were not for the extraordinary gymnastics of the boat. The correspondent marvelled that the captain could still hold to it.

They passed on, nearer to shore—the oiler, the cook, the captain—
and following them went the water-jar, bouncing gaily over the seas.

The correspondent remained in the grip of this strange new enemy—a
current. The shore, with its white slope of sand and its green bluff, topped
with little silent cottages, was spread like a picture before him. It was very

near to him then, but he was impressed as one who in a gallery looks at a scene from Brittany or Holland.

He thought: "I am going to drown? Can it be possible? Can it be possible? Can it be possible?" Perhaps an individual must consider his own death to be the final phenomenon of nature.

But later a wave perhaps whirled him out of this small, deadly current, for he found suddenly that he could again make progress toward the shore. Later still, he was aware that the captain, clinging with one hand to the keel of the dinghy, had his face turned away from the shore and toward him, and was calling his name. "Come to the boat! Come to the boat!"

In his struggle to reach the captain and the boat, he reflected that when one gets properly wearied, drowning must really be a comfortable arrangement, a cessation of hostilities accompanied by a large degree of relief, and he was glad of it, for the main thing in his mind for some months had been horror of the temporary agony. He did not wish to be hurt.

Presently he saw a man running along the shore. He was undressing with most remarkable speed. Coat, trousers, shirt, everything flew magically off him.

"Come to the boat," called the captain.

"All right, captain." As the correspondent paddled, he saw the captain let himself down to bottom and leave the boat. Then the correspondent performed his one little marvel of the voyage. A large wave caught him and flung him with ease and supreme speed completely over the boat and far beyond it. It struck him even then as an event in gymnastics, and a true miracle of the sea. An over-turned boat in the surf is not a plaything to a swimming man.

The correspondent arrived in water that reached only to his waist, but his condition did not enable him to stand for more than a moment. Each wave knocked him into a heap, and the under-tow pulled at him.

Then he saw the man who had been running and undressing, and undressing and running, come bounding into the water. He dragged ashore the cook, and then waded towards the captain, but the captain waved him away, and sent him to the correspondent. He was naked, naked as a tree in winter, but a halo was about his head, and he shone like a saint. He gave a strong pull, and a long drag, and a bully heave at the correspondent's hand. The correspondent, schooled in the minor formulae, said: "Thanks, old man." But suddenly the man cried: "What's that?" He pointed a swift finger. The correspondent said: "Go."

In the shallows, face downward, lay the oiler. His forehead touched sand that was periodically, between each wave, clear of the sea.

The correspondent did not know all that transpired afterward. When he achieved safe ground he fell, striking the sand with each particular part of his body. It was as if he had dropped from a roof, but the thud was grateful to him.

It seemed that instantly the beach was populated with men with blankets, clothes, and flasks, and women with coffeepots and all the remedies sacred to their minds. The welcome of the land to the men from the sea was warm and generous, but a still and dripping shape was carried slowly up the beach, and the land's welcome for it could only be the different and sinister hospitality of the grave.

When it came night, the white waves paced to and fro in the moonlight, and the wind brought the sound of the great sea's voice to the men on shore, and they felt that they could then be interpreters.

STUDY QUESTIONS:

1. The opening sentence of this story has often been commented upon. What is the significance of it? Why did these men not know the color of the sky?

2. Three of the men in the boat are professional seamen, the fourth, the correspondent, is not. What is Crane's point in making the fourth man so different? (Remember, of course, that the story is based on a true happening. Still authors often take liberties with truth. Why did Crane keep the original characters?)

3. Only one of the characters, the oiler, has a name—Billie. What does the anonymity of the other men add to the story? Why, for that matter, should Billie have a name?

4. Comment on the following passage: "When it occurs to a man that nature does not regard him as important, and that she feels she would not maim the universe by disposing of him, he at first wishes to throw bricks at the temple, and he hates deeply the fact that there are no bricks and no temples. Any visible expression of nature would scarcely be pelleted with his jeers.

"Then, if there be no tangible thing to hoot, he feels, perhaps, the desire to confront a personification and indulge in pleas, bowed to one knee, and with hands supplicant, saying, 'Yes, but I love myself.'

"A high cold star on a winter's night is the word he feels that she says to him. Thereafter he knows the pathos of his situation."

What is Crane saying here?

5. What is the special irony in the fact that it is the oiler who dies?

6. What is Crane's point in having the correspondent reflect that "perhaps an individual must consider his own death to be the final phenomenon of nature"?

THE UNDEFEATED

Ernest Hemingway, who died in 1961, was born in Oak Park, Illinois, in 1898. His father was a physician, who often took his son on hunting and fishing trips in northern Michigan. Hemingway was a man who liked to be near excitement, where men are required to face up to danger, for he believed that the test of manliness is the way a man behaves when confronted with the possibility of imminent death. He participated in and wrote about World War I, the Spanish Civil War (1935–38), and World War II. His favorite sports were bull fighting, big game hunting, deep sea fishing and skiing, sports that he often wrote about. In other words, he lived the kind of life he wrote about, celebrating strength, courage, and constant action. The qualities he disliked most were fear and sentimentality. Among his best known novels are *A Farewell to Arms* (1929), *For Whom the Bell Tolls* (1940), and *The Old Man and the Sea* (1952).

Hemingway's style has been much imitated by many other contemporary writers. It seems very much like ordinary speech; the thoughts of his characters are expressed naturally and plainly. An English critic, Bonamy Dobrée, had this to say about Hemingway's manner of writing: "Mr. Hemingway gets his effects largely by repetition and by using the simplest words and ideas. And, oddly enough, he gives the impression of being sentimental by the avoidance of the sentimental, by being as matter-of-fact as possible. His lines are very simple, and it is by saying the same thing over and over again that he impresses them on you." *vernacular* *newspaper review*

The situation presented in "The Undefeated" is a familiar one in modern life: after the popularity and skill of a once great sports figure are gone, what does he do? Manuel Garcia was once a public idol as a matador, but now he has to beg for a chance to enter the bull ring. When he does manage to get a fight, he does a miserable job. The fans boo him and even, as is the custom with bull-fight audiences when they are disappointed in a matador's performance, throw things into the ring. Manuel knows his failure and their displeasure, but in another way he seems insensitive to both. He has to carry on with what he was once good at. Is it in this sense that he is "undefeated"? Or is it that in his persistence and devotion he maintains real dignity, even though his greatness is gone?

Hemingway presents Manuel as a pitiable figure, but the reader respects him. Why? How do the other characters of the story feel about him? This is a story of paradoxes, of victory in defeat, of admiration and respect in failure. Manuel Garcia's catastrophe is really a triumph.

Manuel Garcia climbed the stairs to Don Miguel Retana's office. He set down his suitcase and knocked on the door. There was no answer. Manuel, standing in the hallway, felt there was someone in the room. He felt it through the door.

"Retana," he said, listening.

There was no answer.

He's there, all right, Manuel thought.

"Retana," he said and banged the door.

"Who's there?" said someone in the office.

"Me, Manolo," Manuel said.

"What do you want?" asked the voice.

"I want to work," Manuel said.

Something in the door clicked several times and it swung open. Manuel went in, carrying his suitcase.

A little man sat behind a desk at the far side of the room. Over his head was a bull's head, stuffed by a Madrid taxidermist; on the walls were framed photographs and bullfight posters.

The little man sat looking at Manuel.

"I thought they'd killed you," he said.

Manuel knocked with his knuckles on the desk. The little man sat looking at him across the desk.

"How many corridas'[1] you had this year?" Retana asked.

"One," he answered.

"Just that one?" the little man asked.

"That's all."

"I read about it in the papers," Retana said. He leaned back in the chair and looked at Manuel.

Manuel looked up at the stuffed bull. He had seen it often before. He felt a certain family interest in it. It had killed his brother, the promising one, about nine years ago. Manuel remembered the day. There was a brass plate on the oak shield the bull's head was mounted on. Manuel could not read it, but he imagined it was in memory of his brother. Well, he had been a good kid.

The plate said: "The Bull 'Mariposa' of the Duke of Veragua, which accepted 9 varas for 7 caballos[2], and caused the death of Antonio Garcia, Novillero, April 27, 1909."

Retana saw him looking at the stuffed bull's head.

"The lot the Duke sent me for Sunday will make a scandal," he said, "They're all bad in the legs. What do they say about them at the Café?"

"I don't know," Manuel said. "I just got in."

"Yes," Retana said. "You still have your bag."

He looked at Manuel, leaning back behind the big desk.

"Sit down," he said. "Take off your cap."

Manuel sat down; his cap off, his face was changed. He looked pale, and his coleta[3] pinned forward on his head, so that it would not show under the cap, gave him a strange look.

"You don't look well," Retana said.

"I just got out of the hospital," Manuel said.

"I heard they'd cut your leg off," Retana said.

"No," said Manuel. "It got all right."

Retana leaned forward across the desk and pushed a wooden box of cigarettes toward Manuel.

[1] Corridas. This word can mean either the bullring or the fight itself. Here, of course, it means the fight.

[2] 9 varas for 7 caballos. 9 shafts or pics for 7 horses. The picadors on horseback drive the metal shafts into the bulls. This bull disposed of seven horses.

[3] Coleta. The pig-tail that matadors wear.

"Have a cigarette," he said.

"Thanks."

Manuel lit it.

"Smoke?" he said, offering the match to Retana.

"No," Retana waved his hand, "I never smoke."

Retana watched him smoking.

"Why don't you get a job and go to work?" he said.

"I don't want to work," Manuel said. "I am a bullfighter."

"There aren't any bullfighters any more," Retana said.

"I'm a bullfighter," Manuel said.

"Yes, while you're in there," Retana said.

Manuel laughed.

Retana sat, saying nothing and looking at Manuel.

"I'll put you in a nocturnal if you want," Retana offered.

"When?" Manuel asked.

"Tomorrow night."

"I don't like to substitute for anybody," Manuel said. That was the way they all got killed. That was the way Salvator got killed. He tapped with his knuckles on the table.

"It's all I've got," Retana said.

"Why don't you put me on next week?" Manuel suggested.

"You wouldn't draw," Retana said. "All they want is Litri and Rubito and La Torre. Those kids are good."

"They'd come to see me get it," Manuel said, hopefully.

"No, they wouldn't. They don't know who you are any more."

"I've got a lot of stuff," Manuel said.

"I'm offering to put you on tomorrow night," Retana said. "You can work with young Hernandez and kill two novillos[4] after the Charlots."

"Whose novillos?" Manuel asked.

"I don't know. Whatever stuff they've got in the corrals. What the veterinaries won't pass in the daytime."

"I don't like to substitute," Manuel said.

"You can take it or leave it," Retana said. He leaned forward over the papers. He was no longer interested. The appeal that Manuel had made to him for a moment when he thought of the old days was gone. He would like to get him to substitute for Larita because he could get him cheaply. He could get others cheaply too. He would like to help him though. Still he had given him the chance. It was up to him.

[4] Novillos. Under-age or over-age bulls of low quality.

"How much do I get?" Manuel asked. He was still playing with the idea of refusing. But he knew he could not refuse.

"Two hundred and fifty pesetas," Retana said. He had thought of five hundred, but when he opened his mouth it said two hundred and fifty.

"You pay Villalta seven thousand," Manuel said.

"You're not Villalta," Retana said.

"I know it," Manuel said.

"He draws it, Manolo," Retana said in explanation.

"Sure," said Manuel. He stood up. "Give me three hundred, Retana."

"All right," Retana agreed. He reached in the drawer for a paper.

"Can I have fifty now?" Manuel asked.

"Sure," said Retana. He took a fifty-peseta note out of his pocketbook and laid it, spread out flat, on the table.

Manuel picked it up and put it in his pocket.

"What about a cuadrilla[5]?" he asked.

"There's the boys that always work for me nights," Retana said. "They're all right."

"How about picadors?" Manuel asked.

"They're not much," Retana admitted.

"I've got to have one good pic," Manuel said.

"Get him then," Retana said. "Go and get him."

"Not out of this," Manuel said. "I'm not paying for any cuadrilla out of sixty duros."

Retana said nothing but looked at Manuel across the big desk.

"You know I've got to have one good pic," Manuel said.

Retana said nothing but looked at Manuel from a long way off.

"It isn't right," Manuel said.

Retana was still considering him, leaning back in his chair, considering him from a long way away.

"There're the regular pics," he offered.

"I know," Manuel said. "I know your regular pics."

Retana did not smile. Manuel knew it was over.

"All I want is an even break," Manuel said reasoningly. "When I go out there I want to be able to call my shots on the bull. It only takes one good picador."

He was talking to a man who was no longer listening.

"If you want something extra," Retana said, "go and get it. There will

---

[5] Cuadrilla. Any one of the assistants to the matador.

be a regular cuadrilla out there. Bring as many of your own pics as you want. The charlotada[6] is over by 10:30."

"All right," Manuel said. "If that's the way you feel about it."

"That's the way," Retana said.

"I'll see you tomorrow night," Manuel said.

"I'll be out there," Retana said.

Manuel picked up his suitcase and went out.

"Shut the door," Retana called.

Manuel looked back. Retana was sitting forward and looking at some papers. Manuel pulled the door tight until it clicked.

He went down the stairs and out of the door into the hot brightness of the street. It was very hot in the street and the light on the white buildings was sudden and hard on his eyes. He walked down the shady side of the steep street toward the Puerta del Sol. The shade felt solid and cool as running water. The heat came suddenly as he crossed the intersecting streets. Manuel saw no one he knew in all the people he passed.

Just before the Puerta del Sol he turned into a café.

It was quiet in the café. There were a few men sitting at tables against the wall. At one table four men played cards. Most of the men sat against the wall smoking, empty coffee-cups and liqueur-glasses before them on the tables. Manuel went through the long room to a small room in back. A man sat at a table in the corner asleep. Manuel sat down at one of the tables.

A waiter came in and stood beside Manuel's table.

"Have you seen Zurito?" Manuel asked him.

"He was in before lunch," the waiter answered. "He won't be back before five o'clock."

"Bring me some coffee and milk and a shot of the ordinary," Manuel said.

The waiter came back into the room carrying a tray with a big coffee-glass and a liqueur-glass on it. In his left hand he held a bottle of brandy. He swung these down to the table and a boy who had followed him poured coffee and milk into the glass from two shiny, spouted pots with long handles.

Manuel took off his cap and the waiter noticed his pigtail pinned forward on his head. He winked at the coffee-boy as he poured out the brandy into the little glass beside Manuel's coffee. The coffee-boy looked at Manuel's pale face curiously.

"You fighting here?" asked the waiter, corking up the bottle.

6 Charlotada. A preliminary, comic fight.

"Yes," Manuel said. "Tomorrow."

The waiter stood there, holding the bottle on one hip.

"You in the Charlie Chaplins[7]?" he asked.

The coffee-boy looked away, embarrassed.

"No. In the ordinary."

"I thought they were going to have Chaves and Hernandez," the waiter said.

"No. Me and another."

"Who? Chaves or Hernandez?"

"Hernandez, I think."

"What's the matter with Chaves?"

"He got hurt."

"Where did you hear that?"

"Retana."

"Hey Looie," the waiter called to the next room, "Chaves got cogida[8]."

Manual had taken the wrapper off the clumps of sugar and dropped them into his coffee. He stirred it and drank it down, sweet, hot, and warming in his empty stomach. He drank off the brandy.

"Give me another shot of that," he said to the waiter.

The waiter uncorked the bottle and poured the glass full, slopping another drink into the saucer. Another waiter had come up in front of the table. The coffee-boy was gone.

"Is Chaves hurt bad?" the second waiter asked Manuel.

"I don't know," Manuel said, "Retana didn't say."

"A hell of a lot he cares," the tall waiter said. Manuel had not seen him before. He must have just come up.

"If you stand in with Retana in this town, you're a made man," the tall waiter said. "If you aren't in with him, you might just as well go out and shoot yourself."

"You said it," the other waiter who had come in said. "You said it then."

"You're right I said it," said the tall waiter. "I know what I'm talking about when I talk about that bird."

"Look what he's done for Villalta," the first waiter said.

"And that ain't all," the tall waiter said. "Look what he's done for Marcial Lalanda. Look what he's done for Nacional."

"You said it, kid," agreed the short waiter.

Manuel looked at them, standing talking in front of his table. He had

[7] Charlie Chaplins. Burlesque or comic bull-fights.
[8] Cogida. Tossed by a bull.

drunk his second brandy. They had forgotten about him. They were not interested in him.

"Look at that bunch of camels," the tall waiter went on. "Did you ever see this Nacional II?"

"I seen him last Sunday, didn't I?" the original waiter said.

"He's a giraffe," the short waiter said.

"What did I tell you?" the tall waiter said. "Those are Retana's boys."

"Say, give me another shot of that," Manuel said. He had poured the brandy the waiter had slopped over in the saucer into his glass and drank it while they were talking.

The original waiter poured his glass full mechanically, and the three of them went out of the room talking.

In the far corner the man was still asleep, snoring slightly on the intaking breath, his head back against the wall.

Manuel drank his brandy. He felt sleepy himself. It was too hot to go out into the town. Besides there was nothing to do. He wanted to see Zurito. He would go to sleep while he waited. He kicked his suitcase under the table to be sure it was there. Perhaps it would be better to put it back under the seat, against the wall. He leaned down and shoved it under. Then he leaned forward on the table and went to sleep.

When he woke there was someone sitting across the table from him. It was a big man with a heavy brown face like an Indian. He had been sitting there some time. He had waved the waiter away and sat reading the paper and occasionally looking down at Manuel, asleep, his head on the table. He read the paper laboriously, forming the words with his lips as he read. When it tired him he looked at Manuel. He sat heavily in the chair, his black Cordoba hat tipped forward.

Manuel sat up and looked at him.

"Hello, Zurito," he said.

"Hello, kid," the big man said.

"I've been asleep." Manuel rubbed his forehead with the back of his fist.

"I thought maybe you were."

"How's everything?"

"Good. How is everything with you?"

"Not so good."

They were both silent. Zurito, the picador, looked at Manuel's white face. Manuel looked down at the picador's enormous hands folding the paper to put away in his pocket.

"I got a favor to ask you, Manos," Manuel said.

Manosduros was Zurito's nickname. He never heard it without think-ing of his huge hands. He put them forward on the table self-consciously.

"Let's have a drink," he said.

"Sure," said Manuel.

The waiter came and went and came again. He went out of the room looking back at the two men at the table.

"What's the matter, Manolo?" Zurito set down his glass.

"Would you pic two bulls for me tomorrow night?" Manuel asked, looking up at Zurito across the table.

"No," said Zurito. "I'm not pic-ing."

Manuel looked down at his glass. He had expected that answer; now he had it. Well, he had it.

"I'm sorry, Manolo, but I'm not pic-ing." Zurito looked at his hands.

"That's all right," Manuel said.

"I'm too old," Zurito said.

"I just asked you," Manuel said.

"Is it the nocturnal tomorrow?"

"That's it. I figured if I had just one good pic, I could get away with it."

"How much are you getting?"

"Three hundred pesetas."

"I get more than that for pic-ing."

"I know," said Manuel. "I didn't have any right to ask you."

"What do you keep on doing it for?" Zurito asked. "Why don't you cut off your coleta, Manolo?"

"I don't know," Manuel said.

"You're pretty near as old as I am," Zurito said.

"I don't know," Manuel said. "I got to do it. If I can fix it so that I get an even break, that's all I want. I got to stick with it, Manos."

"No, you don't."

"Yes, I do. I've tried keeping away from it."

"I know how you feel. But it isn't right. You ought to get out and say out."

"I can't do it. Besides, I've been going good lately."

Zurito looked at his face.

"You've been in the hospital."

"But I was going great when I got hurt."

Zurito said nothing. He tipped the cognac out of his saucer into his glass.

"The papers said they never saw a better faena[9]," Manuel said.
Zurito looked at him.

"You know when I get going I'm good," Manuel said.

"You're too old," the picador said.

"No," said Manuel. "You're ten years older than I am."

"With me it's different."

"I'm not too old," Manuel said.

They sat silent, Manuel watching the picador's face.

"I was going great till I got hurt," Manuel offered.

"You ought to have seen me, Manos," Manuel said, reproachfully.

"I don't want to see you," Zurito said. "It makes me nervous."

"You haven't seen me lately.'"

"I've seen you plenty."

Zurito looked at Manuel, avoiding his eyes.

"You ought to quit it, Manolo."

"I can't," Manuel said. "I'm going good now, I tell you."

Zurito leaned forward, his hands on the table.

"Listen. I'll pic for you and if you don't go big tomorrow night, you'll
quit. See? Will you do that?"

"Sure."

Zurito leaned back, relieved.

"You got to quit," he said. "No monkey business. You got to cut the
coleta."

"I won't have to quit," Manuel said. "You watch me. I've got the stuff."

Zurito stood up. He felt tired from arguing.

"You got to quit," he said. "I'll cut your coleta myself."

"No, you won't," Manuel said. "You won't have a chance."

Zurito called the waiter.

"Come on," said Zurito. "Come on up to the house."

Manuel reached under the seat for his suitcase. He was happy. He
knew Zurito would pic for him. He was the best picador living. It was all
simple now.

"Come on up to the house and we'll eat," Zurito said.

Manuel stood in the patio de caballos waiting for the Charlie Chaplins
to be over. Zurito stood beside him. Where they stood it was dark. The
high door that led into the bull-ring was shut. Above them they heard a
shout, then another shout of laughter. Then there was silence. Manuel liked
the smell of the stables about the patio de caballos. It smelled good in the

[9] Faena. The crucial moment of the bull-fight when the matador is alone with the bull.

dark. There was another roar from the arena and then applause, prolonged applause, going on and on.

"You ever seen these fellows?" Zurito asked, big and looming beside Manuel in the dark.

"No," Manuel said.

"They're pretty funny," Zurito said. He smiled to himself in the dark.

The high, double, tight-fitting door into the bull-ring swung open and Manuel saw the ring in the hard light of the arc-lights, the plaza, dark all the way around, rising high; around the edge of the ring were running and bowing two men dressed like tramps, followed by a third in the uniform of a hotel bell-boy who stooped and picked up the hats and canes thrown down onto the sand and tossed them back up into the darkness.

The electric light went on in the patio.

"I'll climb onto one of those ponies while you collect the kids", Zurito said.

Behind them came the jingle of the mules, coming out to go into the arena and be hitched onto the dead bull.

The members of the cuadrilla, who had been watching the burlesque from the runway between the barrera and the seats, came walking back and stood in a group talking, under the electric light in the patio. A good-looking lad in a silver-and-orange suit came up to Manuel and smiled.

"I'm Hernandez," he said and put out his hand.

Manuel shook it.

"They're regular elephants we've got tonight," the boy said cheerfully.

"They're big ones with horns," Manuel agreed.

"You drew the worst lot," the boy said.

"That's all right," Manuel said. "The bigger they are, the more meat for the poor."

"Where did you get that one?" Hernandez grinned.

"That's an old one," Manuel said. "You line up your cuadrilla, so I can see what I've got."

"You've got some good kids," Hernandez said. He was very cheerful. He had been on twice before in nocturnals and was beginning to get a following in Madrid. He was happy the fight would start in a few minutes.

"Where are the pics?" Manuel asked.

"They're back in the corrals fighting about who gets the beautiful horses," Hernandez grinned.

The mules came through the gate in a rush, the whips snapping, bells jangling and the young bull ploughing a furrow of sand.

They formed up for the paseo[10] as soon as the bull had gone through.

Manuel and Hernandez stood in front. The youths of the cuadrillas were behind, their heavy capes furled over their arms. In back, the four picadors, mounted, holding their steel-tipped push-poles erect in the half-dark of the corral.

"It's a wonder Retana wouldn't give us enough light to see the horses by," one picador said.

"He knows we'll be happier if we don't get too good a look at these skins," another pic answered.

"This thing I'm on barely keeps me off the ground," the first picador said.

"Well, they're horses."

"Sure, they're horses."

They talked, sitting their gaunt horses in the dark.

Zurito said nothing. He had the only steady horse of the lot. He had tried him, wheeling him in the corrals and he responded to the bit and the spurs. He had taken the bandage off his right eye and cut the strings where they had tied his ears tight shut at the base. He was a good, solid horse, solid on his legs. That was all he needed. He intended to ride him all through the corrida. He had already, since he had mounted, sitting in the half-dark in the big, quilted saddle, waiting for the paseo, pic-ed through the whole corrida in his mind. The other picadors went on talking on both sides of him. He did not hear them.

The two matadors stood together in front of their three peones, their capes furled over their left arms in the same fashion. Manuel was thinking about the three lads in back of him. They were all three Madrilenos, like Hernandez, boys about nineteen. One of them, a gypsy, serious, aloof, and dark-faced, he liked the look of. He turned.

"What's your name, kid?" he asked the gypsy.

"Fuentes," the gypsy said.

"That's a good name," Manuel said.

The gypsy smiled, showing his teeth.

"You take the bull and give him a little run when he comes out," Manuel said.

"All right," the gypsy said. His face was serious. He began to think about just what he would do.

"Here she goes," Manuel said to Hernandez.

"All right. We'll go."

[10] Paseo. Opening parade.

Heads up, swinging with the music, their right arms swinging free, they stepped out, crossing the sanded arena under the arc-lights, the cuadrillas opening out behind, the picadors riding after; behind came the bull-ring servants and the jingling mules. The crowd applauded Hernandez as they marched across the arena. Arrogant, swinging, they looked straight ahead as they marched.

They bowed before the president, and the procession broke up into its component parts. The bullfighters went over to the barrera and changed their heavy mantles for the light fighting capes. The mules went out. The picadors galloped jerkily around the ring, and two rode out the gate they had come in by. The servants swept the sand smooth.

Manuel drank a glass of water poured for him by one of Retana's deputies, who was acting as his manager and swordhandler. Hernandez came over from speaking with his own manager.

"You got a good hand, kid," Manuel complimented him.

"They like me," Hernandez said happily.

"How did the paseo go?" Manuel asked Retana's man.

"Like a wedding," said the handler. "Fine. You came out like Joselito and Belmonte."

Zurito rode by, a bulky equestrian statue. He wheeled his horse and faced him toward the toril on the far side of the ring where the bull would come out. It was strange under the arc-light. He pic-ed in the hot afternoon sun for big money. He didn't like this arc-light business. He wished they would get started.

Manuel went up to him.

"Pic him, Manos," he said. "Cut him down to size for me."

"I'll pic him, kid." Zurito spat on the sand. "I'll make him jump out of the ring."

"Lean on him, Manos," Manuel said.

"I'll lean on him," Zurito said. "What's holding it up?"

"He's coming now," Manuel said.

Zurito sat there, his feet in the box-stirrups, his great legs in the buckskin-covered armor gripping the horse, the reins in his left hand, the long pic held in his right hand, his broad hat well down over his eyes to shade them from the lights, watching the distant door of the toril. His horse's ears quivered. Zurito patted him with his left hand.

The red door of the toril swung back and for a moment Zurito looked into the empty passageway far across the arena. Then the bull came out in a rush, skidding on his four legs as he came out under the lights, then charging in a gallop, moving softly in a fast gallop, silent except as he woofed through wide nostrils as he charged, glad to be free after the dark pen.

In the first row of seats, slightly bored, leaning forward to write on the cement wall in front of his knees, the substitute bullfight critic of *El Heraldo* scribbled: "Campagnero, Negro, 42, came out at 90 miles an hour with plenty of gas—"

Manuel, leaning against the barrera, watching the bull, waved his hand and the gypsy ran out, trailing his cape. The bull, in full gallop, pivoted and charged the cape, his head down, his tail rising. The gypsy moved in a zig-zag, and as he passed, the bull caught sight of him and abandoned the cape to charge the man. The gyp sprinted and vaulted the red fence of the barrera as the bull struck it with his horns. He tossed into it twice with his horns, banging into the wood blindly.

The critic of *El Heraldo* lit a cigarette and tossed the match at the bull, then wrote in his note-book, "large and with enough horns to satisfy the cash customers, Campagnero showed a tendency to cut into the terrain of the bullfighters."

Manuel stepped out on the hard sand as the bull banged into the fence. Out of the corner of his eye he saw Zurito sitting the white horse close to the barrera, about a quarter of the way around the ring to the left. Manuel held the cape close in front of him, a fold in each hand, and shouted at the bull. "Huh! Huh!" The bull turned, seemed to brace against the fence as he charged in a scramble, driving into the cape as Manuel side-stepped, pivoted on his heels with the charge of the bull, and swung the cape just ahead of the horns. At the end of the swing he was facing the bull again and held the cape in the same position close in front of his body, and pivoted again as the bull recharged. Each time, as he swung, the crowd shouted.

Four times he swung with the bull, lifting the cape so it billowed full, and each time bringing the bull around to charge again. Then, at the end of the fifth swing, he held the cape against his hip and pivoted, so the cape swung out like a ballet dancer's skirt and wound the bull around himself like a belt, to step clear, leaving the bull facing Zurito on the white horse, come up and planted firm, the horse facing the bull, its ears forward, its lips nervous, Zurito, his hat over his eyes, leaning forward, the long pole sticking out before and behind in a sharp angle under his right arm, held half-way down, the triangular iron point facing the bull.

El Heraldo's second-string critic, drawing on his cigarette, his eyes on the bull, wrote: "The veteran Manolo designed a series of acceptable veronicas,[11] ending in a very Belmontistic[12] recorte[13] that earned applause from the regulars, and we entered the tercio of the cavalry."[14]

Zurito sat his horse, measuring the distance between the bull and the end of the pic. As he looked, the bull gathered himself together and charged, his eyes on the horse's chest. As he lowered his head to hook, Zurito sunk the point of the pic in the swelling hump of muscle above the bull's shoulder, leaned all his weight on the shaft, and with his left hand pulled the white horse into the air, front hoofs pawing, and swung him on the right as he pushed the bull under and through so the horns passed safely under the horse's belly and the horse came down, quivering, the bull's tail brushing his chest as he charged the cape Hernandez offered him.

Hernandez ran sideways, taking the bull out and away with the cape, toward the other picador. He fixed him with a swing of the cape, squarely facing the horse and rider, and stepped back. As the bull saw the horse he charged. The picador's lance slid along his back, and as the shock of the charge lifted the horse, the picador was already halfway out of the saddle, lifting his right leg clear as he missed with the lance and falling to the left side to keep the horse between him and the bull. The horse, lifted and gored, crashed over with the bull driving into him, the picador gave a shove with his boots against the horse and lay clear, waiting to be lifted and hauled away and put on his feet.

Manuel let the bull drive into the fallen horse; he was in no hurry, the picador was safe; besides, it did a picador like that good to worry. He'd stay on longer next time. Lousy pics! He looked across the sand at Zurito a little way out from the barrera, his horse rigid, waiting.

"Huh!" he called to the bull, "Tomar!" holding the cape in both hands so it would catch his eye. The bull detached himself from the horse and charged the cape, and Manuel, running sideways and holding the cape spread wide, stopped, swung on his heels, and brought the bull sharply around facing Zurito.

"Campagnero accepted a pair of varas for the death of one rosinante[15], with Hernandez and Manolo at the quites," *El Heraldo's* critic wrote. "He

[11] Veronica. A movement with the cape to bring the bull close.

[12] Belmontistic. For Juan Belmonte, a famous bull-fighter.

[13] Recorte. Quick pass with the cape.

[14] The tercio of the cavalry. This is sports writer jargon, meaning that the picadors are beginning their work.

[15] Rosinante. The horse. The critic is making a common noun out of the name of the horse of Don Quixote in Cervantes' famous story.

pressed on the iron and clearly showed he was no horse-lover. The veteran Zurito resurrected some of his old stuff with the pike-pole, notably the suerte—"[16]

"Olé! Olé!" the man sitting beside him shouted. The shout was lost in the roar of the crowd, and he slapped the critic on the back. The critic looked up to see Zurito, directly below him, leaning far out over his horse, the length of the pic rising in a sharp angle under his armpit, holding the pic almost by the point, bearing down with all his weight, holding the bull off, the bull pushing and driving to get at the horse, and Zurito, far out, on top of him, holding him, holding him, and slowly pivoting the horse against the pressure, so that at last he was clear. Zurito felt the moment when the horse was clear and the bull could come past, and relaxed the absolute steel lock of his resistance, and the triangular steel point of the pic ripped in the bull's hump of shoulder muscle as he tore loose to find Hernandez's cape before his muzzle. He charged blindly into the cape and the boy took him out into the open arena.

Zurito sat patting his horse and looking at the bull charging the cape that Hernandez swung for him out under the bright light while the crowd shouted.

"You see that one?" he said to Manuel.

"It was a wonder," Manuel said.

"I got him that time," Zurito said. "Look at him now."

At the conclusion of a closely turned pass of the cape the bull slid to his knees. He was up at once, but far out across the sand Manuel and Zurito saw the shine of the pumping flow of blood, smooth against the black of the bull's shoulder.

"I got him that time," Zurito said.

"He's a good bull," Manuel said.

"If they gave me another shot at him, I'd kill him," Zurito said.

"They'll change the thirds on us," Manuel said.

"Look at him now," Zurito said.

"I got to go over there," Manuel said, and started on a run for the other side of the ring, where the monos were leading a horse out by the bridle toward the bull, whacking him on the legs with rods and all, in a procession, trying to get him toward the bull, who stood, dropping his head, pawing, unable to make up his mind to charge.

Zurito, sitting his horse, walking him toward the scene, not missing any detail, scowled.

[16] Suerte. It can mean a deft movement, but here it probably means luck or skill.

Finally the bull charged, the horse leaders ran for the barrera, the picador hit too far back, and the bull got under the horse, lifted him, threw him onto his back.

Zurito watched. The monos[17], in their red shirts, running out to drag the picador clear. The picador, now on his feet, swearing and flopping his arms. Manuel and Hernandez standing ready with their capes. And the bull, the great, black bull, with a horse on his back, hooves dangling, the bridle caught in the horns. Black bull with a horse on his back, staggering short-legged, then arching his neck and lifting, thrusting, charging to slide the horse off, horse sliding down. Then the bull into a lunging charge at the cape Manuel spread for him.

The bull was slower now, Manuel felt. He was bleeding badly. There was a sheen of blood all down his flank.

Manuel offered him the cape again. There he came, eyes open, ugly, watching the cape. Manuel stepped to the side and raised his arms, tightening the cape ahead of the bull for the veronica.

Now he was facing the bull. Yes, his head was going down a little. He was carrying it lower. That was Zurito.

Manuel flopped the cape; there he comes; he side-stepped and swung in another veronica. He's shooting awfully accurately, he thought. He's had enough fight, so he's watching now. He's hunting now. Got his eye on me. But I always give him the cape.

He shook the cape at the bull; there he comes; he side-stepped. Awful close that time. I don't want to work that close to him.

The edge of the cape was wet with blood where it had swept along the bull's back as he went by.

All right, here's the last one.

Manuel, facing the bull, having turned with him each charge, offered the cape with his two hands. The bull looked at him. Eyes watching, horns straight forward, the bull looked at him, watching.

"Huh!" Manuel said, "Toro!"[18] and leaning back, swung the cape forward. Here he comes. He side-stepped, swung the cape in back of him, and pivoted, so the bull followed a swirl of cape and then was left with nothing, fixed by the pass, dominated by the cape. Manuel swung the cape under his muzzle with one hand, to show the bull was fixed, and walked away.

There was no applause.

Manuel walked across the sand toward the barrera, while Zurito rode

[17] Monos. Men who do the ordinary labor around the ring.
[18] Toro. Spanish word for Bull. Matadors shout this regularly during the fight.

out of the ring. The trumpet had blown to change the act to the planting of the banderillos[19] while Manuel had been working with the bull. He had not consciously noticed it. The monos were spreading canvas over the two dead horses and sprinkling sawdust around them.

Manuel came up to the barrera for a drink of water. Retana's man handed him the heavy porous jug.

Fuentes, the tall gypsy, was standing holding a pair of banderillos, holding them together, slim, red sticks, fish-hook points out. He looked at Manuel.

"Go on out there," Manuel said.

The gypsy trotted out. Manuel set down the jug and watched. He wiped his face with his handkerchief.

The critic of *El Heraldo* reached for the bottle of warm champagne that stood between his feet, took a drink, and finished his paragraph.

"—the aged Manolo rated no applause for a vulgar series of lances with the cape and we entered the third of the palings."

Alone in the center of the ring the bull stood, still fixed. Fuentes, tall, flat-backed, walking toward him arrogantly, his arms spread out, the two slim, red sticks, one in each hand, held by the fingers, points straight forward. Fuentes walked forward. Back of him and to one side was a peon with a cape. The bull looked at him and was no longer fixed.

His eyes watched Fuentes, now standing still. Now he leaned back, calling to him. Fuentes twitched the two banderillos and the light on the steel points caught the bull's eye.

His tail went up and he charged.

He came straight, his eyes on the man. Fuentes stood still, leaning back, the banderillos pointing forward. As the bull lowered his head to hook, Fuentes leaned backward, his arms came together and rose, his two hands touching, the banderillos two descending red lines, and leaning forward drove the points into the bull's shoulder, leaning far in over the bull's horns and pivoting on the two upright sticks, his legs tight together, his body curving to one side to let the bull pass.

"Olé!" from the crowd.

The bull was hooking wildly, jumping like a trout, all four feet off the ground. The red shaft of the banderillos tossed as he jumped.

Manuel standing at the barrera, noticed that he hooked always to the right.

---

[19] Banderillos. Sharp, pointed and very colorful sticks which are driven into the bull.

"Tell him to drop the next pair on the right," he said to the kid who started to run out to Fuentes with the new banderillos.

A heavy hand fell on his shoulder. It was Zurito.

"How do you feel, kid?" he asked.

Manuel was watching the bull.

Zurito leaned forward on the barrera, leaning the weight of his body on his arms. Manuel turned to him.

"You're going good," Zurito said.

Manuel shook his head. He had nothing to do now until the next third. The gypsy was very good with the banderillos. The bull would come to him in the next third in good shape. He was a good bull. It had all been easy up to now. The final stuff with the sword was all he worried over. He did not really worry. He did not even think about it. But standing there he had a heavy sense of apprehension. He looked out at the bull, planning his faena, his work with the red cloth that was to reduce the bull, to make him manageable.

The gypsy was walking out toward the bull again, walking heel-and-toe, insultingly, like a ballroom dancer, the red shafts of the banderillos twitching with his walk. The bull watched him, not fixed now, hunting him, but waiting to get close enough so he could be sure of getting him, getting the horns into him.

As Fuentes walked forward the bull charged. Fuentes ran across the quarter of a circle as the bull charged and, as he passed running backward, stopped, swung forward, rose to his toes, arm straight out, and sunk the banderillos straight down into the tight of the big shoulder muscles as the bull missed him.

The crowd were wild about it.

"That kid won't stay in this night stuff long," Retana's man said to Zurito.

"He's good," Zurito said.

"Watch him now."

They watched.

Fuentes was standing with his back against the barrera. Two of the cuadrilla were back of him, with their capes ready to flop over the fence to distract the bull.

The bull, with his tongue out, his barrel heaving, was watching the gypsy. He thought he had him now. Back against the red planks. Only a short charge away. The bull watched him.

The gypsy bent back, drew back his arms, the banderillos pointing at the bull. He called to the bull, stamped one foot. The bull was suspicious. He wanted a man. No more barbs in the shoulder.

Fuentes walked a little closer to the bull. Bent back. Called again. Somebody in the crowd shouted a warning.

"He's too damn close," Zurito said.

"Watch him," Retana's man said.

Leaning back, inciting the bull with the banderillos, Fuentes jumped, both feet off the ground. As he jumped the bull's tail rose and he charged. Fuentes came down on his toes, arms straight out, whole body arching forward, and drove the shafts straight down as he swung his body clear of the right horn.

The bull crashed into the barrera where the flopping capes had attracted his eye as he lost the man.

The gypsy came running along the barrera toward Manuel, taking the applause of the crowd. His vest was ripped where he had not quite cleared the point of the horn. He was happy about it, showing it to the spectators. He made the tour of the ring. Zurito saw him go by, smiling, pointing at his vest. He smiled.

Somebody else was planting the last pair of banderillos. Nobody was paying any attention.

Retana's man tucked a baton inside the red cloth of a muleta[20], folded the cloth over it, and handed it over the barrera to Manuel. He reached in the leather sword-case, took out a sword, and holding it by its leather scabbard, reached it over the fence to Manuel. Manuel pulled the blade out by the red hilt and the scabbard felt limp.

He looked at Zurito. The big man saw he was sweating.

"Now you get him, kid." Zurito said.

Manuel nodded.

"He's in good shape," Zurito said.

"Just like you want him," Retana's man assured him.

Manuel nodded.

The trumpeter, up under the roof, blew for the final act, and Manuel walked across the arena toward where, up in the dark boxes, the president must be.

In the front row of seats the substitute bullfight critic of *El Heraldo* took a long drink of the warm champagne. He had decided it was not worth while to write a running story and would write up the corrida back in the office. What the hell was it anyway? Only a nocturnal. If he missed any-

---

[20] Muleta. The red cloth covering the sword. Matadors use the sword for the kill.

thing he would get it out of the morning papers. He took another drink of the champagne. He had a date at Maxim's at twelve. Who were these bullfighters anyway? Kids and bums. A bunch of bums. He put his pad of paper in his pocket and looked over toward Manuel, standing very much alone in the ring, gesturing with his hat in a salute toward a box he could not see high up in the dark plaza. Out in the ring the bull stood quiet, looking at nothing.

"I dedicate this bull to you, Mr. President, and to the public of Madrid, the most intelligent and generous of the world," was what Manuel was saying. It was a formula. He said it all. It was a little long for nocturnal use.

He bowed at the dark, straightened, tossed his hat over his shoulder, and, carrying the muleta in his left hand and the sword in his right, walked out toward the bull.

Manuel walked toward the bull. The bull looked at him; his eyes were quick. Manuel noticed the way the banderillos hung down on his left shoulder and the steady sheen of blood from Zurito's pic-ing. He noticed the way the bull's feet were. As he walked forward, holding the muleta in his left hand and the sword in his right, he watched the bull's feet. The bull could not charge without gathering his feet together. Now he stood square on them, dully.

Manuel walked toward him, watching his feet. This was all right. He could do this. He must work to get the bull's head down, so he could go in past the horns and kill him. He did not think about the sword, not about killing the bull. He thought about one thing at a time. The coming things oppressed him, though. Walking forward, watching the bull's feet, he saw successively his eyes, his wet muzzle, and the wide, forward-pointing spread of his horns. The bull had light circles about his eyes. His eyes watched Manuel. He felt he was going to get this little one with the white face.

Standing still now and spreading the red cloth of the muleta with the sword, pricking the point into the cloth so that the sword, now held in his left hand, spread the red flannel like the jib of a boat, Manuel noticed the points of the bull's horns. One of them was splintered from banging against the barrera. The other was sharp as a porcupine quill. Manuel noticed while spreading the muleta that the white base of the horn was stained red. While he noticed these things he did not lose sight of the bull's feet. The bull watched Manuel steadily.

He's on the defensive now, Manuel thought. He's reserving himself. I've got to bring him out of that and get his head down. Always get his head down. Zurito had his head down once, but he's come back. He'll bleed when I start him going and that will bring it down.

Holding the muleta, with the sword in his left hand widening it in front of him, he called to the bull.

The bull looked at him.

He leaned back insultingly and shook the wide-spread flannel.

The bull saw the muleta. It was a bright scarlet under the arc-light. The bull's legs tightened.

Here he comes. Whoosh! Manuel turned as the bull came and raised the muleta so that it passed over the bull's horns and swept down his broad back from head to tail. The bull had gone clean up in the air with the charge. Manuel had not moved.

At the end of the pass the bull turned like a cat coming around a corner and faced Manuel.

He was on the offensive again. His heaviness was gone. Manuel noted the fresh blood shining down the black shoulder and dripping down the bull's leg. He drew the sword out of the muleta and held it in his right hand. The muleta held low down in his left hand, leaning toward the left, he called to the bull. The bull's legs tightened, his eyes on the muleta. Here he comes, Manuel thought. Yuh!

He swung with the charge, sweeping the muleta ahead of the bull, his feet firm, the sword following the curve, a point of light under the arcs.

The bull recharged as the pase natural finished and Manuel raised the muleta for a pase de pecho.[21] Firmly planted, the bull came by his chest under the raised muleta. Manuel leaned his head back to avoid the clattering banderillo shafts. The hot, black bull body touched his chest as it passed.

Too damn close, Manuel thought. Zurito, leaning on the barrera, spoke rapidly to the gypsy, who trotted out toward Manuel with a cape Zurito pulled his hat down low and looked out across the arena at Manuel.

Manuel was facing the bull again, the muleta held low and to the left. The bull's head was down as he watched the muleta.

"If it was Belmonte doing that stuff, they'd go crazy," Retana's man said.

Zurito said nothing. He was watching Manuel out in the center of the arena.

"Where did the boss dig this fellow up?" Retana's man asked.

[21] Pase de pecho. "Pass by the chest." A difficult movement for the matador. The muleta must be in the left hand rather than the right.

"Out of the hospital," Zurito said.

"That's where he's going damn quick," Retana's man said.

Zurito turned on him.

"Knock on that," he said, pointing to the barrera.

"I was just kidding, man," Retana's man said.

"Knock on the wood."

Retana's man leaned forward and knocked three times on the barrera.

"Watch the faena," Zurito said.

Out in the center of the ring, under the lights, Manuel was kneeling, facing the bull, and as he raised the muleta in both hands the bull charged, tail up.

Manuel swung his body clear and, as the bull recharged, brought around the muleta in a half-circle that pulled the bull to his knees.

"Why, that one's a great bullfighter," Retana's man said.

"No, he's not," said Zurito.

Manuel stood up and, the muleta in his left hand, the sword in his right, acknowledged the applause from the dark plaza.

The bull had humped himself up from his knees and stood waiting, his head hung low.

Zurito spoke to two of the other lads of the cuadrilla and they ran out to stand back of Manuel with their capes. There were four men back of him now. Hernandez had followed him since he first came out with the muleta. Fuentes stood watching, his cape held against his body, tall, in repose, watching lazy-eyed. Now the two came up. Hernandez motioned them to stand one at each side. Manuel stood alone, facing the bull.

Manuel waved back the men with the capes. Stepping back cautiously, they saw his face was white and sweating.

Didn't they know enough to keep back? Did they want to catch the bull's eye with the capes after he was fixed and ready? He had enough to worry about without that kind of thing.

The bull was standing, his four feet square, looking at the muleta. Manuel furled the muleta in his left hand. The bull's eyes watched it. His body was heavy on his feet. He carried his head low, but not too low.

Manuel lifted the muleta at him. The bull did not move. Only his eyes watched.

He's all lead, Manuel thought. He's all square. He's framed right. He'll take it.

He thought in bullfight terms. Sometimes he had a thought and the particular piece of slang would not come into his mind and he could not realize the thought. His instincts and his knowledge worked automatically, and his brain worked slowly and in words. He knew all about bulls. He did not have to think about them. He just did the right thing. His eyes noted things and his body performed the necessary measures without thought. If he thought about it, he would be gone.

Now, facing the bull, he was conscious of many things at the same time. There were the horns, the one splintered, the other smoothly sharp, the need to profile himself toward the left horn, lance himself short and straight, lower the muleta so the bull would follow it, and, going in over the horns, put the sword all the way into a little spot about as big as a five-peseta piece straight in back of the neck, between the sharp pitch of the bull's shoulders. He must do all this and must then come out from between the horns. He was conscious he must do all this, but his only thought was in words: "Corto y derecho."

"Corto y derecho," he thought, furling the muleta. Short and straight. Corto y derecho, he drew the sword out of the muleta, profiled on the splintered left horn, dropped the muleta across his body, so his right hand with the sword on the level with his eye made the sign of the cross, and, rising on his toes, sighted along the dipping blade of the sword at the spot high up between the bull's shoulders.

Corto y derecho, he launched himself on the bull.

There was a shock, and he felt himself go up in the air. He pushed on the sword as he went up and over, and it flew out of his hand. He hit the ground and the bull was on him. Manuel, lying on the ground, kicked at the bull's muzzle with his slippered feet. Kicking, kicking, the bull after him, missing him in his excitement, bumping him with his head, driving the horns into the sand. Kicking like a man keeping a ball in the air, Manuel kept the bull from getting a clean thrust at him.

Manuel felt the wind on his back from the capes flopping at the bull, and then the bull was gone, gone over him in a rush. Dark, as his belly went over. Not even stepped on.

Manuel stood up and picked up the muleta. Fuentes handed him the sword. It was bent where it had struck the shoulderblade. Manuel straightened it on his knee and ran toward the bull, standing now beside one of the dead horses. As he ran, his jacket flopped where it had been ripped under his arm pit.

"Get him out of there," Manuel shouted to the gypsy. The bull had smelled the blood of the dead horse and ripped into the canvas-cover with his horns. He charged Fuentes's cape, with the canvas hanging from his

splintered horn, and the crowd laughed. Out in the ring, he tossed his head
to rid himself of the canvas. Hernandez, running up from behind him,
grabbed the end of the canvas and neatly lifted it off the horn.

The bull followed it in a half-charge and stopped still. He was on the
defensive again. Manuel was walking toward him with the sword and muleta.
Manuel swung the muleta before him. The bull would not charge

Manuel profiled toward the bull, sighting along the dipping blade of
the sword. The bull was motionless, seemingly dead on his feet, incapable
of another charge.

Manuel rose to his toes, sighting along the steel, and charged.

Again there was the shock and he felt himself being borne back in a
rush, to strike hard on the sand. There was no chance of kicking this time.
The bull was on top of him. Manuel lay as though dead, his head on his
arms, and the bull bumped him. Bumped his back, bumped his face in the
sand. He felt the horn go into the sand between his folded arms. The bull
hit him in the small of the back. His face drove into the sand. The horn drove
through one of his sleeves and the bull ripped it off. Manuel was tossed clear
and the bull followed the capes.

Manuel got up, found the sword and muleta, tried the point of the sword
with his thumb, and then ran toward the barrera for a new sword.

Retana's man handed him the sword over the edge of the barrera.

"Wipe off your face," he said.

Manuel, running again toward the bull, wiped his bloody face with his
handkerchief. He had not seen Zurito. Where was Zurito?

The cuadrilla had stepped away from the bull and waited with their
capes. The bull stood, heavy and dull again after the action.

Manuel walked toward him with the muleta. He stopped and shook it.
The bull did not respond. He passed it right and left, left and right before
the bull's muzzle. The bull's eyes watched it and turned with the swing, but
he would not charge. He was waiting for Manuel.

Manuel was worried. There was nothing to do but go in. Corto y
derecho. He profiled close to the bull, crossed the muleta in front of his
body and charged. As he pushed in the sword, he jerked his body to the left
to clear the horn. The bull passed him and the sword shot up in the air,
twinkling under the arc-lights, to fall red-hilted on the sand.

Manuel ran over and picked it up. It was bent and he straightened it
over his knee.

As he came running toward the bull, fixed again now, he passed
Hernandez standing with his cape.

"He's all bone," the boy said encouragingly.

Manuel nodded, wiping his face. He put the bloody handkerchief in his pocket.

There was the bull. He was close to the barrera now. Damn him. Maybe he was all bone. Maybe there was not any place for the sword to go in. The hell there wasn't! He'd show them.

He tried a pass with the muleta and the bull did not move. Manuel chopped the muleta back and forth in front of the bull. Nothing doing.

He furled the muleta, drew the sword out, profiled it and drove in on the bull. He felt the sword buckle as he shoved it in, leaning his weight on it, and then it shot high in the air, end-over-ending into the crowd. Manuel had jerked clear as the sword jumped.

The first cushions[22] thrown down out of the dark missed him. Then one hit him in the face, his bloody face looking toward the crowd. They were coming down fast. Spotting the sand. Somebody threw an empty champagne-bottle from close range. It hit Manuel on the foot. He stood there watching the dark, where the things were coming from. Then something whished through the air and struck by him. Manuel leaned over and picked it up. It was his sword. He straightened it over his knee and gestured with it to the crowd.

"Thank you," he said. "Thank you."

Oh, the dirty bastards! Dirty bastards! Oh, the lousy, dirty bastards! He kicked into a cushion as he ran.

There was the bull. The same as ever. All right, you dirty, lousy bastard!

Manuel passed the muleta in front of the bull's black muzzle.

Nothing doing.

You won't! All right. He stepped close and jammed the sharp peak of the muleta into the bull's damp muzzle.

The bull was on him as he jumped back and as he tripped on a cushion he felt the horn go into him, into his side. He grabbed the horn with his two hands and rode backward, holding tight onto the place. The bull tossed him and he was clear. He lay still. It was all right. The bull was gone.

He got up coughing and feeling broken and gone. The dirty bastards!

"Give me the sword," he shouted. "Give me the stuff."

Fuentes came up with the muleta and the sword.

Hernandez put his arm around him.

[22] The first cushions. Patrons of the bull ring express their dissatisfaction by throwing things into the ring, chiefly the cushions on which they have been sitting.

"Go on to the infirmary, man," he said. "Don't be a damn fool."

"Get away from me," Manuel said. "Get to hell away from me."

He twisted free. Hernandez shrugged his shoulders. Manuel ran toward the bull.

There was the bull standing, heavy, firmly planted.

All right, you bastard! Manuel drew the sword out of the muleta, sighted with the same movement, and flung himself onto the bull. He felt the sword go in all the way. Right up to the guard. Four fingers and his thumb into the bull. The blood was hot on his knuckles, and he was on top of the bull.

The bull lurched with him as he lay on, and seemed to sink; then he was standing clear. He looked at the bull going down slowly over on his side, then suddenly four feet in the air.

Then he gestured at the crowd, his hand warm from the bull blood.

All right, you bastards! He wanted to say something, but he started to cough. It was hot and choking. He looked down for the muleta. He must go over and salute the president. President, hell! He was sitting down looking at something. It was the bull. His four feet up. Thick tongue out. Things crawling around on his belly and under his legs. Crawling where the hair was thin. Dead bull. To hell with the bull! To hell with them all! He started to get to his feet and commenced to cough. He sat down again, coughing. Somebody came and pushed him up.

They carried him across the ring to the infirmary, running with him across the sand, standing blocked at the gate as the mules came in, then around under the dark passageway, men grunting as they took him up the stairway, and then laid him down.

The doctor and two men in white were waiting for him. They laid him out on the table. They were cutting away his shirt. Manuel felt tired. His whole chest felt scalding inside. He started to cough and they held something to his mouth. Everybody was very busy.

There was an electric light in his eyes. He shut his eyes.

He heard someone coming very heavily up the stairs. Then he did not hear it. Then he heard a noise far off. That was the crowd. Well, somebody would have to kill his other bull. They had cut away all his shirt. The doctor smiled at him. There was Retana.

"Hello, Retana!" Manuel said. He could not hear his voice.

Retana smiled at him and said something. Manuel could not hear it.

Zurito stood beside the table, bending over where the doctor was working. He was in his picador clothes, without his hat.

Zurito said something to him. Manuel could not hear it.

Zurito was speaking to Retana. One of the men in white smiled and handed Retana a pair of scissors. Retana gave them to Zurito. Zurito said something to Manuel. He could not hear it.

To hell with this operating-table. He'd been on plenty of operating-tables before. He was not going to die. There would be a priest if he was going to die.

Zurito was saying something to him. Holding up the scissors.

That was it. They were going to cut off his coleta. They were going to cut off his pigtail.

Manuel sat up on the operating-table. The doctor stepped back, angry. Someone grabbed him and held him.

"You couldn't do a thing like that, Manos," he said.

He heard suddenly, clearly, Zurito's voice.

"That's all right," Zurito said. "I won't do it. I was joking."

"I was going good," Manuel said. "I didn't have any luck. That was all."

Manuel lay back. They had put something over his face. It was all familiar. He inhaled deeply. He felt very tired. He was very, very tired. They took the thing away from his face.

"I was going good," Manuel said weakly. "I was going great."

Retana looked at Zurito and started for the door.

"I'll stay here with him," Zurito said.

Retana shrugged his shoulders.

Manuel opened his eyes and looked at Zurito.

"Wasn't I going good, Manos?" he asked, for confirmation.

"Sure," said Zurito. "You were going great."

The doctor's assistant put the cone over Manuel's face and he inhaled deeply. Zurito stood awkwardly, watching.

STUDY QUESTIONS:

1. Write an interpretation of the following paragraph. In what sense is it a character description of Manuel?

"He thought in bull-fight terms. Sometimes he had a thought and the particular piece of slang would not come into his mind and he could not realize the thought. His instincts and his knowledge worked automatically, and his brain worked slowly and in words. He knew all about bulls. He did not have to think about them. He just did the right thing. His eyes noted things and his body performed the necessary measures without thought. If he thought about it, he would be gone."

2. Contrast Zurito and Hernandez in their loyalty to Manuel. What do they admire in him? What purpose does the gypsy Fuentes serve in the story?

3. Several times in the story Hemingway shifts to the point of view of the bull. What is gained by this shift?

4. What does the newspaper critic add to the story? Why does Hemingway remove him before the end of the bull-fight?

5. Very few bull-fights would ever be quite so disastrously bloody and violent as this one. How is this excessive violence appropriate to the theme of the story?

6. Why does Zurito refrain from cutting off Manuel's coleta at the end?

THE HIGH HILL

MARY DEASY

Mary Deasy is young, American and pretty and makes her home in Cincinnati, Ohio. She has published several novels and a number of short stories like "The High Hill," which appeared first in *Harper's*. Her work deals chiefly with the events of everyday life—family relationships, problems of adjustment to new environments, schools, and the boys and girls in them. For the most part, they are quiet stories, filled with human warmth and sympathy and quite different from the stories of Ernest Hemingway.

"The High Hill" is an interesting study in ironic contrasts, which says in part that popularity and even leadership can sometimes be acquired for the wrong reasons. It is only after her classmates think that Elvy Morgum has taken Miss Janiek's ring that they "accept" her and want to associate with her above any other of their friends. This is a great blow to Miss Farrell, the idealistic young teacher, who wanted them to come to like Elvy for reasons of kindness and brotherhood—Elvy with her limp, ragged clothes and general unattractiveness. But there are surprises in the story, each of which has a special kind of delight for the reader and not the least of which is the meaning of the title, not fully revealed until the end of the story.

The characters are excellently drawn; the contrast between hard-boiled Miss Janiek (hard-boiled on the surface, that is) and Miss Farrell does much to set the tone of the story. Our sympathies are with Miss Farrell, but the plot of the story says that Miss Janiek has her uses, too. Both teachers are proved right—and wrong—and this is the story's way of saying that life is often hard to predict and that it is not usually a simple matter of "mercy, loyalty, and understanding," as Miss Farrell says, though these considerations are very important.

A story like "The High Hill" borders dangerously on the sentimental. The author has to be very careful. There are fine touches everywhere to show that Mary Deasy knew this danger and, more important, knew how to deal with it. Generally, this is a bright, happy story, but there are a few moments of ugliness in it, too—enough to make us realize the truth of Huck Finn's observation that "human beings *can* be awful cruel to one another."

Twenty years ago, when I was six years old and went to school for the first time, the new theories of child education hadn't made much impression yet on the public school system, and we still sat all day in one varnished, black-boarded, chalk-smelling room, fighting our way through the thorny prickles of the alphabet, and laying the first staggering foundations of the art of writing. Miss Farrell, our teacher, was red-haired and young and Irish, and she threw herself into the labor of instruction with an earnestness that left her sometimes, I suppose, full of the tears of a sense of desperate inadequacy behind the flushed cheeks, the curling hair, the dark-blue eyes with the Celtic shadows beneath them, that were all that we, with our pride in the possession of a young, pretty teacher, could see.

No doubt she had her moments of self-searching and frightened emptiness, when it must have seemed to her that she was failing both in the task for which the school board had hired her, that of making literate citizens out of us, and in the task which she had imposed on herself, of leading us into the paths of the passionate conviction of human brotherhood that was the mixed legacy of her Irish blood and her American birth. I can remember her eager voice sounding the words that came to us, secure in the closed hidden valley in which children live, with a meaning still too evanescent for us to grasp—words that said *love* and *mercy* and *tolerance*, ripe round syllables that broke and vanished in the thin harsh air of our simpler world.

Miss Janiek, from the third-grade room across the hall, talked to her about it after school, sitting in Miss Farrell's big varnished chair behind the desk, while Miss Farrell, standing beside her, gave her half her attention, the other half being directed at those of us who had stayed behind to erase the blackboards and gather the chalk neatly into white dusty boxes.

"They're little savages," Miss Janiek said. "The whole lot of them." We felt her gaze wandering over us with the darkness, the tenderness, the pungent vitality in it that we sensed without understanding. "Sitting there and watching a person with those blank clear eyes of theirs," she said. And then: "School-teaching! The women who bore those children don't understand them, and yet they expect us to take a good three dozen of them and get inside their minds somehow, put knowledge and skill and morality there—And you're lucky if after three years you've taught them to hold a pen, and add two pairs of figures, and squeeze out the meaning of a row of letters set end to end, that spell out a sentence nobody from the beginning of time was ever interested in reading: *The cat runs, the dog jumps—*"

"No," Miss Farrell said. "There's more than that." She said the words again: *mercy,* and *loyalty,* and *understanding.* "We learned," she said. "Somebody taught us. We weren't born knowing, any more than they were. Now it's our turn to teach—"

"We're going now, Miss Farrell," Sisley Ross said.

We may forget the others, the anonymous outgrown faces, the long-ago names of earliest schoolfellows; but none of us will forget Sisley Ross, because she was the girl with the spun-sugar curls and the cornflower-blue eyes and the pink-and-white dresses, the doll-heroine of our earnest dreams, as perfect and as unattainable as if, fashioned of wax or bisque, she had sat serenely staring from a shop-window, with a price tag, on which there appeared a figure beyond the most fantastic imagined limits of our parents' generosity, dangling quietly from one wrist. She stood in the doorway now; Margot Berry was beside her, waiting to walk home with her, daring any of us, with the imperious, watchful glance of her light-blue eyes, to dispute her prerogative.

"C-a-t, cat," Miss Janiek said. Her eyes brooded over us fiercely. "Teach them that, if you've got to earn your salary. Teach them the immutable rule of two plus two."

"Good night, Miss Farrell," Sisley said. "Good night, Miss Janiek."

"Good night, children," Miss Farrell said. And to Miss Janiek: "There's more than that. You know it, too."

Miss Janiek wore on the third finger of her left hand a gold ring with a diamond held in it by tiny prongs of gold. It was an engagement ring, but she was not engaged any more, because the man who had given her the ring had been a flier in the war (having given up teaching the French language safely and quietly in a city high school to fly the French skies, where there was no need for any language but the stuttering burst of a machine gun), and he had been killed, so that she was left with nothing but the ring, and a photograph, and a memory that seemed queerer company each year for the dark heavy face and the invariable shapeless brown dresses that she wore. There was something about her that reminded us vaguely of our own mothers, as if, without in the least resembling them, she brought to us the same aura of maternal warmth; we knew this instinctively, reading behind manner and speech to the warmth inside, while the other teachers wondered audibly at the attraction she had for us, she who rarely said a word to us that was not spoken in a tone of fierce and desperate exasperation.

I remember the day she brought Elvy Morgum into our room. It was in the morning, and we had just sat down in our places when the door banged open and she came in, thrusting before her a girl of our own age—a small girl, hatless, her features narrow, with a curiously granitelike sharpness about them, beneath a harsh tangle of hair, above an old black cut-down coat of worn velveteen.

"Here's another one for you," she shouted to Miss Farrell, in her clear loud voice. "Elvy, or Elvira, Morgum; it doesn't seem to make much difference; there are Morgums all over the place this morning, and none of them, not even the oldest, seems to know. They tell me there are four more, younger than this one, still at home, so it looks as if you'll have them in permanent supply, as long as they stay in the neighborhood."

With her hand still on Elvy Morgum's shoulder, she gave her a slight thrust forward toward Miss Farrell's desk. We watched as Elvy moved reluctantly across the front of the room, seeing the hitch and drag of one foot as she walked. She stopped beside Miss Farrell's desk, and Miss Farrell said clearly, stretching out one hand to her: "Elvy Morgum. What a pretty name."

"Pretty or not, it's what she'll have to do with till the Lord or a man releases her," Miss Janiek said. "The one I've got is Theophilus, as near as I can make it out. The whole herd of them came wandering in here this morning without parent or guardian, so there's a little confusion about some of the biographical data."

Miss Farrell shook her head; she was smiling, looking over at Miss Janiek.

"I'm one of nine myself," she said. "It's an active life—especially for the mother." She looked back at Elvy Morgum. "I have six brothers and two sisters, Elvy," she said to her. "Would you like to tell me how many you have?"

Elvy stood there at the front of the room without speaking. She looked at Miss Farrell with a dark, wary look, taking her all in, the white soft blouse and the blue skirt and the eyes that were smiling at her, waiting for her to speak.

"The whole set of them are like that," Miss Janiek said "Silent. Wild. You'd think there wasn't a tongue in the lot of them. You'll have to take time."

She took Elvy's hand, and brought her down the aisle, and let her sit at a desk behind Sisley Ross's. Sisley turned round to look at her, not smiling, only staring at her curiously, with her sweet blue-eyed doll's stare.

"This is Sisley Ross, Elvy," Miss Farrell said. "Sisley, would you like to show Elvy where to put her coat?"

"Yes, Miss Farrell," Sisley said.

Even her voice was a doll's prompt obedient pipe at the proper pressure of a button. We watched her go down the aisle, plump and firm in her pink dress and ruffles, with Elvy Morgum toiling slowly behind, hitch and drag, hitch and drag, her figure witchlike in profile above the bunchy black coat.

That was sometime late in January. By mid-February Miss Farrell must have hidden even more often than before the tears of her sense of desperate inadequacy behind the flushed cheeks and the blue Celtic eyes that she showed to us; for she had watched us now every day, for almost a month, sitting before her in an unredeemed and unembarrassed thwarting of every one of the bright words that she had said to us so often. She saw us, no doubt, looking at her with the clear stare of childhood, equally without malice and without mercy, while, behind Sisley Ross, Elvy Morgum crouched in taciturn isolation, the misfit, the unwanted, who wandered alone on the fringe of our games at recess, and trailed home alone after school was out.

For, in spite of Miss Farrell, she had no friends, and when the fourteenth of February arrived, and we were given permission, during the last half-hour of our school-time, to exchange the Valentines we had bought for each other, scrawling the names that we could scarcely write on the backs of the double heart-shaped bits of paper with the printed verses inside that we could scarcely read, none was left on her desk by little Jasper Corrin, who had been appointed, because he was the best reader in the class, to be our postman.

On Sisley's desk the bright heart-shaped folders fluttered in heaps.

None of us had forgotten to send her our tributes, and half-a-dozen of the boys, with spending-money burning in their pockets and admiration burning in their hearts, had lumped the whole sum of money and adoration in one extravagant lacy token, all gilt and froth, that lay on her desk now with its sender's name or a bashful—*Guess Who?*—staggering earnestly across beneath the pierced hearts and the chaste pink-ribboned cupids. We watched as Jasper, walking up and down the aisles with his big box, paused again beside Sisley's desk and laid on it a huge red heart frilled round with stiff white paper. She turned it over without excitement, though it was the handsomest of the lot, and we watched her index finger tracing slowly the letters of the name.

"It's from Elvy Morgum," she announced presently, a little astonishment creeping into her voice.

We looked into Elvy's dark, taciturn face, lit now with a kind of radiant terror of shyness as Sisley turned round to her, all of us wondering by what magical process a Morgum, to whom two-for-a-penny was always half-a-penny too dear, had come into possession of the most magnificent Valentine we had seen that day. But at the same moment there was a cry, sharp and clear, one almost of triumph, and we turned to see Margot Berry standing in her place across the aisle, pointing a steady finger at the great red heart on Sisley's desk.

"It's mine," she said. "*I* gave it to Sisley. *I* bought it for her with my own money."

She came over and picked up the Valentine and showed us the eraser marks over which Elvy had written her name. If we looked closely we could see the *Margot* too, violently erased but still printing the paper with the neat heavy marks of Margot's signature, beneath the narrow scrawl that said *Elvy Morgum.*

"She stole it," Margot said. "She stole it out of the box at noontime and put her name on it instead of mine. I can prove it's mine. Miss Farrell—"

We watched Miss Farrell come down the aisle and pick up the red heart and look at it, and all the while Margot's voice went clamoring on, and Miss Farrell did not even look at her, or tell her to stop. After a while she said to Elvy, in a voice that did not sound angry to us, but full only of an amazed and tremulous desperation: "Did you take the Valentine, Elvy?"

We looked at Elvy again. She was sitting at her desk with her hands shut tight together in her lap and her head thrust forward a little, so that her dark hair fell and hid her face. She didn't say anything, and Miss Farrell asked again: "Did you take it because you wanted a pretty Valentine to give to Sisley? Is that it, Elvy?"

"She stole it," Margot said again. "It was mine; I paid for it with my own money."

"Hush," Miss Farrell said.

She looked at the three of them: at Sisley, suspended in polite waiting amazement, at Margot's red clamorous face, at Elvy's bunched stubborn figure crouched in her seat.

"It was very wrong of you to take Margot's Valentine, Elvy," she said (she was doing what the school board expected of her, I learned to understand later, standing there for morality, and the legal statutes of the state of Indiana, and the Ten Commandments themselves, all at one time; but there was something more she wanted to stand there for too, something that said *love* and said *mercy* and said *understanding*, something that rose like a high hill in the sunlight, above the hidden valley of childhood in which we lived). "If you'd come to me," she said to Elvy, "I'd have helped you make Sisley a Valentine, one even prettier than this. We could have made it together, and then it would have been yours to give to her." She turned to us suddenly, her face pink and shining with her earnestness. "You *do* understand, all of you," she said, "that Elvy only took the Valentine because she wanted something nice to give to Sisley? She didn't take it for herself. You *do* understand that, don't you?"

"She stole it," Margot said. "She did too steal it. I'm going to tell my father."

She looked round in clear unbending triumph at our closed and sober and approving faces.

Then it was the day that Miss Janiek lost her ring. Or it wasn't that she had lost it, she said, because she knew exactly where she had put it, on the ledge of the window in the washroom when she had washed her hands; only when she had gone back for it, it was gone, and not even a ring that had been worn as long as that one had been, she said, could have learned how to walk out of a room alone.

"One of those little savages took it," she said, sitting in the big chair behind Miss Farrell's desk on that cold March afternoon after school, her dark eyes brooding over our inadequacies as we industriously pounded erasers together out the window. "Yours, or mine, or poor little Collins' down the hall," she said. "What they'll do with it, heaven only knows. They haven't any more idea of its value—which I must say isn't large, the salaries of high-school teachers in 1917 being what they were—than a tribe of Choctaw Indians in the year 1491."

Miss Farrell said, "Don't. Don't say that. You know you don't mean—"

She was standing behind us, looking out the window at the street below, quiet now after the long rush and chatter of the lines of children streaming from the school, lying straight and deserted except for a single figure toiling slowly along in an old black velveteen coat. Without looking around, we knew what sort of expression there would be in Miss Farrell's eyes as she stood there watching Elvy Morgum disappear down the street, because as much to her as to us the tale of the lost ring must have come as a sudden whisper of sinister conjecture leading deviously to the little figure in the old black coat. I don't know how it was that we *knew*, as soon as we heard the tale of the ring, as certainly as if we had been there watching the sharp profile, the pure eyes, bent over the glittering bauble on the window-ledge, looking at it for a long moment, in terrific indecision, before the grubby fingers, darting forth suddenly, snatched up the round of gold broken by the winking diamond-blaze, and concealed it swiftly in a faded gingham pocket, along with perhaps a half-sucked lemon drop, a rusty penpoint, and a bit of blue glass that she had picked up off the street. But we *knew*, and the knowledge was like something hidden and wicked inside us, as if we, by our absolute yet wholly groundless assurance, were somehow sharing in the darkness of Elvy's crime.

The next day, at recess time, Miss Farrell kept Elvy back in the classroom while the rest of us trooped outside to the sunlit schoolyard. We stood in tight clusters under the bare limbs of the two big oak trees in the north corner of the yard, our games abandoned, standing where we could watch the windows of the classroom, as if we thought that what was happening there was something lurid and violent, that would flash out its meaning to us through the blank long panes. But all that did happen was that after a little while we saw the side door of the school open and Elvy come out. She came across the yard, pausing at a few feet's distance from us, not joining us, but staying on the fringe of things, as she had done ever since she had first come among us. After a while it was Margot who spoke.

"What did she say to you?" she asked.

There was excitement, almost a kind of respect, in the silence with which we waited for her answer. We watched her standing there before us, her eyes going from one to the other of us as if they could not quite believe what they saw: the excitement, the respect, the fearful admiration. She took a step toward us, hesitating on the drag of her lame foot.

"She didn't say anything. I wasn't afraid of her," she said.

Her voice was hoarse, not loud, as if she didn't use it often and it was a little out of practice. We remembered then that we had hardly ever heard it; even when Miss Farrell asked her a question in school, usually she only got up and stood there, silent, her head thrust forward a little, poised stubbornly like the head of a small granite idol.

"Miss Janiek lost her ring," Margot said in a loud voice, as if it were something she was a little afraid to say. "She left it in the washroom; she told Miss Farrell she left it there. Maybe if she doesn't get it back she'll go tell the principal."

Elvy stood there looking at us without moving; her eyes were watching Sisley Ross, seeing the way the pink had come up in her cheeks from the excitement.

"I wouldn't be afraid," Elvy said.

Her voice was still hoarse, but more excited and strained, the way the boys' voices sounded when they were boasting to each other about the things they could do.

"Not even if you were the one that took it?" Margot said daringly.

"Nobody ever said I took it," Elvy said. She was answering Margot, but she seemed to be talking to Sisley all along. "I wouldn't be afraid, even if they did say I took it," she said. We heard her breath coming fast between the words, as if she had been running hard. "I wouldn't be afraid," she said. "Even if I did take it—"

Watching her, we could see the pocket of her dress bulging slightly, fancying the secret hoard inside, the half-sucked lemon drop, the rusty penpoint, and, at the bottom, hard and dangerous and bright, the round of gold and the winking diamond. Something like a sigh escaped us, a long exhalation of fearful admiration. A girl in blue held out a handful of jacks suddenly.

"We're going to play jacks," she said to Elvy. "Do you want to play too? You can have first turn."

She smiled at Elvy, questioningly, almost timidly, but Elvy kept on looking at Sisley Ross.

"Are you going to play?" she said to her, in that same hoarse, unbelieving voice.

Sisley shook her head. "No," she said. "I don't think I want to play. I think I just want to walk around the yard." She waited a minute, watching Elvy, her pink-and-white face serene yet asking. "Do you think you'd like to come, too?" she said.

We saw them go off together across the yard, side by side in the March sunlight, walking slowly, so that Elvy could keep up. They were still walk-

ing together when the bell rang and it was time for us to go back into the
school again.

It is hard to explain what happened to us after that. Such things—the
sudden mob-shift, the peculiar fascination of the deed too dark for our own
doing—are always difficult to analyze, though no one who has ever thrilled to
the adventures of Jesse James or Robin Hood, or has lived to see, less innocently, the pathological submission of whole peoples to the mere smell and
rattle of a lawless violence, is without the knowledge of what they are like.

For our own part, from the moment when, seized with the conviction
that Elvy Morgum had dared things beyond the farthest range of our
audacity, we watched her walk away with Sisley Ross under our very eyes,
we could only fall deeper into the pit of the submission which our wicked
knowledge had dug for us. I remember that Elvy was wary at first, half-sus-
picious, it seemed, that we might suddenly take back again this strange gift
of supremacy that we had thrust on her; but as the days passed and we did
nothing, her confidence grew, and she began to queen it over us with a kind
of frightened taciturnity. She had grasped the fact that her ascendancy over
us rested on her ability to represent to us a more violent nature than any of
us owned, and she was doing her best, in her small inarticulate way, to keep
up to the pitch of the character that we expected of her.

Not, I suppose, that it made a great deal of difference to her whether
we bowed to her or not, as long as Sisley Ross remained impressed. We used
to watch the two of them, Elvy and Sisley, walking home together, arm in
arm, after school; and there were times when Miss Farrell and Miss Janiek
watched them too, standing—as on the day that Margot and I heard them
talking together—before the windows in our empty classroom, where they
could look out over the street below.

That afternoon Margot and I were pasting on the end window the Easter
lilies we had cut from stiff white paper (they were the best in the class, chosen
after heated competition), and no doubt Miss Farrell and Miss Janiek
believed that we could not hear them, for they were keeping their voices
low, standing close together at the other end of the room. Miss Janiek said:
"Well, she's in the middle of it now. I thought that was what you wanted.
Wasn't it?"—and we heard Miss Farrell answer her, her voice sounding quick
and unhappy, different from the way it did when she spoke to us: "But not
like that. I wanted them to be her friends—"

"Why not like that?" Miss Janiek said. "Why isn't it as good a way as
any? It's their world; they've made the laws; and they're satisfied—"

"No," said Miss Farrell. "It isn't the right way. It can never be the right way."

We could see her face in profile—the short, earnest, slightly tiptilted nose, the round chin, the curve of the forehead beneath the bright curling hair, and, behind it, the turn of Miss Janiek's dark head on its powerful neck, the two of them together like the picture of Day and Night in our readers.

"Why isn't it the right way?" Miss Janiek said. "Isn't it the way we do things ourselves in our world, only for the thin breath of fine words that we grudge even the few moments it takes us to say? Are you trying to make them better than we are ourselves?"

"Yes," Miss Farrell said.

Margot and I looked at each other, not understanding, each looking at the other to see if she understood. Then we heard Miss Janiek saying, in a low harsh voice that sounded somehow as if she had just been crying, or was just going to cry: "I don't care; I don't care about any of it. I've got my own thirty-six, and next year they'll be Collins' thirty-six, and the next year someone else's; and by the time they're fifteen years old, if they remember me at all, they'll remember me only as a kind of ogress who kept them in sometimes after school, and made them recite tables and learn the difference between Christopher Columbus and George Washington, when all they wanted was to be outside in the sun—"

Miss Farrell slipped her hand inside Miss Janiek's arm.

"No," she said. "They'll remember you. And not like that, not just the Christopher Columbus and the George Washington part—"

Miss Janiek shook her head.

"I know better," she said. "You're young; you're not used to losing things yet." Then she sounded as if she were trying to laugh. "Lord," she said, "I've even lost my ring, my little round of golden faith, with a diamond in it to remind me that even I was once thought prized and rare."

They did not say that it was Elvy Morgum who had taken the ring, but we stayed secure in our wicked knowledge and our dark, resenting admiration till another afternoon, this time a dripping day late in April, when half a dozen of us, Elvy Morgum and Sisley Ross among us, had stayed behind to help decorate the classroom for May Day. We had finished the decorations, and had on rain capes and overshoes already, when someone came marching in at the open door of the classroom. It was Miss Janiek, and she was holding her left hand stretched out in front of her, looking as if she did not

quite believe what she saw there—the gleaming golden circle, the bright
flash of the diamond.

"In a pawn shop," she cried out, in her strong voice, to Miss Farrell.
"A pawn shop, of all places in the world! Along with the little cheap fur
jackets, the loving cups, the lost treasured junk of a hundred lives—"

Miss Farrell exclaimed: "But who—?"

She stood before Miss Janiek at the front of the room, her hands tightening on the paste-smeared chain of blue paper rings that she held. Then
we all listened while Miss Janiek told the story of the ring. She told it fast,
so that we did not have time to translate its meaning into the actualities of
our own world as she went along; all that we grasped was a set of wildly
colored pictures, like a sequence out of one of the adventure strips in the
comic papers, with a gum-chewing janitress, a detective, and a pawn-shop
operator who was also a receiver of stolen goods, all pinwheeling together
in a terrific welter of cunning and crime. I remember how we stood there,
quietly, in our rain capes and hoods, while Miss Janiek brought her story
to a close, and then, half-laughing, though there were almost tears in her eyes:
"And think of the ring in the middle of all that," she said; "the poor old thing
that's gone sedately up and down with me for ten years in my lone spinster
existence, after its one romantic moment when Ralph set it on my finger,
and I swore I'd wear it forever; because how was I to imagine then that it
was going to make more of an actuality of a frizz-haired janitress' dream of
owning an imitation seal jacket than of my own dream of marriage and a
home?"

She talked to Miss Farrell, and we kept standing there gravely, understanding and yet not understanding what was being said, with our child's
ability to take only what was comprehensible and interesting to us out of
the words, letting the rest flow by as if we had never heard it. Then it was
Margot Berry who turned first and looked at Elvy Morgum, staring at her
with her face reddening slowly with the triumph of accusation, and pointing
a finger, and saying at last, clearly, as if she were damning her forever with
the words: "*You* didn't take it. You never. You never dared."

We could hear Miss Farrell and Miss Janiek still talking, over near
the desk, but we were not listening to them any more, because we were
watching Elvy standing there in front of us, with her eyes going back and
forth under the harsh tangle of her hair. She didn't have on a rain cape;
she had on the old black velveteen coat she always wore, and all at once,
seeing her standing there in the old black coat, we wanted to make loud,
boastful, cruel laughter in the quiet room—the ancient instinct to mock

and trample the fallen leader rising in us as simply and as innocently as if
we had been the children of the earliest man; before there were any words
that said *love* and said *understanding* and said *brotherhood*. I remember
Elvy's small rusty pleading voice replying to Margot—"I never said I did.
I never said I took it"—the words dying away as her eyes went quickly
from one to the other of our faces, seeing the clear unforgiving stare repeated in each. After that she didn't say anything; she only stood there,
poised on her sound leg, with her head thrust a little forward in her old
attitude of unasking and unhopeful waiting.

"I'm going to walk home with Sisley," Margot said suddenly. She
looked round at us, challenging us, challenging Elvy Morgum, to dispute
her right. "You can all come along, if you want. Everybody can come but
Elvy Morgum."

Then I remember how she moved toward the door, grasping Sisley's
hand tightly in her own. I can see us all as if for a moment time
had stopped and we were suspended in the moment of decision—Sisley
and Margot by the door, Elvy standing alone, her desperate gaze lost in the
tangle of her falling hair, the rest of us just poised to move, herdlike, out
the door behind Margot. I can see Miss Farrell's startled face, the sudden
leap into it of an awareness of the crisis, and Miss Janiek's dark gaze
brooding over us. And then, breaking into the silence, Sisley's voice, not so
prompt, not so clear, a little desperate itself, but determined with no doll-
determination, with no graceful doll-surrender to the pressed button of
others' opinion.

"No," she said. "I'm going to walk home with Elvy Morgum."

She pulled her hand out of Margot's and started back into the room
toward Elvy. I heard Miss Janiek say something, and I turned around, and
there was Miss Farrell standing beside the desk with a look on her face
that I did not understand till many years later, because I thought then that she
was going to cry, and it took me that long to find out that that is the way
people look when they have wanted something for a long time (the bright
words, the high hill), and at last someone gives it to them ungrudgingly
and beautifully.

"Would you like to walk home with me, Elvy?" Sisley said.

"Well, will you look at that!" Miss Janiek said.

"I'm looking," Miss Farrell said. "I'm looking."

STUDY QUESTIONS:

1. Miss Deasy makes both Miss Farrell and Miss Janiek attractive characters, and yet they seem quite different. In what ways are they different and in
what ways are they alike? Probably an elementary school, or, for that matter, a
high school, needs both kinds of teacher. Why?

2. What does the author show about Elvy, when she first appears? Does
Miss Deasy "overdo" Elvy, that is, does she seem a little too pathetic on her
first appearance?

3. What is it within the other children, in your opinion, that causes them
to make a popular idol of Elvy when they think she has stolen Miss Janiek's
ring?

4. How do you think Miss Janiek would have handled the problem of the
theft of the valentine?

5. Discuss the position of the narrator in the story. Obviously, she represents herself as one of the other students. What would seem to be the occasion
for her to remember these events now that she is an adult? How does she show
the growth of her own understanding?

MR. KNOW-ALL

WILLIAM SOMERSET MAUGHAM

William Somerset Maugham (1874–   ) in a long and distinguished career is another of those prolific authors able to write just about anything. He has produced novels, short stories, plays, autobiography, and literary criticism. Actually he started out to be a doctor. He received his degree in medicine from St. Thomas Hospital in London but never practiced. His novel *Of Human Bondage* (1915) deals with the experiences of a medical student and is probably his best known work, although such other novels as *Cakes and Ale* (1930) and *The Moon and Sixpence* (1919) have also been both popular and critical successes. His plays include *The Circle* (1921), *Our Betters* (1923), and *The Constant Wife* (1927). His short stories have been very popular with magazine readers and have appeared with amazing frequency. "Mr. Know-All" first appeared in Cosmopolitan.

Mr. Maugham has generally preferred to write stories of considerable ingenuity of plot in which events take a decidedly ironic turn, and the reader, along with the narrator of the story usually, gets an unexpectedly new understanding of life or human character. In this sense, he is in the tradition of Guy de Maupassant, the great author of the French short story. It is not the intention of the author of this kind of story to trick the reader or to tease him but only to warn him against making casual and easy judgments about what he sees. The narrator in "Mr. Know-All," although his evaluation of Mr. Kelada seems valid enough to the reader, is in for a discovery which reveals that he may have made up his mind too fast.

This story is remarkable for its tightness of form. It reveals long, exacting practice in the writing of the short story. The events are expertly paced. Actually the story is built around a single dramatic incident, but this incident must be prepared for with precision of detail and just the right amount of preliminary movement. Furthermore, the use of a narrator gives the author a chance to keep out of the story himself and let the reader see the events more dramatically, and even, to a certain extent, as in "Mr. Know-All," to make his own interpretations. Only a very practiced writer can turn out a story like "Mr. Know-All."

I was prepared to dislike Max Kelada even before I knew him. The war had just finished and the passenger traffic in the ocean-going lines was heavy. Accommodation was very hard to get and you had to put up with whatever the agents chose to offer you. You could not hope for a cabin to yourself and I was thankful to be given one in which there were only two berths. But when I was told the name of my companion my heart sank. It suggested closed port-holes and the night air rigidly excluded. It was bad enough to share a cabin for fourteen days with anyone (I was going from San Francisco to Yokohama), but I should have looked upon it with less dismay if my fellow-passenger's name had been Smith or Brown.

When I went on board I found Mr. Kelada's luggage already below. I did not like the look of it; there were too many labels on the suitcases, and the wardrobe trunk was too big. He had unpacked his toilet things, and I observed that he was a patron of the excellent Monsieur Coty[1]; for I saw on the washing-stand his scent, his hair-wash and his brilliantine. Mr. Kelada's brushes, ebony with his monogram in gold, would have been all the better for a scrub. I did not at all like Mr. Kelada. I made my way into the smoking-room. I called for a pack of cards and began to play patience[2]. I had scarcely started before a man came up to me and asked me if he was right in thinking my name was so-and-so.

[1] Monsieur Coty. Manufacturer of comparatively inexpensive toiletries for both men and women.

[2] Play "patience." Americans would probably say "solitaire."

"I am Mr. Kelada," he added, with a smile that showed a row of flashing teeth, and sat down.

"Oh, yes, we're sharing a cabin, I think."

"Bit of luck, I call it. You never know who you're going to be put in with. I was jolly glad when I heard you were English. I'm all for us English sticking together when we're abroad, if you understand what I mean."

I blinked.

"Are you English?" I asked, perhaps tactlessly.

"Rather. You don't think I look like an American, do you? British to the backbone, that's what I am."

To prove it, Mr. Kelada took out of his pocket a passport and airily waved it under my nose.

King George has many strange subjects. Mr. Kelada was short and of a sturdy build, clean-shaven and dark-skinned, with a fleshy, hooked nose and very large, lustrous and liquid eyes. His long black hair was sleek and curly. He spoke with a fluency in which there was nothing English and his gestures were exuberant. I felt pretty sure that a closer inspection of that British passport would have betrayed the fact that Mr. Kelada was born under a bluer sky than is generally seen in England.

"What will you have?" he asked me.

I looked at him doubtfully. Prohibition[3] was in force and to all appearances the ship was bone-dry. When I am not thirsty I do not know which I dislike more, ginger-ale or lemon-squash. But Mr. Kelada flashed an oriental smile at me.

"Whiskey and soda or a dry Martini, you have only to say the word."

From each of his hip-pockets he fished a flask and laid them on the table before me. I chose the Martini, and calling the steward he ordered a tumbler of ice and a couple of glasses.

"A very good cocktail," I said.

"Well, there are plenty more where that came from, and if you've got any friends on board, you tell them you've got a pal who's got all the liquor in the world."

Mr. Kelada was chatty. He talked of New York and of San Francisco. He discussed plays, pictures, and politics. He was patriotic. The Union Jack is an impressive piece of drapery, but when it is flourished by a gentleman from Alexandria or Beirut, I cannot but feel that it loses somewhat in dignity. Mr. Kelada was familiar. I do not wish to put on airs, but I

---

[3] Prohibition. The period in America between 1919 and 1933, when the manufacture, sale and use of alcoholic beverages, except for medicinal purposes, was prohibited by Federal law.

cannot help feeling that it is seemly in a total stranger to put mister before my name when he addresses me. Mr. Kelada, doubtless to set me at my ease, used no such formality. I did not like Mr. Kelada. I had put aside the cards when he sat down, but now, thinking that for this first occasion our conversation had lasted long enough, I went on with my game.

"The three on the four," said Mr. Kelada.

There is nothing more exasperating when you are playing patience than to be told where to put the card you have turned up before you have had a chance to look for yourself.

"It's coming out, it's coming out," he cried. "The ten on the knave."

With rage and hatred in my heart I finished. Then he seized the pack.

"Do you like card tricks?"

"No, I hate card tricks," I answered.

"Well, I'll just show you this one."

He showed me three. Then I said I would go down to the dining-room and get my seat at table.

"Oh, that's all right," he said. "I've already taken a seat for you. I thought that as we were in the same state-room we might just as well sit at the same table."

I did not like Mr. Kelada.

I not only shared a cabin with him and ate three meals a day at the same table, but I could not walk round the deck without his joining me. It was impossible to snub him. It never occurred to him that he was not wanted. He was certain that you were as glad to see him as he was to see you. In your own house you might have kicked him downstairs and slammed the door in his face without the suspicion dawning on him that he was not a welcome visitor. He was a good mixer, and in three days knew everyone on board. He ran everything. He managed the sweeps, conducted the auctions, collected money for prizes at the sports, got up quoit and golf matches, organised the concert and arranged the fancy dress ball. He was everywhere and always. He was certainly the best-hated man in the ship. We called him Mr. Know-All, even to his face. He took it as a compliment. But it was at meal times that he was most intolerable. For the better part of an hour then he had us at his mercy. He was hearty, jovial, loquacious and argumentative. He knew everything better than anybody else, and it was an affront to his overweening vanity that you should disagree with him. He would not drop a subject, however unimportant, till he had brought you round to his way of thinking. The possibility that he could be mistaken never occurred to him. He was the chap who knew. We sat at the doctor's table. Mr. Kelada would certainly

have had it all his own way, for the doctor was lazy and I was frigidly indifferent, except for a man called Ramsay who sat there also. He was
as dogmatic as Mr. Kelada and resented bitterly the Levantine's cocksureness.
The discussions they had were acrimonious and interminable.

Ramsay was in the American Consular Service, and was stationed at
Kobe. He was a great heavy fellow from the Middle West, with loose fat
under a tight skin, and he bulged out of his ready-made clothes. He was on
his way back to resume his post, having been on a flying visit to New York
to fetch his wife, who had been spending a year at home. Mrs. Ramsay was
a very pretty little thing, with pleasant manners and a sense of humour. The
Consular Service is ill paid, and she was dressed always very simply; but
she knew how to wear her clothes. She achieved an effect of quiet distinction. I should not have paid any particular attention to her but that she possessed a quality that may be common enough in women, but nowadays is
not obvious in their demeanour. You could not look at her without being
struck by her modesty. It shone in her like a flower on a coat.

One evening at dinner the conversation by chance drifted to the subject
of pearls. There had been in the papers a good deal of talk about the culture
pearls which the cunning Japanese were making, and the doctor remarked
that they must inevitably diminish the value of real ones. They were very good
already; they would soon be perfect. Mr. Kelada, as was his habit, rushed
the new topic. He told us all that was to be known about pearls. I do not
believe Ramsay knew anything about them at all, but he could not resist the
opportunity to have a fling at the Levantine, and in five minutes we were in
the middle of a heated argument. I had seen Mr. Kelada vehement and voluble before, but never so voluble and vehement as now. At last something
that Ramsay said stung him, for he thumped the table and shouted:

"Well, I ought to know what I am talking about. I'm going to Japan
just to look into this Japanese pearl business. I'm in the trade and there's
not a man in it who won't tell you that what I say about pearls goes. I know
all the best pearls in the world and what I don't know about pearls isn't
worth knowing."

Here was news for us, for Mr. Kelada, with all his loquacity, had never
told anyone what his business was. We only knew vaguely that he was going
to Japan on some commercial errand. He looked round the table triumphantly.

"They'll never be able to get a culture pearl that an expert like me can't
tell with half an eye." He pointed to a chain that Mrs. Ramsay wore. "You
take my word for it, Mrs. Ramsay, that chain you're wearing will never be
worth a cent less than it is now."

Mrs. Ramsay in her modest way flushed a little and slipped the chain inside her dress. Ramsay leaned forward. He gave us all a look and a smile flickered in his eyes.

"That's a pretty chain of Mrs. Ramsay's, isn't it?"

"I noticed it at once," answered Mr. Kelada. "Gee, I said to myself, those are pearls all right."

"I didn't buy it myself, of course. I'd be interested to know how much you think it cost."

"Oh, in the trade somewhere round fifteen thousand dollars. But if it was bought on Fifth Avenue I shouldn't be surprised to hear that anything up to thirty thousand was paid for it."

Ramsay smiled grimly.

"You'll be surprised to hear that Mrs. Ramsay bought that string at a department store the day before we left New York, for eighteen dollars."

Mr. Kelada flushed.

"Rot. It's not only real, but it's as fine a string for its size as I've ever seen."

"Will you bet on it? I'll bet you a hundred dollars it's imitation."

"Done."

"Oh, Elmer, you can't bet on a certainty," said Mrs. Ramsay.

She had a little smile on her lips and her tone was gently deprecating.

"Can't I? If I get a chance of easy money like that I should be all sorts of a fool not to take it."

"But how can it be proved?" she continued. "It's only my word against Mr. Kelada's."

"Let me look at the chain, and if it's imitation I'll tell you quickly enough. I can afford to lose a hundred dollars," said Mr. Kelada.

"Take it off, dear. Let the gentleman look at it as much as he wants."

Mrs. Ramsay hesitated a moment. She put her hands to the clasp.

"I can't undo it," she said. "Mr. Kelada will just have to take my word for it."

I had a sudden suspicion that something unfortunate was about to occur, but I could think of nothing to say.

Ramsay jumped up.

"I'll undo it."

He handed the chain to Mr. Kelada. The Levantine took a magnifying glass from his pocket and closely examined it. A smile of triumph spread over his smooth and swarthy face. He handed back the chain. He was about to speak. Suddenly he caught sight of Mrs. Ramsay's face. It was so white that she looked as though she were about to faint. She was staring at him with wide and terrified eyes. They held a desperate appeal; it was so clear that I wondered why her husband did not see it.

Mr. Kelada stopped with his mouth open. He flushed deeply. You could almost *see* the effort he was making over himself.

"I was mistaken," he said. "It's a very good imitation, but of course as soon as I looked through my glass I saw that it wasn't real. I think eighteen dollars is just about as much as the damned thing's worth."

He took out his pocket-book and from it a hundred-dollar note. He handed it to Ramsay without a word.

"Perhaps that'll teach you not to be so cocksure another time, my young friend," said Ramsay as he took the note.

I noticed that Mr. Kelada's hands were trembling.

The story spread over the ship as stories do, and he had to put up with a good deal of chaff that evening. It was a fine joke that Mr. Know-All had been caught out. But Mrs. Ramsay retired to her state-room with a headache.

Next morning I got up and began to shave. Mr. Kelada lay on his bed smoking a cigarette. Suddenly there was a small scraping sound and I saw a letter pushed under the door. I opened the door and looked out. There was nobody there. I picked up the letter and saw that it was addressed to Max Kelada. The name was written in block letters. I handed it to him.

"Who's this from?" He opened it. "Oh!"

He took out of the envelope, not a letter, but a hundred-dollar note. He looked at me and again he reddened. He tore the envelope into little bits and gave them to me.

"Do you mind just throwing them out of the port-hole?"

I did as he asked, and then I looked at him with a smile.

"No one likes being made to look a perfect damned fool," he said.

"Were the pearls real?"

"If I had a pretty little wife I shouldn't let her spend a year in New York while I stayed at Kobe," said he.

At that moment I did not entirely dislike Mr. Kelada. He reached out for his pocket-book and carefully put in it the hundred-dollar note.

STUDY QUESTIONS:

1. This is a story not so much of the surprise-ending type as of that which leads the reader to a result totally different from what he expected. In "Mr. Know-All" this is accomplished through Mr. Kelada's unexpected display of decency in protecting Mrs. Ramsay's secret. Is there anything in the early part of the story which prepares the reader for what Mr. Kelada does?

2. Characterize the narrator of the story. How do you interpret the next-to-last sentence, "At that moment I did not entirely dislike Mr. Kelada"? Does it mean more than it says or is it to be taken quite literally?

3. The paragraph on p. 78 which begins, "I not only shared a cabin with him . . ." has interesting stylistic effects, especially in its rapid movement. In a very brief space Mr. Maugham gives us a great amount of time and a great amount of detail. How is this accomplished? Study particularly the forms and patterns of his sentences.

4. How plausible is this story; that is, how willing are you to accept that it may have happened?

THE STRANGE CASE OF DR. JEKYLL AND MR. HYDE

ROBERT LOUIS STEVENSON

Born in Edinburgh and dying in Samoa, Robert Louis Stevenson (1850–1894) united in himself such complex qualities it is hard to sum up the books and the man; yet in a sense it is easy to see why he created Dr. Jekyll and Mr. Hyde. He himself was a bundle of lively contradictions. He was Scotch, he believed in the moral destiny of human beings, but he loved rogues and vagabonds. He was an invalid all his life and therefore demanded that one should live picturesquely and adventurously. Though he did not practice the profession, he was trained as an engineer, and simultaneously wanted to be romantic and also a skillful constructor of tales. He was an unsuccessful dramatist whose stories teem with drama, and a successful critic whose essays are more often directed to the question of how to live than they are to how to write. He published "The Strange Case of Dr. Jekyll and Mr. Hyde" in 1886, a story that has haunted English readers ever since, so much so that these two proper names have taken on a proverbial character.

"The Strange Case of Dr. Jekyll and Mr. Hyde" can be thought of as a "long" short story or as a concentrated novel. As a short story it meets the primary requisite of one important kind of story—it leads up to a fate-

ful change in the fortune and the character of the "hero." As a condensed
novel its ten named sections are like ten chapters, each of which ends with
a puzzling action, and each of which in turn leads the reader deeper and
deeper into the darkened heart of man, so that, when we come to the final
statement, we are prepared to believe in a mystery story that has turned
into a morality play, and begin to shudder at the possibilities latent in all
of us.

But there is more to the problem of meaning than the question
whether this narrative is short story or novel. It is a mixture of contradictory, yet conventional elements so freshly fused we do not feel they are
old. In the first place, the concept of an utterly evil person has long troubled
the world, as names like Cain, Judas, the Wandering Jew, and Faust (or, if
you prefer, Mephistopheles) amply show. This concept is essential to
Stevenson's purpose. Then there is a contribution of long standing from
science fantasy and from medieval romance—the Magic Potion, which will
prolong youth, change character, or transport the drinker into another
world. A third element is the Faithful Servant, and a fourth is the Faithful Friend.

Stevenson fuses these components into the pattern of a detective story.
Note that the title refers to a strange case, just as the casebook of Sherlock
Holmes is made up of crimes difficult to solve and as the novels of Erle
Stanley Gardner are each called "The Case of———." In the hands of a less
skillful author a story made up of so many traditional materials might break,
but Stevenson is so adroit in mixing them together, he is so clever in post-
poning the final solution of the riddle, that he holds attention and shocks
the reader into a new perception of the potentialities for good and ill in
any human being. Perhaps it was sheer genius that led him in this story to
anticipate some of the findings of modern psychology about personality and
its troubles.

STORY OF THE DOOR

Mr. Utterson the lawyer was a man of a rugged countenance that was
never lighted by a smile; cold, scanty and embarrassed in discourse; backward in sentiment; lean, long, dusty, dreary and yet somehow lovable. At
friendly meetings, and when the wine was to his taste, something eminently
human beaconed from his eye; something indeed which never found its way
into his talk, but which spoke not only in these silent symbols of the after-
dinner face, but more often and loudly in the acts of his life. He was austere
with himself; drank gin when he was alone, to mortify a taste for vintages;

and though he enjoyed the theatre, had not crossed the doors of one for twenty years. But he had an approved tolerance for others; sometimes wondering, almost with envy, at the high pressure of spirits involved in their misdeeds; and in any extremity inclined to help rather than to reprove. "I incline to Cain's heresy[1]," he used to say quaintly: "I let my brother go to the devil in his own way." In this character, it was frequently his fortune to be the last reputable acquaintance and the last good influence in the lives of downgoing men. And to such as these, so long as they came about his chambers, he never marked a shade of change in his demeanour.

No doubt the feat was easy to Mr. Utterson; for he was undemonstrative at the best, and even his friendship seemed to be founded in a similar catholicity of good-nature. It is the mark of a modest man to accept his friendly circle ready-made from the hands of opportunity; and that was the lawyer's way. His friends were those of his own blood or those whom he had known the longest; his affections, like ivy, were the growth of time, they implied no aptness in the object. Hence, no doubt, the bond that united him to Mr. Richard Enfield, his distant kinsman, the well-known man about town. It was a nut to crack for many, what these two could see in each other, or what subject they could find in common. It was reported by those who encountered them in their Sunday walks, that they said nothing, looked singularly dull, and would hail with obvious relief the appearance of a friend. For all that, the two men put the greatest store by these excursions, counted them the chief jewel of each week, and not only set aside occasions of pleasure, but even resisted the calls of business, that they might enjoy them uninterrupted.

It chanced on one of these rambles that their way led them down a by-street in a busy quarter of London. The street was small and what is called quiet, but it drove a thriving trade on the week-days. The inhabitants were all doing well, it seemed, and all emulously hoping to do better still, and laying out the surplus of their gains in coquetry; so that the shop fronts stood along that thoroughfare with an air of invitation, like rows of smiling saleswomen. Even on Sunday, when it veiled its more florid charms and lay comparatively empty of passage, the street shone out in contrast to its dingy neighbourhood, like a fire in a forest; and with its freshly painted shutters, well-polished brasses, and general cleanliness and gaiety of note, instantly caught and pleased the eye of the passenger.

Two doors from one corner, on the left hand going east, the line was

---

[1] Cain's heresy. In *Genesis* IV: 9, Cain, when the Lord asks him where Abel is, whom has just murdered, responds: "Am I my brother's keeper?"

broken by the entry of a court; and just at that point, a certain sinister block of building thrust forward its gable on the street. It was two storeys high; showed no window, nothing but a door on the lower storey and a blind forehead of discoloured wall on the upper; and bore in every feature, the marks of prolonged and sordid negligence. The door, which was equipped with neither bell nor knocker, was blistered and distained. Tramps slouched into the recess and struck matches on the panels; children kept shop upon the steps; the schoolboy had tried his knife on the mouldings; and for close on a generation, no one had appeared to drive away these random visitors or to repair their ravages.

Mr. Enfield and the lawyer were on the other side of the by-street; but when they came abreast of the entry, the former lifted up his cane and pointed.

"Did you ever remark that door?" he asked; and when his companion had replied in the affirmative, "It is connected in my mind," added he, "with a very odd story."

"Indeed?" said Mr. Utterson, with a slight change of voice, "and what was that?"

"Well, it was this way," returned Mr. Enfield: "I was coming home from some place at the end of the world, about three o'clock of a black winter morning, and my way lay through a part of town where there was literally nothing to be seen but lamps. Street after street, and all the folks asleep —street after street, all lighted up as if for a procession and all as empty as a church—till at last I got into that state of mind when a man listens and listens and begins to long for the sight of a policeman. All at once, I saw two figures: one a little man who was stumping along eastward at a good walk, and the other a girl of maybe eight or ten who was running as hard as she was able down a cross street. Well, sir, the two ran into one another naturally enough at the corner; and then came the horrible part of the thing; for the man trampled calmly over the child's body and left her screaming on the ground. It sounds nothing to hear, but it was hellish to see. It wasn't like a man; it was like some damned Juggernaut.[2] I gave a view halloa, took to my heels, collared my gentleman, and brought him back to where there was already quite a group about the screaming child. He was perfectly cool and made no resistance, but gave me one look, so ugly that it brought out the sweat on me like running. The people who had turned out were the girl's

---

[2] Juggernaut. At Orissa in India, the statue of Juggernaut was annually dragged on an enormous car through the streets, and crazed worshippers threw themselves under its wheels to be crushed to death.

own family; and pretty soon, the doctor, for whom she had been sent, put in his appearance. Well, the child was not much the worse, more frightened, according to the Sawbones; and there you might have supposed would be an end to it. But there was one curious circumstance. I had taken a loathing to my gentleman at first sight. So had the child's family, which was only natural. But the doctor's case was what struck me. He was the usual cut and dry apothecary, of no particular age and colour, with a strong Edinburgh accent, and about as emotional as a bagpipe. Well, sir, he was like the rest of us; every time he looked at my prisoner, I saw that Sawbones turn sick and white with the desire to kill him. I knew what was in his mind, just as he knew what was in mine; and killing being out of the question, we did the next best. We told the man we could and would make such a scandal out of this, as should make his name stink from one end of London to the other. If he had any friends or any credit, we undertook that he should lose them. And all the time, as we were pitching it in red hot, we were keeping the women off him as best we could, for they were as wild as harpies. I never saw a circle of such hateful faces; and there was the man in the middle, with a kind of black, sneering coolness—frightened too, I could see that—but carrying it off, sir, really like Satan. 'If you choose to make capital out of this accident,' said he, 'I am naturally helpless. No gentleman but wishes to avoid a scene,' says he. 'Name your figure' Well, we screwed him up to a hundred pounds for the child's family; he would have clearly liked to stick out; but there was something about the lot of us that meant mischief, and at last he struck. The next thing was to get the money; and where do you think he carried us but to that place with the door?— whipped out a key, went in, and presently came back with the matter of ten pounds in gold and a cheque for the balance on Coutts's,[3] drawn payable to bearer and signed with a name that I can't mention, though it's one of the points of my story, but it was a name at least very well known and often printed. The figure was stiff; but the signature was good for more than that, if it was only genuine. I took the liberty of pointing out to my gentleman that the whole business looked apocryphal, and that a man does not, in real life, walk into a cellar door at four in the morning and come out of it with another man's cheque for close upon a hundred pounds. But he was quite easy and sneering. 'Set your mind at rest,' says he, 'I will stay with you till the banks open and cash the cheque myself.' So we all set off, the doctor, and the child's father, and our friend and myself, and passed the rest of the night in my chambers; and next day, when we had break-

[3] Coutts's. Coutts and Co., a famous banking house, a synonym for financial respectability.

fasted, went in a body to the bank. I gave in the cheque myself, and said I had every reason to believe it was a forgery. Not a bit of it. The cheque was genuine."

"Tut-tut," said Mr. Utterson.

"I see you feel as I do," said Mr. Enfield. "Yes, it's a bad story. For my man was a fellow that nobody could have to do with, a really damnable man; and the person that drew the cheque is the very pink of the proprieties, celebrated too, and (what makes it worse) one of your fellows who do what they call good. Black mail, I suppose; an honest man paying through the nose for some of the capers of his youth. Black Mail House is what I call that place with the door, in consequence. Though even that, you know, is far from explaining all," he added, and with the words fell into a vein of musing.

From this he was recalled by Mr. Utterson asking rather suddenly: "And you don't know if the drawer of the cheque lives there?"

"A likely place, isn't it?" returned Mr. Enfield. "But I happen to have noticed his address; he lives in some square or other."

"And you never asked about the—place with the door?" said Mr. Utterson.

"No, sir: I had a delicacy," was the reply. "I feel very strongly about putting questions; it partakes too much of the style of the day of judgment. You start a question, and it's like starting a stone. You sit quietly on the top of a hill; and away the stone goes, starting others; and presently some bland old bird (the last you would have thought of) is knocked on the head in his own back garden and the family have to change their name. No, sir, I make it a rule of mine: the more it looks like Queer Street the less I ask."

"A very good rule, too," said the lawyer.

"But I have studied the place for myself," continued Mr. Enfield. "It seems scarcely a house. There is no other door, and nobody goes in or out of that one but, once in a great while, the gentleman of my adventure. There are three windows looking on the court on the first floor; none below; the windows are always shut but they're clean. And then there is a chimney which is generally smoking; so somebody must live there. And yet it's not so sure; for the buildings are so packed together about that court, that it's hard to say where one ends and another begins."

The pair walked on again for a while in silence; and then "Enfield," said Mr. Utterson, "that's a good rule of yours."

"Yes, I think it is." returned Enfield.

"But for all that," continued the lawyer, "there's one point I want to ask: I want to ask the name of that man who walked over the child."

"Well," said Mr. Enfield, "I can't see what harm it would do. It was a man of the name of Hyde."

"Hm," said Mr. Utterson. "What sort of a man is he to see?"

"He is not easy to describe. There is something wrong with his appearance; something displeasing, something downright detestable. I never saw a man I so disliked, and yet I scarce know why. He must be deformed somewhere; he gives a strong feeling of deformity, although I couldn't specify the point. He's an extraordinary looking man, and yet I really can name nothing out of the way. No, sir; I can make no hand of it; I can't describe him. And it's not want of memory; for I declare I can see him this moment."

Mr. Utterson again walked some way in silence and obviously under a weight of consideration. "You are sure he used a key?" he inquired at last.

"My dear sir . . ." began Enfield, surprised out of himself.

"Yes, I know," said Utterson; "I know it must seem strange. The fact is, if I do not ask you the name of the other party, it is because I know it already. You see, Richard, your tale has gone home. If you have been inexact in any point, you had better correct it."

"I think you might have warned me," returned the other with a touch of sullenness. "But I have been pedantically exact, as you call it. The fellow had a key; and what's more, he has it still. I saw him use it, not a week ago."

Mr. Utterson sighed deeply but said never a word; and the young man presently resumed. "Here is another lesson to say nothing," said he. "I am ashamed of my long tongue. Let us make a bargain never to refer to this again."

"With all my heart," said the lawyer. "I shake hands on that, Richard."

SEARCH FOR MR. HYDE

That evening Mr. Utterson came home to his bachelor house in sombre spirits and sat down to dinner without relish. It was his custom of a Sunday, when this meal was over, to sit close by the fire, a volume of some dry divinity on his reading desk, until the clock of the neighbouring church rang out the hour of twelve, when he would go soberly and gratefully to bed. On this night, however, as soon as the cloth was taken away, he took up a candle and went into his business room. There he opened his safe, took from the most private part of it a document endorsed on the envelope as

Dr. Jekyll's Will, and sat down with a clouded brow to study its contents. The will was holograph[4], for Mr. Utterson, though he took charge of it now that it was made, had refused to lend the least assistance in the making of it; it provided not only that, in case of the decease of Henry Jekyll, M.D., D.C.L., L.L.D., F.R.S., etc. all his possessions were to pass into the hands of his "friend and benefactor Edward Hyde," but that in case of Dr. Jekyll's "disappearance or unexplained absence for any period exceeding three calendar months," the said Edward Hyde should step into the said Henry Jekyll's shoes without further delay and free from any burden or obligation, beyond the payment of a few small sums to the members of the doctor's household. This document had long been the lawyer's eyesore. It offended him both as a lawyer and as a lover of the sane and customary sides of life, to whom the fanciful was the immodest. And hitherto it was his ignorance of Mr. Hyde that had swelled his indignation; now, by a sudden turn, it was his knowledge. It was already bad enough when the name was but a name of which he could learn no more. It was worse when it began to be clothed upon with detestable attributes; and out of the shifting, insubstantial mists that had so long baffled his eye, there leaped up the sudden, definite presentment of a fiend.

  "I thought it was madness," he said, as he replaced the obnoxious paper in the safe, "and now I begin to fear it is disgrace."

  With that he blew out his candle, put on a greatcoat, and set forth in the direction of Cavendish Square, that citadel of medicine, where his friend, the great Dr. Lanyon, had his house and received his crowding patients. "If anyone knows, it will be Lanyon," he had thought.

  The solemn butler knew and welcomed him; he was subjected to no stage of delay, but ushered direct from the door to the dining-room where Dr. Lanyon sat alone over his wine. This was a hearty, healthy, dapper, red-faced gentleman, with a shock of hair prematurely white, and a boisterous and decided manner. At sight of Mr. Utterson, he sprang up from his chair and welcomed him with both hands. The geniality, as was the way of the man, was somewhat theatrical to the eye; but it reposed on genuine feeling. For these two were old friends, old mates both at school and college, both thorough respecters of themselves and of each other, and, what does not always follow, men who thoroughly enjoyed each other's company.

  After a little rambling talk, the lawyer led up to the subject which so disagreeably preoccupied his mind.

----

[4] Holograph. It was entirely in the handwriting of the person in whose name it appears. Most wills in the period of the story were written out by a law clerk and merely signed by the testator, the person making the will.

"I suppose, Lanyon," said he, "you and I must be the two oldest friends that Henry Jekyll has?"

"I wish the friends were younger," chuckled Dr. Lanyon. "But I suppose we are. And what of that? I see little of him now."

"Indeed?" said Utterson. "I thought you had a bond of common interest."

"We had," was the reply. "But it is more than ten years since Henry Jekyll became too fanciful for me. He began to go wrong, wrong in mind; and though of course I continue to take an interest in him for old sake's sake, as they say, I see and I have seen devilish little of the man. Such unscientific balderdash," added the doctor, flushing suddenly purple, "would have estranged Damon and Pythias."[5]

This little spirit of temper was somewhat of a relief to Mr. Utterson. "They have only differed on some point of science," he thought; and being a man of no scientific passions (except in the matter of conveyancing), he even added: "It is nothing worse than that!" He gave his friend a few seconds to recover his composure, and then approached the question he had come to put. "Did you ever come across a protégé of his—one Hyde?" he asked.

"Hyde?" repeated Lanyon. "No. Never heard of him. Since my time."

That was the amount of information that the lawyer carried back with him to the great, dark bed on which he tossed to and fro, until the small hours of the morning began to grow large. It was a night of little ease to his toiling mind, toiling in mere darkness and besieged by questions.

Six o'clock struck on the bells of the church that was so conveniently near to Mr. Utterson's dwelling, and still he was digging at the problem. Hitherto it had touched him on the intellectual side alone; but now his imagination also was engaged, or rather enslaved; and as he lay and tossed in the gross darkness of the night and the curtained room, Mr. Enfield's tale went by before his mind in a scroll of lighted pictures. He would be aware of the great field of lamps of a nocturnal city; then of the figure of a man walking swiftly; then of a child running from the doctor's; and then these met, and that human Juggernaut trod the child down and passed on regardless of her screams. Or else he would see a room in a rich house, where his friend lay asleep, dreaming and smiling at his dreams; and then the door of that room would be opened, the curtains of the bed plucked apart, the sleeper recalled, and lo! there would stand by his side a figure to whom power was given, and even at that dead hour, he must rise and do its bidding. The figure in these two phases haunted the lawyer all

[5] Damon and Pythias. Proverbial fast friends of Greek mythology.

night; and if at any time he dozed over, it was but to see it glide more stealth-
ily through sleeping houses, or move the more swiftly and still the more
swiftly, even to dizziness, through wider labyrinths of lamplighted city, and at
every street corner crush a child and leave her screaming. And still the figure had no face by which he might know it; even in his dreams, it had no
face, or one that baffled him and melted before his eyes; and thus it was that
there sprang up and grew apace in the lawyer's mind a singularly strong,
almost an inordinate, curiosity to behold the features of the real Mr. Hyde.
If he could but once set eyes on him, he thought the mystery would lighten
and perhaps roll altogether away, as was the habit of mysterious things when
well examined. He might see a reason for his friend's strange preference or
bondage (call it which you please) and even for the startling clause of the
will. At least it would be a face worth seeing: the face of a man who was
without bowels of mercy: a face which had but to show itself to raise up, in
the mind of the unimpressionable Enfield, a spirit of enduring hatred.

From that time forward, Mr. Utterson began to haunt the door in the
by-street of shops. In the morning before office hours, at noon when
business was plenty, and time scarce, at night under the face of the fogged
city moon, by all lights and at all hours of solitude or concourse, the
lawyer was to be found on his chosen post.

"If he be Mr. Hyde," he had thought, "I shall be Mr. Seek."

And at last his patience was rewarded. It was a fine dry night; frost in
the air; the streets as clean as a ballroom floor; the lamps, unshaken by any
wind, drawing a regular pattern of light and shadow. By ten o'clock, when
the shops were closed, the by-street was very solitary and, in spite of
the low growl of London from all round, very silent. Small sounds carried
far; domestic sounds out of the houses were clearly audible on either
side of the roadway; and the rumour of the approach of any passenger
preceded him by a long time. Mr. Utterson had been some minutes at his
post, when he was aware of an odd, light footstep drawing near. In
the course of his nightly patrols, he had long grown accustomed to
the quaint effect with which the footfalls of a single person, while he is still
a great way off, suddenly spring out distinct from the vast hum and clatter
of the city. Yet his attention had never before been so sharply and
decisively arrested; and it was with a strong, superstitious prevision of
success that he withdrew into the entry of the court.

The steps drew swiftly nearer, and swelled out suddenly louder as
they turned the end of the street. The lawyer, looking forth from the entry,
could soon see what manner of man he had to deal with. He was small and
very plainly dressed, and the look of him, even at that distance, went some-

how strongly against the watcher's inclination. But he made straight for the door, crossing the roadway to save time; and as he came, he drew a key from his pocket like one approaching home.

Mr. Utterson stepped out and touched him on the shoulder as he passed. "Mr. Hyde, I think?"

Mr. Hyde shrank back with a hissing intake of the breath. But his fear was only momentary; and though he did not look the lawyer in the face, he answered coolly enough: "That is my name. What do you want?"

"I see you are going in," returned the lawyer. "I am an old friend of Dr. Jekyll's—Mr. Utterson of Gaunt Street—you must have heard of my name; and meeting you so conveniently, I thought you might admit me."

"You will not find Dr. Jekyll; he is from home," replied Mr. Hyde, blowing in the key. And then suddenly, but still without looking up, "How did you know me?" he asked.

"On your side," said Mr. Utterson, "will you do me a favour?"

"With pleasure," replied the other. "What shall it be?"

"Will you let me see your face?" asked the lawyer.

Mr. Hyde appeared to hesitate, and then, as if upon some sudden reflection, fronted about with an air of defiance; and the pair stared at each other pretty fixedly for a few seconds. "Now I shall know you again," said Mr. Utterson. "It may be useful."

"Yes," returned Mr. Hyde, "it is as well we have met; and *à propos,* you should have my address." And he gave a number of a street in Soho.

"Good God!" thought Mr. Utterson, "can he, too, have been thinking of the will?" But he kept his feelings to himself and only grunted in acknowledgment of the address.

"And now," said the other, "how did you know me?"

"By description," was the reply.

"Whose description?"

"We have common friends," said Mr. Utterson.

"Common friends?" echoed Mr. Hyde, a little hoarsely. "Who are they?"

"Jekyll, for instance," said the lawyer.

"He never told you," cried Mr. Hyde, with a flush of anger. "I did not think you would have lied."

"Come," said Mr. Utterson, "that is not fitting language."

The other snarled aloud into a savage laugh; and the next moment, with extraordinary quickness, he had unlocked the door and disappeared into the house.

The lawyer stood awhile when Mr. Hyde had left him, the picture of disquietude. Then he began slowly to mount the street, pausing every step or two and putting his hand to his brow like a man in mental perplexity. The problem he was thus debating as he walked, was one of a class that is rarely solved. Mr. Hyde was pale and dwarfish, he gave an impression of deformity without any nameable malformation, he had a displeasing smile, he had borne himself to the lawyer with a sort of murderous mixture of timidity and boldness, and he spoke with a husky, whispering and somewhat broken voice; all these were points against him, but not all of these together could explain the hitherto unknown disgust, loathing and fear with which Mr. Utterson regarded him. "There must be something else," said the perplexed gentleman. "There *is* something more, if I could find a name for it. God bless me, the man seems hardly human! Something troglodytic, shall we say? or can it be the old story of Dr. Fell? or is it the mere radiance of a foul soul that thus transpires through, and transfigures, its clay continent? The last, I think; for, O my poor old Harry Jekyll, if ever I read Satan's signature upon a face, it is on that of your new friend."

Round the corner from the by-street, there was a square of ancient, handsome houses, now for the most part decayed from their high estate and let in flats and chambers to all sorts and conditions of men; map-engravers, architects, shady lawyers and the agents of obscure enterprises. One house, however, second from the corner, was still occupied entire; and at the door of this, which wore a great air of wealth and comfort, though it was now plunged in darkness except for the fanlight, Mr. Utterson stopped and knocked. A well-dressed, elderly servant opened the door.

"Is Dr. Jekyll at home, Poole?" asked the lawyer.

"I will see, Mr. Utterson," said Poole, admitting the visitor, as he spoke, into a large, low-roofed, comfortable hall, paved with flags, warmed (after the fashion of a country house) by a bright, open fire, and furnished with costly cabinets of oak. "Will you wait here by the fire, sir? or shall I give you a light in the dining-room?"

"Here, thank you," said the lawyer, and he drew near and leaned on the tall fender. This hall, in which he was now left alone, was a pet fancy of his friend the doctor's; and Utterson himself was wont to speak of it as the pleasantest room in London. But tonight there was a shudder in his blood; the face of Hyde sat heavy on his memory; he felt (what was rare with him) a nausea and distaste of life; and in the gloom of his spirits, he seemed to read a menace in the flickering of the firelight on the polished cabinets and the uneasy starting of the shadow on the roof. He was ashamed of his relief, when Poole presently returned to announce that Dr. Jekyll was gone out.

"I saw Mr. Hyde go in by the old dissecting-room door, Poole," he said. "Is that right, when Dr. Jekyll is from home?"

"Quite right, Mr. Utterson, sir," replied the servant. "Mr. Hyde has a key."

"Your master seems to repose a great deal of trust in that young man, Poole," resumed the other musingly.

"Yes, sir, he do indeed," said Poole. "We have all orders to obey him."

"I do not think I ever met Mr. Hyde?" asked Utterson.

"O, dear no, sir. He never *dines* here," replied the butler. "Indeed we see very little of him on this side of the house; he mostly comes and goes by the laboratory."

"Well, good-night, Poole."

"Good-night, Mr. Utterson."

And the lawyer set out homeward with a very heavy heart. "Poor Harry Jekyll," he thought, "my mind misgives me he is in deep waters! He was wild when he was young; a long while ago to be sure; but in the law of God, there is no statute of limitations.[6] Ay, it must be that; the ghost of some old sin, the cancer of some concealed disgrace: punishment coming, *pede claudo*,[7] years after memory has forgotten and self-love condoned the fault." And the lawyer, scared by the thought, brooded awhile on his own past, groping in all the corners of memory, lest by chance some Jack-in-the-Box of an old iniquity should leap to light there. His past was fairly blameless; few men could read the rolls of their life with less apprehension; yet he was humbled to the dust by the many ill things he had done, and raised up again into a sober and fearful gratitude by the many he had come so near to doing, yet avoided. And then by a return on his former subject, he conceived a spark of hope. "This Master Hyde, if he were studied," thought he, "must have secrets of his own; black secrets,

[6] Statute of limitations. A legal provision whereby after the lapse of a given number of years one cannot be prosecuted for a crime.

[7] Pede claudo. This phrase occurs in the last line of a poem by Horace, and requires a little explanation. We know from the opening of the story that Mr. Utterson, a conservative man, has had a conservative education; and it is therefore appropriate he should quote from Horace (*Carmina*, III:2): raro antecedentem scelestum/deseruit pede Poena claudo, which Dean Swift translated: "And though the villain 'scape a while, he feels/Slow vengeance, like a blood-hound, at his heels."

by the look of him; secrets compared to which poor Jekyll's worst would be like sunshine. Things cannot continue as they are. It turns me cold to think of this creature stealing like a thief to Harry's bedside; poor Harry, what a wakening! And the danger of it; for if this Hyde suspects the existence of the will, he may grow impatient to inherit. Ay, I must put my shoulder to the wheel—if Jekyll will but let me," he added, "if Jekyll will only let me." For once more he saw before his mind's eye, as clear as transparency, the strange clauses of the will.

DR. JEKYLL WAS QUITE AT EASE

A fortnight later, by excellent good fortune, the doctor gave one of his pleasant dinners to some five or six old cronies, all intelligent, reputable men and all judges of good wine; and Mr. Utterson so contrived that he remained behind after the others had departed. This was no new arrangement, but a thing that had befallen many scores of times. Where Utterson was liked, he was liked well. Hosts loved to detain the dry lawyer, when the light-hearted and loose-tongued had already their foot on the threshold; they liked to sit awhile in his unobtrusive company, practising for solitude, sobering their minds in the man's rich silence after the expense and strain of gaiety. To this rule, Dr. Jekyll was no exception; and as he now sat on the opposite side of the fire—a large, well-made, smooth-faced man of fifty, with something of a slyish cast perhaps, but every mark of capacity and kindness—you could see by his looks that he cherished for Mr. Utterson a sincere and warm affection.

"I have been wanting to speak to you, Jekyll," began the latter. "You know that will of yours?"

A close observer might have gathered that the topic was distasteful; but the doctor carried it off gaily. "My poor Utterson," said he, "you are unfortunate in such a client, I never saw a man so distressed as you were by my will; unless it were that hide-bound pedant, Lanyon, at what he called my scientific heresies. O, I know he's a good fellow—you needn't frown—an excellent fellow, and I always mean to see more of him; but a hide-bound pedant for all that; an ignorant, blatant pedant. I was never more disappointed in any man than Lanyon."

"You know I never approved of it," pursued Utterson, ruthlessly disregarding the fresh topic.

"My will? Yes, certainly, I know that," said the doctor, a trifle sharply. "You have told me so."

"Well, I tell you so again," continued the lawyer. "I have been learning something of young Hyde."

The large handsome face of Dr. Jekyll grew pale to the very lips, and there came a blackness about his eyes. "I do not care to hear more," said he. "This is a matter I thought we had agreed to drop."

"What I heard was abominable," said Utterson.

"It can make no change. You do not understand my position," returned the doctor, with a certain incoherency of manner. "I am painfully situated, Utterson; my position is a very strange—a very strange one. It is one of those affairs that cannot be mended by talking."

"Jekyll," said Utterson, "you know me: I am a man to be trusted. Make a clean breast of this in confidence; and I make no doubt I can get you out of it."

"My good Utterson," said the doctor, "this is very good of you, this is downright good of you, and I cannot find words to thank you in. I believe you fully; I would trust you before any man alive, ay, before myself, if I could make the choice; but indeed it isn't what you fancy; it is not as bad as that; and just to put your good heart at rest, I will tell you one thing: the moment I choose, I can be rid of Mr. Hyde. I give you my hand upon that; and I thank you again and again; and I will just add one little word, Utterson, that I'm sure you'll take in good part: this is a private matter, and I beg of you to let it sleep."

Utterson reflected a little, looking in the fire.

"I have no doubt you are perfectly right," he said at last, getting to his feet.

"Well, but since we have touched upon this business, and for the last time I hope," continued the doctor, "there is one point I should like you to understand. I have really a very great interest in poor Hyde. I know you have seen him; he told me so; and I fear he was rude. But I do sincerely take a great, a very great interest in that young man; and if I am taken away, Utterson, I wish you to promise me that you will bear with him and get his rights for him. I think you would, if you knew all; and it would be a weight off my mind if you would promise."

"I can't pretend that I shall ever like him," said the lawyer.

"I don't ask that," pleaded Jekyll, laying his hand upon the other's arm; "I only ask for justice; I only ask you to help him for my sake, when I am no longer here."

Utterson heaved an irrepressible sigh. "Well," said he, "I promise."

THE CAREW MURDER CASE

Nearly a year later, in the month of October, 18—, London was startled by a crime of singular ferocity and rendered all the more notable by the high position of the victim. The details were few and startling. A maid servant living alone in a house not far from the river, had gone upstairs to bed about eleven. Although a fog rolled over the city in the small hours, the early part of the night was cloudless, and the lane, which the maid's window overlooked, was brilliantly lit by the full moon. It seems she was romantically given, for she sat down upon her box,[8] which stood immediately under the window, and fell into a dream of musing. Never (she used to say, with streaming tears, when she narrated that experience), never had she felt more at peace with all men or thought more kindly of the world. And as she so sat she became aware of an aged beautiful gentleman with white hair, drawing near along the lane; and advancing to meet him, another and very small gentleman, to whom at first she paid less attention. When they had come within speech (which was just under the maid's eyes) the older man bowed and accosted the other with a very pretty manner of politeness. It did not seem as if the subject of his address were of great importance; indeed, from his pointing, it sometimes appeared as if he were only inquiring his way; but the moon shone on his face as he spoke, and the girl was pleased to watch it, it seemed to breathe such an innocent and old-world kindness of disposition, yet with something high too, as of a well-founded self-content. Presently her eye wandered to the other, and she was surprised to recognise in him a certain Mr. Hyde, who had once visited her master and for whom she had conceived a dislike. He had in his hand a heavy cane, with which he was trifling; but he answered never a word, and seemed to listen with an ill-contained impatience. And then all of a sudden he broke out in a great flame of anger, stamping with his foot, brandishing the cane, and carrying on (as the maid described it) like a madman. The old gentleman took a step back, with the air of one very much surprised and a trifle hurt; and at that Mr. Hyde broke out of all bounds and clubbed him to the earth. And next moment, with ape-like fury, he was trampling his victim under foot and hailing down a storm of blows, under which the bones were audibly shattered and the body jumped upon the roadway. At the horror of these sights and sounds, the maid fainted.

[8] Box, i.e., equivalent to a trunk.

It was two o'clock when she came to herself and called for the police. The murderer was gone long ago; but there lay his victim in the middle of the lane, incredibly mangled. The stick with which the deed had been done, although it was of some rare and very tough and heavy wood, had broken in the middle under the stress of this insensate cruelty; and one splintered half had rolled in the neighbouring gutter—the other, without doubt, had been carried away by the murderer. A purse and gold watch were found upon the victim: but no cards or papers, except a sealed and stamped envelope, which he had been probably carrying to the post, and which bore the name and address of Mr. Utterson.

This was brought to the lawyer the next morning, before he was out of bed; and he had no sooner seen it, and been told the circumstances, than he shot out a solemn lip. "I shall say nothing till I have seen the body," said he; "this may be very serious. Have the kindness to wait while I dress." And with the same grave countenance he hurried through his breakfast and drove to the police station, whither the body had been carried. As soon as he came into the cell, he nodded.

"Yes," said he, "I recognise him. I am sorry to say that this is Sir Danvers Carew."

"Good God sir," exclaimed the officer, "is it possible?" And the next moment his eye lighted up with professional ambition. "This will make a deal of noise," he said. "And perhaps you can help us to the man." And he briefly narrated what the maid had seen, and showed the broken stick.

Mr. Utterson had already quailed at the name of Hyde; but when the stick was laid before him, he could doubt no longer; broken and battered as it was, he recognised it for one that he had himself presented many years before to Henry Jekyll.

"Is this Mr. Hyde a person of small stature?" he inquired. "Particularly small and particularly wicked-looking, is what the maid calls him," said the officer.

Mr. Utterson reflected; and then, raising his head, "If you will come with me in my cab," he said, "I think I can take you to his house."

It was by this time about nine in the morning, and the first fog of the season. A great chocolate-coloured pall lowered over heaven, but the wind was continually charging and routing these embattled vapours; so that as the cab crawled from street to street, Mr. Utterson beheld a marvelous number of degrees and hues of twilight; for here it would be dark like the back-end of evening; and there would be a glow of a rich, lurid brown, like the light of some strange conflagration; and here, for a moment, the fog would be quite broken up, and a haggard shaft of daylight would glance in between the swirling wreaths. The dismal quarter of Soho seen under these changing glimpses, with its muddy ways, and slatternly passengers, and its lamps, which had never been extinguished or had been kindled afresh to combat this mournful reinvasion of darkness, seemed, in the lawyer's eyes, like a district of some city in a nightmare. The thoughts of his mind, besides, were of the gloomiest dye; and when he glanced at the companion of his drive, he was conscious of some touch of that terror of the law and the law's officers, which may at times assail the most honest.

As the cab drew up before the address indicated, the fog lifted a little and showed him a dingy street, a gin palace, a low French eating house, a shop for the retail of penny numbers[9] and twopenny salads, many ragged children huddled in the doorways, and many women of many different nationalities passing out, key in hand, to have a morning glass; and the next moment the fog settled down again upon that part, as brown as umber, and cut him off from his blackguardly surroundings. This was the home of Henry Jekyll's favourite; of a man who was heir to a quarter of a million sterling.

An ivory-faced and silvery-haired old woman opened the door. She had an evil face, smoothed by hypocrisy: but her manners were excellent. Yes, she said, this was Mr. Hyde's, but he was not at home; he had been in that night very late, but he had gone away again in less than an hour; there was nothing strange in that; his habits were very irregular, and he was often absent; for instance, it was nearly two months since she had seen him till yesterday.

"Very well, then, we wish to see his rooms," said the lawyer; and when the woman began to declare it was impossible, "I had better tell you who this person is," he added. "This is Inspector Newcomen of Scotland Yard."

A flash of odious joy appeared upon the woman's face. "Ah!" she said. "he is in trouble! What has he done?"

Mr. Utterson and the inspector exchanged glances. "He don't seem a very popular character," observed the latter. "And now, my good woman, just let me and this gentleman have a look about us."

In the whole extent of the house, which but for the old woman remained otherwise empty, Mr. Hyde had only used a couple of rooms; but these were furnished with luxury and good taste. A closet was filled with wine; the plate was of silver, the napery elegant; a good picture hung upon the walls, a gift (as Utterson supposed) from Henry Jekyll, who was

9 Penny numbers. Installments of melodramatic fiction sold for a penny.

much of a connoisseur; and the carpets were of many plies and agreeable in colour. At this moment, however, the rooms bore every mark of having been recently and hurriedly ransacked; clothes lay about the floor, with their pockets inside out; lock-fast drawers stood open; and on the hearth there lay a pile of grey ashes, as though many papers had been burned. From these embers the inspector disinterred the butt end of a green cheque book, which had resisted the action of the fire; the other half of the stick was found behind the door; and as this clinched his suspicions, the officer declared himself delighted. A visit to the bank, where several thousand pounds were found to be lying to the murderer's credit, completed his gratification.

"You may depend upon it, sir," he told Mr. Utterson: "I have him in my hand. He must have lost his head, or he never would have left the stick or, above all, burned the cheque book. Why, money's life to a man. We have nothing to do but wait for him at the bank, and get out the handbills[10]."

This last, however, was not so easy of accomplishment; for Mr. Hyde had numbered few familiars—even the master of the servant maid had only seen him twice; his family could nowhere be traced; he had never been photographed; and the few who could describe him differed widely, as common observers will. Only on one point were they agreed; and that was the haunting sense of unexpressed deformity with which the fugitive impressed his beholders.

INCIDENT OF THE LETTER

It was late in the afternoon, when Mr. Utterson found his way to Dr. Jekyll's door, where he was at once admitted by Poole, and carried down by the kitchen offices and across a yard which had once been a garden, to the building which was indifferently known as the laboratory or dissecting rooms. The doctor had bought the house from the heirs of a celebrated surgeon; and his own tastes being rather chemical than anatomical, had changed the destination of the block at the bottom of the garden. It was the first time that the lawyer had been received in that part of his friend's quarters; and he eyed the dingy, windowless structure with curiosity, and gazed round with a distasteful sense of strangeness as he crossed the theatre,[11] once crowded with eager students and now lying gaunt and silent, the tables laden with chemical apparatus, the floor strewn with crates and

[10] Handbills. I.e., posters of the kind found in U.S. post offices describing a criminal who is "wanted".

[11] Theatre. I.e., lecture hall.

littered with packing straw, and the light falling dimly through the foggy cupola. At the further end, a flight of stairs mounted to a door covered with red baize; and through this, Mr. Utterson was at last received into the doctor's cabinet. It was a large room fitted round with glass presses, furnished, among other things, with a cheval-glass and a business table, and looking out upon the court by three dusty windows barred with iron. The fire burned in the grate; a lamp was set lighted on the chimney shelf, for even in the houses the fog began to lie thickly; and there, close up to the warmth, sat Dr. Jekyll, looking deadly sick. He did not rise to meet his visitor, but held out a cold hand and bade him welcome in a changed voice.

"And now," said Mr. Utterson, as soon as Poole had left them, "you have heard the news?"

The doctor shuddered. "They were crying it in the square," he said. "I heard them in my dining-room."

"One word," said the lawyer. "Carew was my client, but so are you, and I want to know what I am doing. You have not been mad enough to hide this fellow?"

"Utterson, I swear to God," cried the doctor, "I swear to God I will never set eyes on him again. I bind my honour to you that I am done with him in this world. It is all at an end. And indeed he does not want my help; you do not know him as I do; he is safe, he is quite safe; mark my words, he will never more be heard of."

The lawyer listened gloomily; he did not like his friend's feverish manner. "You seem pretty sure of him," said he; "and for your sake, I hope you may be right. If it came to a trial, your name might appear."

"I am quite sure of him," replied Jekyll; "I have grounds for certainty that I cannot share with anyone. But there is one thing on which you may advise me. I have—I have received a letter; and I am at a loss whether I should show it to the police. I should like to leave it in your hands, Utterson; you would judge wisely, I am sure; I have so great a trust in you."

"You fear, I suppose, that it might lead to his detection?" asked the lawyer."

"No," said the other, "I cannot say that I care what becomes of Hyde; I am quite done with him. I was thinking of my own character, which this hateful business has rather exposed."

Utterson ruminated awhile; he was surprised at his friend's selfishness, and yet relieved by it. "Well," said he, at last, "let me see the letter."

The letter was written in an odd, upright hand and signed "Edward

Hyde": and it signified, briefly enough, that the writer's benefactor, Dr. Jekyll, whom he had long so unworthily repaid for a thousand generosities, need labour under no alarm for his safety, as he had means of escape on which he placed a sure dependence. The lawyer liked this letter well enough; it put a better colour on the intimacy than he had looked for; and he blamed himself for some of his past suspicions.

"Have you the envelope?" he asked.

"I burned it," replied Jekyll, "before I thought what I was about. But it bore no postmark. The note was handed in."

"Shall I keep this and sleep upon it?" asked Utterson.

"I wish you to judge for me entirely," was the reply. "I have lost confidence in myself."

"Well, I shall consider," returned the lawyer. "And now one word more: it was Hyde who dictated the terms in your will about that disappearance?"

The doctor seemed seized with a qualm of faintness; he shut his mouth tight and nodded.

"I knew it," said Utterson. "He meant to murder you. You had a fine escape."

"I have had what is far more to the purpose," returned the doctor solemnly: "I have had a lesson—O God, Utterson, what a lesson I have had!" And he covered his face for a moment with his hands.

On his way out, the lawyer stopped and had a word or two with Poole. "By the bye," said he, "there was a letter handed in to-day: what was the messenger like?" But Poole was positive nothing had come except by post; "and only circulars by that," he added.

This news sent off the visitor with his fears renewed. Plainly the letter had come by the laboratory door; possibly, indeed, it had been written in the cabinet; and if that were so, it must be differently judged, and handled with the more caution. The newsboys, as he went, were crying themselves hoarse along the footways: "Special edition. Shocking murder of an M.P.[12]" That was the funeral oration of one friend and client; and he could not help a certain apprehension lest the good name of another should be sucked down in the eddy of the scandal. It was, at least, a ticklish decision that he had to make; and self-reliant as he was by habit, he began to cherish a longing for advice. It was not to be had directly; but perhaps, he thought, it might be fished for.

Presently after, he sat on one side of his own hearth, with Mr. Guest,

[12] M.P. Member of Parliament.

his head clerk, upon the other, and midway between, at a nicely calculated distance from the fire, a bottle of a particular old wine that had long dwelt unsunned in the foundations of his house. The fog still slept on the wing above the drowned city, where the lamps glimmered like carbuncles; and through the muffle and smother of these fallen clouds, the procession of the town's life was still rolling in through the great arteries with a sound as of a mighty wind. But the room was gay with firelight. In the bottle the acids were long ago resolved; the imperial dye[13] had softened with time, as the colour grows richer in stained windows; and the glow of hot autumn afternoons on hillside vineyards, was ready to be set free and to disperse the fogs of London. Insensibly the lawyer melted. There was no man from whom he kept fewer secrets than Mr. Guest; and he was not always sure that he kept as many as he meant. Guest had often been on business to the doctor's; he knew Poole; he could scarce have failed to hear of Mr. Hyde's familiarity about the house; he might draw conclusions: was it not as well, then, that he should see a letter which put that mystery to rights? and above all since Guest, being a great student and critic of handwriting, would consider the step natural and obliging? The clerk, besides, was a man of counsel; he could scarce read so strange a document without dropping a remark; and by that remark Mr. Utterson might shape his future course.

"This is a sad business about Sir Danvers," he said.

"Yes, sir, indeed. It has elicited a great deal of public feeling," returned Guest. "The man, of course, was mad."

"I should like to hear your views on that," replied Utterson. "I have a document here in his handwriting; it is between ourselves, for I scarce know what to do about it; it is an ugly business at the best. But there it is; quite in your way: a murderer's autograph."

Guest's eyes brightened, and he sat down at once and studied it with passion. "No sir," he said: "not mad; but it is an odd hand."

"And by all accounts a very odd writer," added the lawyer.

Just then the servant entered with a note.

"Is that from Dr. Jekyll, sir?" inquired the clerk. "I thought I knew the writing. Anything private, Mr. Utterson?"

"Only an invitation to dinner. Why? Do you want to see it?"

"One moment. I thank you, sir," and the clerk laid the two sheets of paper alongside and sedulously compared their contents. "Thank you, sir," he said at last, returning both; "it's a very interesting autograph."

There was a pause, during which Mr. Utterson struggled with himself. "Why did you compare them, Guest?" he inquired suddenly.

13 Imperial dye. I.e., Roman red.

"Well, sir," returned the clerk, "there's a rather singular resemblance; the two hands are in many points identical: only differently sloped."

"Rather quaint," said Utterson.

"It is, as you say, rather quaint," returned Guest.

"I wouldn't speak of this note, you know," said the master.

"No, sir," said the clerk. "I understand."

But no sooner was Mr. Utterson alone that night, than he locked the note into his safe, where it reposed from that time forward. "What!" he thought. "Henry Jekyll forge for a murderer!" And his blood ran cold in his veins.

REMARKABLE INCIDENT OF DR. LANYON

Time ran on; thousands of pounds were offered in reward, for the death of Sir Danvers was resented as a public injury; but Mr. Hyde had disappeared out of the ken of the police as though he had never existed. Much of his past was unearthed, indeed, and all disreputable: tales came out of the man's cruelty, at once so callous and violent; of his vile life, of his strange associates, of the hatred that seemed to have surrounded his career; but of his present whereabouts, not a whisper. From the time he had left the house in Soho on the morning of the murder, he was simply blotted out; and gradually, as time drew on, Mr. Utterson began to recover from the hotness of his alarm, and to grow more at quiet with himself. The death of Sir Danvers was, to his way of thinking, more than paid for by the disappearance of Mr. Hyde. Now that that evil influence had been withdrawn, a new life began for Dr. Jekyll. He came out of his seclusion, renewed relations with his friends, became once more their familiar guest and entertainer; and whilst he had always been known for charities, he was now no less distinguished for religion. He was busy, he was much in the open air, he did good; his face seemed to open and brighten, as if with an inward consciousness of service; and for more than two months, the doctor was at peace.

On the 8th of January Utterson had dined at the doctor's with a small party; Lanyon had been there; and the face of the host had looked from one to the other as in the old days when the trio were inseparable friends. On the 12th, and again on the 14th, the door was shut against the lawyer. "The doctor was confined to the house," Poole said, "and saw no one." On the 15th, he tried again, and was again refused; and having now been used for the last two months to see his friend almost daily, he found this return of solitude to weigh upon his spirits. The fifth night he had in Guest to dine with him; and the sixth he betook himself to Dr. Lanyon's.

There at least he was not denied admittance; but when he came in, he was shocked at the change which had taken place in the doctor's appearance. He had his death-warrant written legibly upon his face. The rosy man had grown pale; his flesh had fallen away; he was visibly balder and older; and yet it was not so much these tokens of a swift physical decay that arrested the lawyer's notice, as a look in the eye and quality of manner that seemed to testify to some deep-seated terror of the mind. It was unlikely that the doctor should fear death; and yet that was what Utterson was tempted to suspect. "Yes," he thought; "he is a doctor, he must know his own state and that his days are counted; and the knowledge is more than he can bear." And yet when Utterson remarked on his ill-looks, it was with an air of great firmness that Lanyon declared himself a doomed man.

"I have had a shock," he said, "and I shall never recover. It is a question of weeks. Well, life has been pleasant; I liked it; yes, sir, I used to like it. I sometimes think if we knew all, we should be more glad to get away."

"Jekyll is ill, too," observed Utterson. "Have you seen him?"

But Lanyon's face changed, and he held up a trembling hand. "I wish to see or hear no more of Dr. Jekyll," he said in a loud, unsteady voice. "I am quite done with that person; and I beg that you will spare me any allusion to one whom I regard as dead."

"Tut-tut," said Mr. Utterson; and then after a considerable pause, "Can't I do anything?" he inquired. "We are three very old friends, Lanyon; we shall not live to make others."

"Nothing can be done," returned Lanyon; "ask himself."

"He will not see me," said the lawyer.

"I am not surprised at that," was the reply. "Some day, Utterson, after I am dead, you may perhaps come to learn the right and wrong of this. I cannot tell you. And in the meantime, if you can sit and talk with me of other things, for God's sake, stay and do so; but if you cannot keep clear of this accursed topic, then in God's name, go, for I cannot bear it."

As soon as he got home, Utterson sat down and wrote to Jekyll, complaining of his exclusion from the house, and asking the cause of this unhappy break with Lanyon; and the next day brought him a long answer, often very pathetically worded, and sometimes darkly mysterious in drift. The quarrel with Lanyon was incurable. "I do not blame our old friend," Jekyll wrote, "but I share his view that we must never meet. I mean from henceforth to lead a life of extreme seclusion; you must not be surprised, nor must you doubt my friendship, if my door is often shut even to you. You must suffer me to go my own dark way. I have brought on myself a punishment and a danger that I cannot name. If I am the chief of sinners, I am the chief of sufferers also. I could not think that this earth contained a place for sufferings and terrors so unmanning; and you can do but one thing, Utterson, to lighten this destiny, and that is to respect my silence." Utterson was amazed; the dark influence of Hyde had been withdrawn, the doctor had returned to his old tasks and amities; a week ago, the prospect had smiled with every promise of a cheerful and an honoured age; and now in a moment, friendship, and peace of mind, and the whole tenor of his life were wrecked. So great and unprepared a change pointed to madness; but in view of Lanyon's manner and words, there must lie for it some deeper ground.

A week afterwards Dr. Lanyon took to his bed, and in something less than a fortnight he was dead. The night after the funeral, at which he had been sadly affected, Utterson locked the door of his business room, and sitting there by the light of a melancholy candle, drew out and set before him an envelope addressed by the hand and sealed with the seal of his dead friend. "PRIVATE: for the hands of G. J. Utterson ALONE, and in case of his predecease to be destroyed unread," so it was emphatically superscribed; and the lawyer dreaded to behold the contents. "I have buried one friend to-day," he thought: "what if this should cost me another?" And then he condemned the fear as a disloyalty, and broke the seal. Within there was another enclosure, likewise sealed, and marked upon the cover as "not to be opened till the death or disappearance of Dr. Henry Jekyll." Utterson could not trust his eyes. Yes, it was disappearance; here again, as in the mad will which he had long ago restored to its author, here again were the idea of a disappearance and the name of Henry Jekyll bracketted. But in the will, that idea had sprung from the sinister suggestion of the man Hyde; it was set there with a purpose all too plain and horrible. Written by the hand of Lanyon, what should it mean? A great curiosity came on the trustee, to disregard the prohibition and dive at once to the bottom of these mysteries; but professional honour and faith to his dead friend were stringent obligations; and the packet slept in the inmost corner of his private safe.

It is one thing to mortify curiosity, another to conquer it; and it may be doubted if, from that day forth, Utterson desired the society of his surviving friend with the same eagerness. He thought of him kindly; but his thoughts were disquieted and fearful. He went to call indeed; but he was perhaps relieved to be denied admittance; perhaps, in his heart, he preferred to speak with Poole upon the doorstep and surrounded by the air and sounds of the open city, rather than to be admitted into that house of voluntary bondage, and to sit and speak with its inscrutable recluse. Poole had, indeed, no very pleasant news to communicate. The doctor, it appeared, now more than ever confined himself to the cabinet over the laboratory, where he would sometimes even sleep; he was out of spirits, he had grown very silent, he did not read; it seemed as if he had something on his mind. Utterson became so used to the unvarying character of these reports, that he fell off little by little in the frequency of his visits.

INCIDENT AT THE WINDOW

It chanced on Sunday, when Mr. Utterson was on his usual walk with Mr. Enfield, that their way lay once again through the by-street; and that when they came in front of the door, both stopped to gaze on it.

"Well," said Enfield, "that story's at an end at least. We shall never see more of Mr. Hyde."

"I hope not," said Utterson. "Did I ever tell you that I once saw him, and shared your feeling of repulsion?"

"It was impossible to do the one without the other," returned Enfield. "And by the way, what an ass you must have thought me, not to know that this was a back way to Dr. Jekyll's! It was partly your own fault that I found it out, even when I did."

"So you found it out, did you?" said Utterson. "But if that be so, we may step into the court and take a look at the windows. To tell you the truth, I am uneasy about poor Jekyll; and even outside, I feel as if the presence of a friend might do him good."

The court was very cool and a little damp, and full of premature twilight, although the sky, high up overhead, was still bright with sunset. The middle one of the three windows was half-way open; and sitting close beside it, taking the air with an infinite sadness of mien, like some disconsolate prisoner, Utterson saw Dr. Jekyll.

"What! Jekyll!" he cried. "I trust you are better."

"I am very low, Utterson," replied the doctor drearily, "very low. It will not last long, thank God."

"You stay too much indoors," said the lawyer. "You should be out, whipping up the circulation like Mr. Enfield and me. (This is my cousin—Mr. Enfield—Dr. Jekyll.) Come now; get your hat and take a quick turn with us."

"You are very good," sighed the other. "I should like to very much; but no, no, no, it is quite impossible; I dare not. But indeed, Utterson, I am very glad to see you; this is really a great pleasure; I would ask you and Mr. Enfield up, but the place is really not fit."

"Why then," said the lawyer, good-naturedly, "the best thing we can do is to stay down here and speak with you from where we are."

"That is just what I was about to venture to propose," returned the doctor with a smile. But the words were hardly uttered, before the smile was struck out of his face and succeeded by an expression of such abject terror and despair, as froze the very blood of the two gentlemen below. They saw it but for a glimpse for the window was instantly thrust down; but that glimpse had been sufficient, and they turned and left the court without a word. In silence, too, they traversed the by-street; and it was not until they had come into a neighbouring thoroughfare, where even upon a Sunday there were still some stirrings of life, that Mr. Utterson at last turned and looked at his companion. They were both pale; and there was an answering horror in their eyes.

"God forgive us, God forgive us," said Mr. Utterson.

But Mr. Enfield only nodded his head very seriously, and walked on once more in silence.

THE LAST NIGHT

Mr. Utterson was sitting by his fireside one evening after dinner, when he was surprised to receive a visit from Poole.

"Bless me, Poole, what brings you here?" he cried; and then taking a second look at him, "What ails you?" he added; "is the doctor ill?"

"Mr. Utterson," said the man, "there is something wrong."

"Take a seat, and here is a glass of wine for you," said the lawyer. "Now, take your time, and tell me plainly what you want."

"You know the doctor's ways, sir," replied Poole, "and how he shuts himself up. Well, he's shut up again in the cabinet; and I don't like it, sir— I wish I may die if I like it. Mr. Utterson, sir, I'm afraid."

"Now, my good man," said the lawyer, "be explicit. What are you afraid of?"

"I've been afraid for about a week," returned Poole, doggedly disregarding the question, "and I can bear it no more."

The man's appearance amply bore out his words; his manner was altered for the worse; and except for the moment when he had first announced his terror, he had not once looked the lawyer in the face. Even now, he sat with the glass of wine untasted on his knee, and his eyes directed to a corner of the floor. "I can bear it no more," he repeated.

"Come," said the lawyer, "I see you have some good reason, Poole; I see there is something seriously amiss. Try to tell me what it is."

"I think there's been foul play," said Poole, hoarsely.

"Foul play!" cried the lawyer, a good deal frightened and rather inclined to be irritated in consequence. "What foul play! What does the man mean?"

"I daren't say, sir," was the answer; "but will you come along with me and see for yourself?"

Mr. Utterson's only answer was to rise and get his hat and greatcoat; but he observed with wonder the greatness of the relief that appeared upon the butler's face, and perhaps with no less, that the wine was still untasted when he set it down to follow.

It was a wild, cold, seasonable night of March, with a pale moon, lying on her back as though the wind had tilted her, and a flying wrack of the most diaphanous and lawny texture. The wind made talking difficult, and flecked the blood into the face. It seemed to have swept the streets unusually bare of passengers, besides; for Mr. Utterson thought he had never seen that part of London so deserted. He could have wished it otherwise; never in his life had he been conscious of so sharp a wish to see and touch his fellow-creatures; for struggle as he might, there was borne in upon his mind a crushing anticipation of calamity. The square, when they got there, was full of wind and dust, and the thin trees in the garden were lashing themselves along the railing. Poole, who had kept all the way a pace or two ahead, now pulled up in the middle of the pavement, and in spite of the biting weather, took off his hat and mopped his brow with a red pocket-handkerchief. But for all the hurry of his coming, these were not the dews of exertion that he wiped away, but the moisture of some strangling anguish; for his face was white and his voice, when he spoke, harsh and broken.

"Well, sir," he said, "here we are, and God grant there be nothing wrong."

"Amen, Poole," said the lawyer.

Thereupon the servant knocked in a very guarded manner; the door was opened on the chain; and a voice asked from within, "Is that you, Poole?"

"It's all right," said Poole. "Open the door."

The hall, when they entered it, was brightly lighted up; the fire was built high; and about the hearth the whole of the servants, men and women, stood huddled together like a flock of sheep. At the sight of Mr. Utterson, the housemaid broke into hysterical whimpering; and the cook, crying out "Bless God! it's Mr. Utterson," ran forward as if to take him in her arms.

"What, what? Are you all here?" said the lawyer peevishly. "Very irregular, very unseemly; your master would be far from pleased."

"They're all afraid," said Poole.

Blank silence followed, no one protesting; only the maid lifted up her voice and now wept loudly.

"Hold your tongue!" Poole said to her, with a ferocity of accent that testified to his own jangled nerves; and indeed, when the girl had so suddenly raised the note of her lamentation, they had all started and turned towards the inner door with faces of dreadful expectation. "And now," continued the butler, addressing the knife-boy[14], "reach me a candle, and we'll get this through hands at once." And then he begged Mr. Utterson to follow him, and led the way to the back garden.

"Now, sir," said he, "you come as gently as you can. I want you to hear, and I don't want you to be heard. And see here, sir, if by any chance he was to ask you in, don't go."

Mr. Utterson's nerves, at this unlooked-for termination, gave a jerk that nearly threw him from his balance; but he recollected his courage and followed the butler into the laboratory building and through the surgical theatre, with its lumber of crates and bottles, to the foot of the stair. Here Poole motioned him to stand on one side and listen; while he himself, setting down the candle and making a great and obvious call on his resolution, mounted the steps and knocked with a somewhat uncertain hand on the red baize of the cabinet door.

"Mr. Utterson, sir, asking to see you," he called; and even as he did so, once more violently signed to the lawyer to give ear.

A voice answered from within: "Tell him I cannot see anyone," it said complainingly.

"Thank you, sir," said Poole, with a note of something like triumph in his voice; and taking up his candle, he led Mr. Utterson back across the yard and into the great kitchen, where the fire was out and the beetles were leaping on the floor.

"Sir," he said, looking Mr. Utterson in the eyes, "was that my master's voice?"

"It seems much changed," replied the lawyer, very pale, but giving look for look.

"Changed? Well, yes, I think so," said the butler. "Have I been twenty years in this man's house, to be deceived about his voice? No, sir; master's made away with; he was made away with eight days ago, when we heard him cry out upon the name of God; and *who's* in there instead of him, and *why* it stays there, is a thing that cries to Heaven, Mr. Utterson!"

"This is a very strange tale, Poole; this is rather a wild tale, my man," said Mr. Utterson, biting his finger. "Suppose it were as you suppose, sup-

[14] Knife boy. A minor servant in charge of the cutlery.

posing Dr. Jekyll to have been—well, murdered, what could induce the murderer to stay? That won't hold water; it doesn't commend itself to reason."

"Well, Mr. Utterson, you are a hard man to satisfy, but I'll do it yet," said Poole. "All this last week (you must know) him, or it, whatever it is that lives in that cabinet, has been crying night and day for some sort of medicine and cannot get it to his mind. It was sometimes his way—the master's, that is—to write his orders on a sheet of paper and throw it on the stair. We've had nothing else this week back; nothing but papers, and a closed door, and the very meals left there to be smuggled in when nobody was looking. Well, sir, every day, ay, and twice and thrice in the same day, there have been orders and complaints, and I have been sent flying to all the wholesale chemists in town. Every time I brought the stuff back, there would be another paper telling me to return it, because it was not pure, and another order to a different firm. This drug is wanted bitter bad, sir, whatever for."

"Have you any of these papers?" asked Mr. Utterson.

Poole felt in his pocket and handed out a crumpled note, which the lawyer, bending nearer to the candle, carefully examined. Its contents ran thus: "Dr. Jekyll presents his compliments to Messrs. Maw. He assures them that their last sample is impure and quite useless for his present purpose. In the year 18—, Dr. J. purchased a somewhat large quantity from Messrs. M. He now begs them to search with most sedulous care, and should any of the same quality be left, to forward it to him at once. Expense is no consideration. The importance of this to Dr. J. can hardly be exaggerated." So far the letter had run composedly enough, but here with a sudden splutter of the pen, the writer's emotion had broken loose. "For God's sake," he added, "find me some of the old."

"This is a strange note," said Mr. Utterson; and then sharply, "How do you come to have it open?"

"The man at Maw's was main[15] angry, sir, and he threw it back to me like so much dirt," returned Poole.

"This is unquestionably the doctor's hand, do you know?" resumed the lawyer.

"I thought it looked like it," said the servant rather sulkily; and then, with another voice, "But what matters hand of write[16]?" he said. "I've seen him!"

[15] Main. Very.
[16] Hand of write. This is what Stevenson printed. Perhaps Poole means handwriting.

"Seen him?" repeated Mr. Utterson. "Well?"

"That's it!" said Poole. "It was this way. I came suddenly into the theatre from the garden. It seems he had slipped out to look for this drug or whatever it is; for the cabinet door was open, and there he was at the far end of the room digging among the crates. He looked up when I came in, gave a kind of cry, and whipped upstairs into the cabinet. It was but for one minute that I saw him, but the hair stood upon my head like quills. Sir, if that was my master, why had he a mask upon his face? If it was my master, why did he cry out like a rat, and run from me? I have served him long enough. And then . . ." The man paused and passed his hand over his face.

"These are all very strange circumstances," said Mr. Utterson, "but I think I begin to see daylight. Your master, Poole, is plainly seized with one of those maladies that both torture and deform the sufferer; hence, for aught I know, the alteration of his voice; hence the mask and the avoidance of his friends; hence his eagerness to find this drug, by means of which the poor soul retains some hope of ultimate recovery—God grant that he be not deceived! There is my explanation; it is sad enough, Poole, ay, and appalling to consider; but it is plain and natural, hangs well together, and delivers us from all exorbitant alarms."

"Sir," said the butler, turning to a sort of mottled pallor, "that thing was not my master, and there's the truth. My master"—here he looked round him and began to whisper—"is a tall, fine build of a man, and this was more of a dwarf." Utterson attempted to protest. "O, sir," cried Poole, "do you think I do not know my master after twenty years? Do you think I do not know where his head comes to in the cabinet door, where I saw him every morning of my life? No, sir, that thing in the mask was never Dr. Jekyll—God knows what it was, but it was never Dr. Jekyll; and it is the belief of my heart that there was murder done."

"Poole," replied the lawyer, "if you say that, it will become my duty to make certain. Much as I desire to spare your master's feelings, much as I am puzzled by this note which seems to prove him to be still alive, I shall consider it my duty to break in that door."

"Ah, Mr. Utterson, that's talking!" cried the butler.

"And now comes the second question," resumed Utterson: "Who is going to do it?"

"Why, you and me, sir," was the undaunted reply.

"That's very well said," returned the lawyer; "and whatever comes of it, I shall make it my business to see you are no loser."

"There is an axe in the theatre," continued Poole; "and you might take the kitchen poker for yourself."

The lawyer took that rude but weighty instrument into his hand, and balanced it. "Do you know, Poole," he said, looking up, "that you and I are about to place ourselves in a position of some peril?"

"You may say so, sir, indeed," returned the butler.

"It is well, then, that we should be frank," said the other. "We both think more than we have said; let us make a clean breast. This masked figure that you saw, did you recognize it?"

"Well, sir, it went so quick, and the creature was so doubled up, that I could hardly swear to that," was the answer. "But if you mean, was it Mr. Hyde?—why, yes, I think it was! You see, it was much of the same bigness; and it had the same quick, light way with it; and then who else could have got in by the laboratory door? You have not forgot, sir, that at the time of the murder he had still the key with him? But that's not all. I don't know, Mr. Utterson, if you ever met this Mr. Hyde?"

"Yes," said the lawyer, "I once spoke with him."

"Then you must know as well as the rest of us that there was something queer about that gentleman—something that gave a man a turn—I don't know rightly how to say it, sir, beyond this: that you felt in your marrow kind of cold and thin."

"I own I felt something of what you describe," said Mr. Utterson.

"Quite so, sir," returned Poole. "Well, when that masked thing like a monkey jumped from among the chemicals and whipped into the cabinet, it went down my spine like ice. O, I know it's not evidence, Mr. Utterson; I'm book-learned enough for that; but a man has his feelings, and I give you my bible-word it was Mr. Hyde!"

"Ay, ay," said the lawyer. "My fears incline to the same point. Evil, I fear, founded—evil was sure to come—of that connection. Ay truly, I believe you; I believe poor Harry is killed; and I believe his murderer (for what purpose, God alone can tell) is still lurking in his victim's room. Well, let our name be vengeance. Call Bradshaw."

The footman came at the summons, very white and nervous.

"Pull yourself together, Bradshaw," said the lawyer. "This suspense, I know, is telling upon all of you; but it is now our intention to make an end of it. Poole, here, and I are going to force our way into the cabinet. If all is well, my shoulders are broad enough to bear the blame. Meanwhile, lest anything should really be amiss, or any malefactor seek to escape by the back, you and the boy must go round the corner with a pair of good sticks and take your post at the laboratory door. We give you ten minutes, to get to your stations."

As Bradshaw left, the lawyer looked at his watch. "And now, Poole, let us get to ours," he said; and taking the poker under his arm, led the way into the yard. The scud had banked over the moon, and it was now quite dark. The wind, which only broke in puffs and draughts into that deep well of building, tossed the light of the candle to and fro about their steps, until they came into the shelter of the theatre, where they sat down silently to wait. London hummed solemnly all around; but nearer at hand, the stillness was only broken by the sounds of a footfall moving to and fro along the cabinet floor.

"So it will walk all day, sir," whispered Poole; "ay, and the better part of the night. Only when a new sample comes from the chemist, there's a bit of a break. Ah, it's an ill conscience that's such an enemy to rest! Ah, sir, there's blood foully shed in every step of it! But hark again, a little closer—put your heart in your ears, Mr. Utterson, and tell me, is that the doctor's foot?"

The steps fell lightly and oddly, with a certain swing, for all they went so slowly; it was different indeed from the heavy creaking tread of Henry Jekyll. Utterson sighed. "Is there never anything else?" he asked.

Poole nodded. "Once," he said. "Once I heard it weeping!"

"Weeping? how that?" said the lawyer, conscious of a sudden chill of horror.

"Weeping like a woman or a lost soul," said the butler. "I came away with that upon my heart, that I could have wept too."

But now the ten minutes drew to an end. Poole disinterred the axe from under a stack of packing straw; the candle was set upon the nearest table to light them to the attack; and they drew near with bated breath to where that patient foot was still going up and down, up and down, in the quiet of the night. "Jekyll," cried Utterson, with a loud voice, "I demand to see you." He paused a moment, but there came no reply. "I give you fair warning, our suspicions are aroused, and I must and shall see you," he resumed; "if not by fair means, then by foul—if not of your consent, then by brute force!"

"Utterson," said the voice, "for God's sake, have mercy!"

"Ah, that's not Jekyll's voice—it's Hyde's!" cried Utterson. "Down with the door, Poole!"

Poole swung the axe over his shoulder; the blow shook the building, and the red baize door leaped against the lock and hinges. A dismal

screech, as of mere animal terror, rang from the cabinet. Up went the axe
again, and again the panels crashed and the frame bounded; four times the
blow fell; but the wood was tough and the fittings were of excellent work-
manship; and it was not until the fifth, that the lock burst and the wreck of
the door fell inwards on the carpet.

The besiegers, appalled by their own riot and the stillness that had
succeeded, stood back a little and peered in. There lay the cabinet before
their eyes in the quiet lamplight, a good fire glowing and chattering on the
hearth, the kettle singing its thin strain, a drawer or two open, papers neatly
set forth on the business table, and nearer the fire, the things laid out for
tea; the quietest room, you would have said, and, but for the glazed presses
full of chemicals, the most commonplace that night in London.

Right in the midst there lay the body of a man sorely contorted and
still twitching. They drew near on tiptoe, turned it on its back and beheld
the face of Edward Hyde. He was dressed in clothes far too large for him,
clothes of the doctor's bigness; the cords of his face still moved with a semblance of life, but life was quite gone: and by the crushed phial in the hand
and the strong smell of kernels that hung upon the air, Utterson knew that
he was looking on the body of a self-destroyer.

"We have come too late," he said sternly, "whether to save or punish.
Hyde is gone to his account; and it only remains for us to find the body of
your master."

The far greater proportion of the building was occupied by the theatre,
which filled almost the whole ground storey and was lighted from above,
and by the cabinet, which formed an upper storey at one end and looked
upon the court. A corridor joined the theatre to the door on the by-street;
and with this the cabinet communicated separately by a second flight
of stairs. There were besides a few dark closets and a spacious cellar. All
these they now thoroughly examined. Each closet needed but a glance, for
all were empty, and all, by the dust that fell from their doors, had stood
long unopened. The cellar, indeed, was filled with crazy lumber, mostly
dating from the times of the surgeon who was Jekyll's predecessor; but even
as they opened the door they were advertised of the uselessness of further
search, by the fall of a perfect mat of cobweb which had for years sealed
up the entrance. Nowhere was there any trace of Henry Jekyll, dead
or alive.

Poole stamped on the flags of the corridor. "He must be buried here,"
he said, hearkening to the sound.

"Or he may have fled," said Utterson, and he turned to examine the door in the by-street. It was locked; and lying near by on the flags, they found the key, already stained with rust.

"This does not look like use," observed the lawyer.

"Use!" echoed Poole. "Do you not see, sir, it is broken? much as if a man had stamped on it."

"Ay," continued Utterson, "and the fractures, too, are rusty." The two men looked at each other with a scare. "This is beyond me, Poole," said the lawyer. "Let us go back to the cabinet."

They mounted the stair in silence and still with an occasional awe-struck glance at the dead body, proceeded more thoroughly to examine the contents of the cabinet. At one table, there were traces of chemical work, various measured heaps of some white salt being laid on glass saucers, as though for an experiment in which the unhappy man had been prevented.

"That is the same drug that I was always bringing him," said Poole; and even as he spoke, the kettle with a startling noise boiled over.

This brought them to the fireside, where the easychair was drawn cosily up, and the tea things stood ready to the sitter's elbow, the very sugar in the cup. There were several books on a shelf; one lay beside the tea things open, and Utterson was amazed to find it a copy of a pious work, for which Jekyll had several times expressed a great esteem, annotated, in his own hand, with startling blasphemies.

Next, in the course of their review of the chamber, the searchers came to the cheval-glass, into whose depths they looked with an involuntary horror. But it was so turned as to show them nothing but the rosy glow playing on the roof, the fire sparkling in a hundred repetitions along the glazed front of the presses, and their own pale and fearful countenances stooping to look in.

"This glass has seen some strange things, sir," whispered Poole.

"And surely none stranger than itself," echoed the lawyer in the same tones. "For what did Jekyll"—he caught himself up at the word with a start, and then conquering the weakness—"what could Jekyll want with it?" he said

"You may say that!" said Poole.

Next they turned to the business table. On the desk, among the neat array of papers, a large envelope was uppermost, and bore, in the doctor's hand, the name of Mr. Utterson. The lawyer unsealed it, and several enclosures fell to the floor. The first was a will, drawn in the same eccentric terms as the one which he had returned six months before, to serve as a testament in case of death and as a deed of gift in case of disappearance;

but in place of the name of Edward Hyde, the lawyer, with indescribable amazement, read the name of Gabriel John Utterson. He looked at Poole, and then back at the paper, and last of all at the dead malefactor stretched upon the carpet.

"My head goes round," he said. "He has been all these days in possession; he had no cause to like me; he must have raged to see himself displaced; and he has not destroyed this document."

He caught up the next paper; it was a brief note in the doctor's hand and dated at the top. "O Poole!" the lawyer cried, "he was alive and here this day. He cannot have been disposed of in so short a space; he must be still alive, he must have fled! And then, why fled? and how? and in that case, can we venture to declare this suicide? O, we must be careful. I foresee that we may yet involve your master in some dire catastrophe."

"Why don't you read it, sir?" asked Poole.

"Because I fear," replied the lawyer solemnly. "God grant I have no cause for it!" And with that he brought the paper to his eyes and read as follows:

My dear Utterson,—When this shall fall into your hands, I shall have disappeared, under what circumstances I have not the penetration to foresee, but my instinct and all the circumstances of my nameless situation tell me that the end is sure and must be early. Go then, and first read the narrative which Lanyon warned me he was to place in your hands; and if you care to hear more, turn to the confession of

Your unworthy and unhappy friend,

HENRY JEKYLL.

"There was a third enclosure?" asked Utterson.

"Here, sir," said Poole, and gave into his hands a considerable packet sealed in several places[17].

The lawyer put it in his pocket. "I would say nothing of this paper. If your master has fled or is dead, we may at least save his credit. It is now ten; I must go home and read these documents in quiet; but I shall be back before midnight, when we shall send for the police."

They went out, locking the door of the theatre behind them; and Utterson, once more leaving the servants gathered about the fire in the hall, trudged back to his office to read the two narratives in which this mystery was now to be explained.

On the ninth of January, now four days ago, I received by the evening delivery a registered envelope, addressed in the hand of my colleague and

[17] Sealed in several places. I.e., with sealing wax.

old school companion, Henry Jekyll. I was a good deal surprised by this; for we were by no means in the habit of correspondence; I had seen the man, dined with him, indeed, the night before; and I could imagine nothing in our intercourse that should justify formality of registration. The contents increased my wonder; for this is how the letter ran:

10th December, 18—.

Dear Lanyon,—You are one of my oldest friends; and although we may have differed at times on scientific questions, I cannot remember, at least on my side, any break in our affection. There was never a day when, if you had said to me, 'Jekyll, my life, my honour, my reason, depend upon you,' I would not have sacrificed my left hand to help you. Lanyon, my life, my honour, my reason, are all at your mercy; if you fail me to-night, I am lost. You might suppose, after this preface, that I am going to ask you for something dishonourable to grant. Judge for yourself.

I want you to postpone all other engagements for to-night—ay, even if you were summoned to the bedside of an emperor; to take a cab, unless your carriage should be actually at the door; and with this letter in your hand for consultation, to drive straight to my house. Poole, my butler, has his orders; you will find him waiting your arrival with a locksmith. The door of my cabinet is then to be forced: and you are to go in alone; to open the glazed press (letter E) on the left hand, breaking the lock if it be shut; and to draw out, *with all its contents as they stand,* the fourth drawer from the top or (which is the same thing) the third from the bottom. In my extreme distress of mind, I have a morbid fear of misdirecting you; but even if I am in error, you may know the right drawer by its contents: some powders, a phial and a paper book. This drawer I beg of you to carry back with you to Cavendish Square exactly as it stands.

That is the first part of the service: now for the second. You should be back, if you set out at once on the receipt of this, long before midnight; but I will leave you that amount of margin, not only in the fear of one of those obstacles that can neither be prevented nor foreseen, but because an hour when your servants are in bed is to be preferred for what will then remain to do. At midnight, then, I have to ask you to be alone in your consulting room, to admit with your own hand into the house a man who will present himself in my name, and to place in his hands the drawer that you will have brought with you from my cabinet. Then you will have played your part and earned my gratitude completely. Five minutes afterwards, if you insist upon an explanation, you will have understood that these ar-

rangements are of capital importance; and that by the neglect of one of them,
fantastic as they must appear, you might have charged your conscience with
my death or the shipwreck of my reason.

Confident as I am that you will not trifle with this appeal, my heart
sinks and my hand trembles at the bare thought of such a possibility. Think
of me at this hour, in a strange place, labouring under a blackness of distress that no fancy can exaggerate, and yet well aware that, if you will but
punctually serve me, my troubles will roll away like a story that is told. Serve
me, my dear Lanyon, and save

Your friend,

H.J.

P.S.—I had already sealed this up when a fresh terror struck upon my
soul. It is possible that the post-office may fail me, and this letter not come
into your hands until to-morrow morning. In that case, dear Lanyon, do my
errand when it shall be most convenient for you in the course of the day;
and once more expect my messenger at midnight. It may then already be
too late; and if that night passes without event, you will know that you have
seen the last of Henry Jekyll.

Upon the reading of this letter, I made sure my colleague was insane;
but till that was proved beyond the possibility of doubt, I felt bound to do
as he requested. The less I understood of this farrago, the less I was in a
position to judge of its importance; and an appeal so worded could not be
set aside without a grave responsibility. I rose accordingly from table, got
into a hansom, and drove straight to Jekyll's house. The butler was awaiting
my arrival; he had received by the same post as mine a registered letter of
instruction, and had sent at once for a locksmith and a carpenter. The
tradesmen came while we were yet speaking; and we moved in a body to
old Dr. Denman's surgical theatre, from which (as you are doubtless aware)
Jekyll's private cabinet is most conveniently entered. The door was very
strong, the lock excellent; the carpenter avowed he would have great trouble
and have to do much damage, if force were to be used; and the locksmith
was near despair. But this last was a handy fellow, and after two hours' work,
the door stood open. The press marked E was unlocked; and I took out the
drawer, had it filled up with straw and tied in a sheet, and returned with it
to Cavendish Square.

Here I proceeded to examine its contents. The powders were neatly
enough made up, but not with the nicety of the dispensing chemist; so that
it was plain they were of Jekyll's private manufacture: and when I opened

one of the wrappers I found what seemed to me a simple crystalline salt of a white colour. The phial, to which I next turned my attention, might have been about half full of a blood-red liquor, which was highly pungent to the sense of smell and seemed to me to contain phosphorus and some volatile ether. At the other ingredients I could make no guess. The book was an ordinary version book and contained little but a series of dates. These covered a period of many years, but I observed that the entries ceased nearly a year ago and quite abruptly. Here and there a brief remark was appended to a date, usually no more than a single word: "double" occurring perhaps six times in a total of several hundred entries; and once very early in the list and followed by several marks of exclamation, "total failure!!!" All this, though it whetted my curiosity, told me little that was definite. Here were a phial of some tincture, a paper of some salt, and the record of a series of experiments that had led (like too many of Jekyll's investigations) to no end of practical usefulness. How could the presence of these articles in my house affect either the honour, the sanity, or the life of my flighty colleague? If his messenger could go to one place, why could he not go to another? And even granting some impediment, why was this gentleman to be received by me in secret? The more I reflected the more convinced I grew that I was dealing with a case of cerebral disease; and though I dismissed my servants to bed, I loaded an old revolver, that I might be found in some posture of self-defence.

Twelve o'clock had scarce rung out over London, ere the knocker sounded very gently on the door. I went myself at the summons, and found a small man crouching against the pillars of the portico.

"Are you come from Dr. Jekyll?" I asked.

He told me "yes" by a constrained gesture; and when I had bidden him enter, he did not obey me without a searching backward glance into the darkness of the square. There was a policeman not far off, advancing with his bull's eye open; and at the sight, I thought my visitor started and made greater haste.

These particulars struck me, I confess, disagreeably; and as I followed him into the bright light of the consulting room, I kept my hand ready on my weapon. Here, at last, I had a chance of clearly seeing him. I had never set eyes on him before, so much was certain. He was small, as I have said; I was struck besides with the shocking expression of his face, with his remarkable combination of great muscular activity and great apparent debility of constitution, and—last but not least—with the odd, subjective disturbance caused by his neighbourhood. This bore some resemblance to incipient rigour, and was accompanied by a marked sinking of the pulse. At the time, I set it down to some idiosyncratic, personal distaste, and merely wondered at the acuteness of the symptoms; but I have since had reason to believe the cause to lie much deeper in the nature of man, and to turn on some nobler hinge than the principle of hatred.

This person (who had thus, from the first moment of his entrance, struck in me what I can only describe as a disgustful curiosity) was dressed in a fashion that would have made an ordinary person laughable; his clothes, that is to say, although they were of rich and sober fabric, were enormously too large for him in every measurement—the trousers hanging on his legs and rolled up to keep them from the ground, the waist of the coat below his haunches, and the collar sprawling wide upon his shoulders. Strange to relate, this ludicrous accoutrement was far from moving me to laughter. Rather, as there was something abnormal and misbegotten in the very essence of the creature that now faced me—something seizing, surprising and revolting—this fresh disparity seemed but to fit in with and to reinforce it; so that to my interest in the man's nature and character, there was added a curiosity as to his origin, his life, his fortune and status in the world.

These observations, though they have taken so great a space to be set down in, were yet the work of a few seconds. My visitor was, indeed, on fire with sombre excitement.

"Have you got it?" he cried. "Have you got it?" And so lively was his impatience that he even laid his hand upon my arm and sought to shake me.

I put him back, conscious at his touch of a certain icy pang along my blood. "Come, sir," said I. "You forget that I have not yet the pleasure of your acquaintance. Be seated, if you please." And I showed him an example, and sat down myself in my customary seat and with as fair an imitation of my ordinary manner to a patient, as the lateness of the hour, the nature of my preoccupations, and the horror I had of my visitor, would suffer me to muster.

"I beg your pardon, Dr. Lanyon," he replied civilly enough. "What you say is very well founded; and my impatience has shown its heels to my politeness. I come here at the instance of your colleague, Dr. Henry Jekyll, on a piece of business of some moment; and I understood . . ." He paused and put his hand to his throat, and I could see, in spite of his collected manner, that he was wrestling against the approaches of the hysteria—"I understood, a drawer . . ."

But here I took pity on my visitor's suspense, and some perhaps on my own growing curiosity.

"There it is, sir," said I, pointing to the drawer, where it lay on the floor behind a table and still covered with the sheet.

He sprang to it, and then paused, and laid his hand upon his heart: I could hear his teeth grate with the convulsive action of his jaws; and his face was so ghastly to see that I grew alarmed both for his life and reason.

"Compose yourself," said I.

He turned a dreadful smile to me, and as if with the decision of despair, plucked away the sheet. At sight of the contents, he uttered one loud sob of such immense relief that I sat petrified. And the next moment, in a voice that was already fairly well under control, "Have you a graduated glass?" he asked.

I rose from my place with something of an effort and gave him what he asked.

He thanked me with a smiling nod, measured out a few minims of the red tincture and added one of the powders. The mixture, which was at first of a reddish hue, began, in proportion as the crystals melted, to brighten in colour, to effervesce audibly, and to throw off small fumes of vapour. Suddenly and at the same moment, the ebullition ceased and the compound changed to a dark purple, which faded again more slowly to a watery green. My visitor, who had watched these metamorphoses with a keen eye, smiled, set down the glass upon the table, and then turned and looked upon me with an air of scrutiny.

"And now," said he, "to settle what remains. Will you be wise? will you be guided? will you suffer me to take this glass in my hand and to go forth from your house without further parley? or has the greed of curiosity too much command of you? Think before you answer, for it shall be done as you decide. As you decide, you shall be left as you were before, and neither richer nor wiser, unless the sense of service rendered to a man in mortal distress may be counted as a kind of riches of the soul. Or, if you shall so prefer to choose, a new province of knowledge and new avenues to fame and power shall be laid open to you, here, in this room, upon the instant; and your sight shall be blasted by a prodigy to stagger the unbelief of Satan."

"Sir," said I, affecting a coolness that I was far from truly possessing, "you speak enigmas, and you will perhaps not wonder that I hear you with no very strong impression of belief. But I have gone too far in the way of inexplicable services to pause before I see the end."

"It is well," replied my visitor. "Lanyon, you remember your vows: what follows is under the seal of our profession. And now, you who have so long been bound to the most narrow and material views, you who have denied the virtue of transcendental medicine, you who have derided your superiors—behold!"

He put the glass to his lips and drank at one gulp. A cry followed; he reeled, staggered, clutched at the table and held on, staring with injected eyes, gasping with open mouth; and as I looked there came, I thought, a change—he seemed to swell—his face became suddenly black and the features seemed to melt and alter—and the next moment, I had sprung to my feet and leaped back against the wall, my arm raised to shield me from that prodigy, my mind submerged in terror.

"O God!" I screamed, and "O God!" again and again; for there before my eyes—pale and shaken, and half fainting, and groping before him with his hands, like a man restored from death—there stood Henry Jekyll!

What he told me in the next hour, I cannot bring my mind to set on paper. I saw what I saw, I heard what I heard, and my soul sickened at it; and yet now when that sight has faded from my eyes, I ask myself if I believe it, and I cannot answer. My life is shaken to its roots; sleep has left me; the deadliest terror sits by me at all hours of the day and night; and I feel that my days are numbered, and that I must die; and yet I shall die incredulous. As for the moral turpitude that man unveiled to me, even with tears of penitence, I cannot, even in memory, dwell on it without a start of horror. I will say but one thing, Utterson, and that (if you can bring your mind to credit it) will be more than enough. The creature who crept into my house that night was, on Jekyll's own confession, known by the name of Hyde and hunted for in every corner of the land as the murderer of Carew.

HASTIE LANYON

HENRY JEKYLL'S FULL STATEMENT OF THE CASE

I was born in the year 18— to a large fortune, endowed besides with excellent parts, inclined by nature to industry, fond of the respect of the wise and good among my fellowmen, and thus, as might have been supposed, with every guarantee of an honourable and distinguished future. And indeed the worst of my faults was a certain impatient gaiety of disposition, such as has made the happiness of many, but such as I found it hard to reconcile with my imperious desire to carry my head high, and wear a more than commonly grave countenance before the public. Hence it came about that I concealed my pleasures; and that when I reached years of reflection, and began to look round me and take stock of my progress and position in the world, I stood already committed to a profound duplicity of life. Many a man would have even blazoned such irregularities as I was guilty of; but from the high views that I had set before me, I regarded and hid them with an almost morbid sense of shame. It was thus rather the exacting nature of my aspirations than any particular degradation in my faults, that made me what I was, and, with even a deeper trench than in the majority of men, severed in me those provinces of good and ill which divide and compound man's dual nature. In this case, I was driven to reflect deeply and inveterately on that hard law of life, which lies at the root of religion and is one of the most plentiful springs of distress. Though so profound a double-dealer, I was in no sense a hypocrite; both sides of me were in dead earnest; I was no more myself when I laid aside restraint and plunged in shame, than when I laboured, in the eye of day, at the furtherance of knowledge or the relief of sorrow and suffering. And it chanced that the direction of my scientific studies, which led wholly towards the mystic and the transcendental, reacted and shed a strong light on this consciousness of the perennial war among my members. With every day, and from both sides of my intelligence, the moral and the intellectual, I thus drew steadily nearer to that truth, by whose partial discovery I have been doomed to such a dreadful shipwreck: that man is not truly one, but truly two. I say two, because the state of my own knowledge does not pass beyond that point. Others will follow, others will outstrip me on the same lines; and I hazard the guess that man will be ultimately known for a mere polity of multifarious, incongruous and independent denizens. I, for my part, from the nature of my life, advanced infallibly in one direction and in one direction only. It was on the moral side, and in my own person, that I learned to recognise the thorough and primitive duality of man; I saw that, of the two natures that contended in the field of my consciousness, even if I could rightly be said to be either, it was only because I was radically both; and from an early date, even before the course of my scientific discoveries had begun to suggest the most naked possibility of such a miracle, I had learned to dwell with pleasure, as a beloved daydream, on the thought of the separation of these elements. If each, I told myself, could be housed in separate identities, life would be relieved of all that was unbearable; the unjust might go his way, delivered from the aspirations and remorse of his more upright twin; and the just could walk steadfastly and securely on his upward path, doing the good things in which he found his pleasure, and no longer exposed to disgrace and penitence by the hands of this extraneous evil. It was the curse of mankind that these incongruous faggots were thus bound together—that in the agonised womb of consciousness, these polar twins should be continuously struggling. How, then, were they dissociated?

I was so far in my reflections when, as I have said, a side light began to shine upon the subject from the laboratory table. I began to perceive more deeply than it has ever yet been stated, the trembling immateriality, the mist-like transience, of this seemingly so solid body in which we walk attired. Certain agents[18] I found to have the power to shake and pluck back that fleshly vestment, even as a wind might toss the curtains of a pavilion. For two good reasons, I will not enter deeply into this scientific branch of my confession. First, because I have been made to learn that the doom and burthen of our life is bound for ever on man's shoulders, and when the attempt is made to cast it off, it but returns upon us with more unfamiliar and more awful pressure. Second, because, as my narrative will make, alas! too evident, my discoveries were incomplete. Enough, then, that I not only recognised my natural body from the mere aura and effulgence of certain of the powers that made up my spirit, but managed to compound a drug by which these powers should be dethroned from their supremacy, and a second form and countenance substituted, none the less natural to me because they were the expression, and bore the stamp of lower elements in my soul.

I hesitated long before I put this theory to the test of practice. I knew well that I risked death; for any drug that so potently controlled and shook the very fortress of identity, might, by the least scruple of an overdose or at the least inopportunity in the moment of exhibition, utterly blot out that immaterial tabernacle which I looked to it to change. But the temptation of a discovery so singular and profound at last overcame the suggestions of alarm. I had long since prepared my tincture; I purchased at once, from a firm of wholesale chemists, a large quantity of a particular salt which I knew, from my experiments, to be the last ingredient required; and late one accursed night, I compounded the elements, watched them boil and smoke together in the glass, and when the ebullition had subsided, with a strong glow of courage, drank off the potion.

The most racking pangs succeeded: a grinding in the bones, deadly nausea, and a horror of the spirit that cannot be exceeded at the hour of birth or death. Then these agonies began swiftly to subside, and I came to myself as if out of a great sickness. There was something strange in my sensations, something indescribably new and, from its very novelty, incredibly sweet. I felt younger, lighter, happier in body; within I was conscious of a heady recklessness, a current of disordered sensual images running like a millrace in my fancy, a solution of the bonds of obligation, an unknown but not an innocent freedom of the soul. I knew myself, at the first breath of this new life, to be more wicked, tenfold more wicked, sold a slave to my

[18] Agents. I.e., chemical compounds.

original evil; and the thought, in that moment, braced and delighted me like wine. I stretched out my hands, exulting in the freshness of these sensations; and in the act, I was suddenly aware that I had lost in stature.

There was no mirror, at that date, in my room; that which stands beside me as I write, was brought there later on and for the very purpose of these transformations. The night, however, was far gone into the morning— the morning, black as it was, was nearly ripe for the conception of the day —the inmates of my house were locked in the most rigorous hours of slumber; and I determined, flushed as I was with hope and triumph, to venture in my new shape as far as to my bedroom. I crossed the yard, wherein the constellations looked down upon me, I could have thought, with wonder, the first creature of that sort that their unsleeping vigilance had yet disclosed to them; I stole through the corridors, a stranger in my own house; and coming to my room, I saw for the first time the appearance of Edward Hyde.

I must here speak by theory alone, saying not that which I know, but that which I suppose to be most probable. The evil side of my nature, to which I had now transferred the stamping efficacy, was less robust and less developed than the good which I had just deposed. Again, in the course of my life, which had been, after all, nine tenths a life of effort, virtue and control, it had been much less exercised and much less exhausted. And hence, as I think, it came about that Edward Hyde was so much smaller, slighter and younger than Henry Jekyll. Even as good shone upon the countenance of the one, evil was written broadly and plainly on the face of the other. Evil besides (which I must still believe to be the lethal side of man) had left on that body an imprint of deformity and decay. And yet when I looked upon that ugly idol in the glass, I was conscious of no repugnance, rather of a leap of welcome. This, too, was myself. It seemed natural and human. In my eyes it bore a livelier image of the spirit, it seemed more express and single, than the imperfect and divided countenance I had been hitherto accustomed to call mine. And in so far I was doubtless right. I have observed that when I wore the semblance of Edward Hyde, none could come near to me at first without a visible misgiving of the flesh. This, as I take it, was because all human beings, as we meet them, are commingled out of good and evil: and Edward Hyde, alone in the ranks of mankind, was pure evil.

I lingered but a moment at the mirror: the second and conclusive experiment had yet to be attempted; it yet remained to be seen if I had lost my identity beyond redemption and must flee before daylight from a house that was no longer mine; and hurrying back to my cabinet, I once more prepared and drank the cup, once more suffered the pangs of dissolution, and came to myself once more with the character, the stature and the face of Henry Jekyll.

That night I had come to the fatal cross-roads. Had I approached my discovery in a more noble spirit, had I risked the experiment while under the empire of generous or pious aspirations, all must have been otherwise, and from these agonies of death and birth, I had come forth an angel instead of a fiend. The drug had no discriminating action; it was neither diabolical nor divine; it but shook the doors of the prisonhouse of my disposition; and like the captives of Philippi[19], that which stood within ran forth. At that time my virtue slumbered; my evil, kept awake by ambition, was alert and swift to seize the occasion; and the thing that was projected was Edward Hyde. Hence, although I had now two characters as well as two appearances, one was wholly evil, and the other was still the old Henry Jekyll, that incongruous compound of whose reformation and improvement I had already learned to despair. The movement was thus wholly toward the worse.

Even at that time, I had not conquered my aversions to the dryness of a life of study. I would still be merrily disposed at times; and as my pleasures were (to say the least) undignified, and I was not only well known and highly considered, but growing towards the elderly man, this incoherency of my life was daily growing more unwelcome. It was on this side that my new power tempted me until I fell in slavery. I had but to drink the cup, to doff at once the body of the noted professor, and to assume, like a thick cloak, that of Edward Hyde. I smiled at the notion; it seemed to me at the time to be humourous; and I made my preparations with the most studious care. I took and furnished that house in Soho, to which Hyde was tracked by the police; and engaged as a housekeeper a creature whom I knew well to be silent and unscrupulous. On the other side, I announced to my servants that a Mr. Hyde (whom I described) was to have full liberty and power about my house in the square; and to parry mishaps, I even called and made myself a familiar object, in my second character. I next drew up that will to which you so much objected; so that if anything befell me in the person of Dr. Jekyll, I could enter on that of Edward Hyde without pecuniary loss. And thus fortified, as I supposed, an every side, I began to profit by the strange immunities of my position.

Men have before hired bravos to transact their crimes, while their own

[19] Philippi. According to Acts XVI, when Paul and Silas were imprisoned at Philippi, an earthquake broke open the doors of the prison and loosed the bands of the prisoners, who, however, did not flee.

person and reputation sat under shelter. I was the first that ever did so for his pleasures. I was the first that could plod in the public eye with a load of genial respectability, and in a moment, like a schoolboy, strip off these lendings[20] and spring headlong into the sea of liberty. But for me, in my impenetrable mantle, the safety was complete. Think of it—I did not even exist! Let me but escape into my laboratory door, give me but a second or two to mix and swallow the draught that I had always standing ready; and whatever he had done, Edward Hyde would pass away like the stain of breath upon a mirror; and there in his stead, quietly at home, trimming the midnight lamp in his study, a man who could afford to laugh at suspicion, would be Henry Jekyll.

The pleasures which I made haste to seek in my disguise were, as I have said, undignified; I would scarce use a harder term. But in the hands of Edward Hyde, they soon began to turn toward the monstrous. When I would come back from these excursions, I was often plunged into a kind of wonder at my vicarious depravity. This familiar[21] that I called out of my own soul, and sent forth alone to do his good pleasure, was a being inherently malign and villainous; his every act and thought centered on self; drinking pleasure with bestial avidity from any degree of torture to another; relentless like a man of stone. Henry Jekyll stood at times aghast before the acts of Edward Hyde; but the situation was apart from ordinary laws, and insidiously relaxed the grasp of conscience. It was Hyde, after all, and Hyde alone, that was guilty. Jekyll was no worse; he woke again to his good qualities seemingly unimpaired; he would even make haste, where it was possible, to undo the evil done by Hyde. And thus his conscience slumbered.

Into the details of the infamy at which I thus connived (for even now I can scarce grant that I committed it) I have no design of entering; I mean but to point out the warnings and the successive steps with which my chastisement approached. I met with one accident, which, as it brought on no consequence, I shall no more than mention. An act of cruelty to a child aroused against me the anger of a passer-by, whom I recognised the other day in the person of your kinsman; the doctor and the child's family joined him; there were moments when I feared for my life; and at last, in order to pacify their too just resentment, Edward Hyde had to bring them to the door, and pay them in a cheque drawn in the name of Henry Jekyll. But this danger was easily eliminated from the future, by opening an account at

[20] Strip off these lendings. In Act III, Scene 4, of "King Lear," Lear in his denunciation of humanity cries, "Off, off, you lendings!—Come, unbutton here."
[21] Familiar. I.e., intimate companion.

another bank in the name of Edward Hyde himself; and when, by sloping my own hand backward, I had supplied my double with a signature, I thought I sat beyond the reach of fate.

Some two months before the murder of Sir Danvers, I had been out for one of my adventures, had returned at a late hour, and woke the next day in bed with somewhat odd sensations. It was in vain I looked about me; in vain I saw the decent furniture and tall proportions of my room in the square; in vain that I recognised the pattern of the bed curtains and the design of the mahogany frame; something still kept insisting that I was not where I was, that I had not wakened where I seemed to be, but in the little room in Soho where I was accustomed to sleep in the body of Edward Hyde. I smiled to myself, and, in my psychological way, began lazily to inquire into the elements of this illusion, occasionally, even as I did so, dropping back into a comfortable morning doze. I was still so engaged when, in one of my more wakeful moments, my eyes fell upon my hand. Now the hand of Henry Jekyll (as you have often remarked) was professional in shape and size: it was large, firm, white and comely. But the hand which I now saw, clearly enough, in the yellow light of a mid-London morning, lying half shut on the bedclothes, was lean, corded, knuckly, of a dusky pallor and thickly shaded with a swart growth of hair. It was the hand of Edward Hyde.

I must have stared upon it for near half a minute, sunk as I was in the mere stupidity of wonder, before terror woke up in my breast as sudden and startling as the crash of cymbals; and bounding from my bed, I rushed to the mirror. At the sight that met my eyes, my blood was changed into something exquisitely thin and icy. Yes, I had gone to bed Henry Jekyll, I had awakened Edward Hyde. How was this to be explained? I asked myself; and then, with another bound of terror—how was it to be remedied? It was well on in the morning; the servants were up; all my drugs were in the cabinet—a long journey down two pairs of stairs, through the back passage, across the open court and through the anatomical theatre, from where I was then standing horror-struck. It might indeed be possible to cover my face; but of what use was that, when I was unable to conceal the alteration in my stature? And then with an overpowering sweetness of relief, it came back upon my mind that the servants were already used to the coming and going of my second self. I had soon dressed, as well as I was able, in clothes of my own size: had soon passed through the house, where Bradshaw stared and drew back at seeing Mr. Hyde at such an hour and in such a strange array; and ten minutes later, Dr. Jekyll had returned to his own shape and was sitting down, with a darkened brow, to make a feint of breakfasting.

Small indeed was my appetite. This inexplicable incident, this reversal of my previous experience, seemed, like the Babylonian finger[22] on the wall, to be spelling out the letters of my judgment; and I began to reflect more seriously than ever before on the issues and possibilities of my double existence. That part of me which I had the power of projecting, had lately been much exercised and nourished; it had seemed to me of late as though the body of Edward Hyde had grown in stature, as though (when I wore that form) I were conscious of a more generous tide of blood; and I began to spy a danger that, if this were much prolonged, the balance of my nature might be permanently overthrown, the power of voluntary change be forfeited, and the character of Edward Hyde become irrevocably mine. The power of the drug had not been always equally displayed. Once, very early in my career, it had totally failed me; since then I had been obliged on more than one occasion to double, and once, with infinite risk of death, to treble the amount; and these rare uncertainties had cast hitherto the sole shadow on my contentment. Now, however, and in the light of that morning's accident, I was led to remark that whereas, in the beginning, the difficulty had been to throw off the body of Jekyll, it had of late gradually but decidedly transferred itself to the other side. All things therefore seemed to point to this; that I was slowly losing hold of my original and better self, and becoming slowly incorporated with my second and worse.

Between these two, I now felt I had to choose. My two natures had memory in common, but all other faculties were most unequally shared between them. Jekyll (who was composite) now with the most sensitive apprehensions, now with a greedy gusto, projected and shared in the pleasures and adventures of Hyde; but Hyde was indifferent to Jekyll, or but remembered him as the mountain bandit remembers the cavern in which he conceals himself from pursuit. Jekyll had more than a father's interest; Hyde had more than a son's indifference. To cast in my lot with Jekyll, was to die to those appetites which I had long secretly indulged and had of late begun to pamper. To cast it in with Hyde, was to die to a thousand interests and aspirations, and to become, at a blow and forever, despised and friendless. The bargain might appear unequal; but there was still another consideration in the scales; for while Jekyll would suffer smartingly in the fires of

[22] Babylonian finger. According to Daniel V, in the Old Testament, Belshazzer, king of Babylon, was interrupted during a feast by an unseen hand that wrote his doom on the palace wall before his eyes.

abstinence, Hyde would be not even conscious of all that he had lost. Strange as my circumstances were, the terms of this debate are as old and commonplace as man; much the same inducements and alarms cast the die for any tempted and trembling sinner; and it fell out with me, as it falls with so vast a majority of my fellows, that I chose the better part and was found wanting in the strength to keep to it.

Yes, I preferred the elderly and discontented doctor, surrounded by friends and cherishing honest hopes; and bade a resolute farewell to the liberty, the comparative youth, the light step, leaping impulses and secret pleasures, that I had enjoyed in the disguise of Hyde. I made this choice perhaps with some unconscious reservation, for I neither gave up the house in Soho, nor destroyed the clothes of Edward Hyde, which still lay ready in my cabinet. For two months, however, I was true to my determination; for two months, I led a life of such severity as I had never before attained to, and enjoyed the compensations of an approving conscience. But time began at last to obliterate the freshness of my alarm; the praises of conscience began to grow into a thing of course; I began to be tortured with throes and longings, as of Hyde struggling after freedom; and at last, in an hour of moral weakness, I once again compounded and swallowed the transforming draught.

I do not suppose that, when a drunkard reasons with himself upon his vice, he is once out of five hundred times affected by the dangers that he runs through his brutish, physical insensibility; neither had I, long as I had considered my position, made enough allowance for the complete moral insensibility and insensate readiness to evil, which were the leading characters of Edward Hyde. Yet it was by these that I was punished. My devil had been long caged, he came out roaring. I was conscious, even when I took the draught, of a more unbridled, a more furious propensity to ill. It must have been this, I suppose, that stirred in my soul that tempest of impatience with which I listened to the civilities of my unhappy victim; I declare, at least, before God, no man morally sane could have been guilty of that crime upon so pitiful a provocation; and that I struck in no more reasonable spirit than that in which a sick child may break a plaything. But I had voluntarily stripped myself of all those balancing instincts by which even the worst of us continues to walk with some degree of steadiness among temptations; and in my case, to be tempted, however slightly, was to fall.

Instantly the spirit of hell awoke in me and raged. With a transport of glee, I mauled the unresisting body, tasting delight from every blow; and it was not till weariness had begun to succeed, that I was suddenly, in the top fit of my delirium, struck through the heart by a cold thrill of terror. A mist dispersed; I saw my life to be forfeit; and fled from the scene of these excesses, at once glorying and trembling, my lust of evil gratified and stimulated, my love of life screwed to the topmost peg. I ran to the house in Soho, and (to make assurance doubly sure) destroyed my papers; thence I set out through the lamplit streets, in the same divided ecstasy of mind, gloating on my crime, light-headedly devising others in the future, and yet still hastening and still hearkening in my wake for the steps of the avenger. Hyde had a song upon his lips as he compounded the draught, and as he drank it, pledged the dead man. The pangs of transformation had not done tearing him, before Henry Jekyll, with streaming tears of gratitude and re-morse, had fallen upon his knees and lifted his clasped hands to God. The veil of self-indulgence was rent from head to foot. I saw my life as a whole: I followed it up from the days of childhood, when I had walked with my father's hand, and through the self-denying toils of my professional life, to arrive again and again, with the same sense of unreality, at the damned hor-rors of the evening. I could have screamed aloud; I sought with tears and prayers to smother down the crowd of hideous images and sounds with which my memory swarmed against me; and still, between the petitions, the ugly face of my iniquity stared into my soul. As the acuteness of this re-morse began to die away, it was succeeded by a sense of joy. The problem of my conduct was solved. Hyde was thenceforth impossible; whether I would or not, I was now confined to the better part of my existence; and O, how I rejoiced to think of it! with what willing humility I embraced anew the restrictions of natural life! with what sincere renunciation I locked the door by which I had so often gone and come, and ground the key under my heel!

The next day, came the news that the murder had been overlooked, that the guilt of Hyde was patent to the world, and that the victim was a man high in public estimation. It was not only a crime, it had been a tragic folly. I think I was glad to know it; I think I was glad to have my better im-pulses thus buttressed and guarded by the terrors of the scaffold. Jekyll was now my city of refuge; let but Hyde peep out an instant, and the hands of all men would be raised to take and slay him.

I resolved in my future conduct to redeem the past; and I can say with honesty that my resolve was fruitful of some good. You know yourself how earnestly, in the last months of the last year, I laboured to relieve suffering; you know that much was done for others, and that the days passed quietly,

almost happily for myself. Nor can I truly say that I wearied of this beneficent and innocent life; I think instead that I daily enjoyed it more
completely; but I was still cursed with my duality of purpose; and as the
first edge of my penitence wore off, the lower side of me, so long indulged,
so recently chained down, began to growl for licence. Not that I dreamed of
resuscitating Hyde; the bare idea of that would startle me to frenzy: no, it was
in my own person that I was once more tempted to trifle with my
conscience; and it was as an ordinary secret sinner that I at last fell before the
assualts of temptation.

There comes an end to all things; the most capacious measure is filled
at last; and this brief condescension to my evil finally destroyed the balance
of my soul. And yet I was not alarmed; the fall seemed natural, like a return to the old days before I had made my discovery. It was a fine, clear,
January day, wet under foot where the frost had melted, but cloudless overhead; and the Regent's Park was full of winter chirrupings and sweet with
spring odours. I sat in the sun on a bench; the animal within me licking the
chops of memory; the spiritual side a little drowsed, promising subsequent
penitence, but not yet moved to begin. After all, I reflected, I was like my
neighbours; and then I smiled, comparing myself with other men, comparing
my active good-will with the lazy cruelty of their neglect. And at the very
moment of that vainglorious thought, a qualm came over me, a horrid
nausea and the most deadly shuddering. These passed away, and left me
faint; and then as in its turn faintness subsided, I began to be aware of a
change in the temper of my thoughts, a greater boldness, a contempt
of danger, a solution of the bonds of obligation. I looked down; my clothes
hung formlessly on my shrunken limbs; the hand that lay on my knee was
corded and hairy. I was once more Edward Hyde. A moment before I had
been safe of all men's respect, wealthy, beloved—the cloth laying for me in
the dining-room at home; and now I was the common quarry of mankind,
hunted, houseless, a known murderer, thrall to the gallows.

My reason wavered, but it did not fail me utterly. I have more than
once observed that, in my second character, my faculties seemed sharpened
to a point and my spirits more tensely elastic; thus it came about that,
where Jekyll perhaps might have succumbed, Hyde rose to the importance
of the moment. My drugs were in one of the presses of my cabinet; how
was I to reach them? That was the problem that (crushing my temples in
my hands) I set myself to solve. The laboratory door I had closed. If
I sought to enter by the house, my own servants would consign me to the
gallows. I saw I must employ another hand, and thought of Lanyon. How

was he to be reached? how persuaded? Supposing that I escaped capture in the streets, how was I to make my way into his presence? and how should I, an unknown and displeasing visitor, prevail on the famous physician to rifle the study of his colleague, Dr. Jekyll? Then I remembered that of my original character, one part remained to me: I could write my own hand; and once I had conceived that kindling spark, the way that I must follow became lighted up from end to end.

Thereupon, I arranged my clothes as best I could, and summoning a passing hansom, drove to an hotel in Portland Street, the name of which I chanced to remember. At my appearance (which was indeed comical enough, however tragic a fate these garments covered) the driver could not conceal his mirth. I gnashed my teeth upon him with a gust of devilish fury; and the smile withered from his face—happily for him—yet more happily for myself, for in another instant I had certainly dragged him from his perch. At the inn, as I entered, I looked about me with so black a countenance as made the attendants tremble; not a look did they exchange in my presence; but obsequiously took my orders, led me to a private room, and brought me wherewithal to write. Hyde in danger of his life was a creature new to me; shaken with inordinate anger, strung to the pitch of murder, lusting to inflict pain. Yet the creature was astute; mastered his fury with a great effort of the will; composed his two important letters, one to Lanyon and one to Poole; and that he might receive actual evidence of their being posted, sent them out with directions that they should be registered. Thenceforward, he sat all day over the fire in the private room, gnawing his nails; there he dined, sitting alone with his fears, the waiter visibly quailing before his eye; and thence, when the night was fully come, he set forth in the corner of a closed cab, and was driven to and fro about the streets of the city. He, I say—I cannot say, I. That child of Hell had nothing human; nothing lived in him but fear and hatred. And when at last, thinking the driver had begun to grow suspicious, he discharged the cab and ventured on foot, attired in his misfitting clothes, an object marked out for observation, into the midst of the nocturnal passengers, these two base passions raged within him like a tempest. He walked fast, hunted by his fears, chattering to himself, skulking through the less frequented thoroughfares, counting the minutes that still divided him from midnight. Once a woman spoke to him, offering, I think, a box of lights[23]. He smote her in the face, and she fled.

When I came to myself at Lanyon's, the horror of my old friend perhaps affected me somewhat: I do not know; it was at least but a drop in the

[23] Lights. I.e., matches.

sea to the abhorrence with which I looked back upon these hours. A change had come over me. It was no longer the fear of the gallows, it was the horror of being Hyde that racked me. I received Lanyon's condemnation partly in a dream; it was partly in a dream that I came home to my own house and got into bed. I slept after the prostration of the day, with a stringent and profound slumber which not even the nightmares that wrung me could avail to break. I awoke in the morning shaken, weakened, but refreshed. I still hated and feared the thought of the brute that slept within me, and I had not of course forgotten the appalling dangers of the day before; but I was once more at home, in my own house and close to my drugs; and gratitude for my escape shone so strong in my soul that it almost rivalled the brightness of hope.

I was stepping leisurely across the court after breakfast, drinking the chill of the air with pleasure, when I was seized again with those indescribable sensations that heralded the change; and I had but the time to gain the shelter of my cabinet, before I was once again raging and freezing with the passions of Hyde. It took on this occasion a double dose to recall me to myself; and alas! six hours after, as I sat looking sadly in the fire, the pangs returned, and the drug had to be re-administered. In short, from that day forth it seemed only by a great effort as of gymnastics, and only under the immediate stimulation of the drug, that I was able to wear the countenance of Jekyll. At all hours of the day and night, I would be taken with the premonitory shudder; above all, if I slept, or even dozed for a moment in my chair, it was always as Hyde that I awakened. Under the strain of this continually impending doom and by the sleeplessness to which I now condemned myself, ay, even beyond what I had thought possible to man, I became, in my own person, a creature eaten up and emptied by fever, languidly weak both in body and mind, and solely occupied by one thought: the horror of my other self. But when I slept, or when the virtue of the medicine wore off, I would leap almost without transition (for the pangs of transformation grew daily less marked) into the possession of a fancy brimming with images of terror, a soul boiling with causeless hatreds, and a body that seemed not strong enough to contain the raging energies of life. The powers of Hyde seemed to have grown with the sickliness of Jekyll. And certainly the hate that now divided them was equal on each side. With Jekyll, it was a thing of vital instinct. He had now seen the full deformity of that creature that shared with him some of the phenomena of consciousness, and was co-heir with him to death: and beyond these links of community, which in themselves made the most poignant part of his distress, he thought of Hyde, for all his energy of life, as of something not only hellish but inorganic. This was the shocking thing; that the slime of the pit seemed to utter cries and voices; that the amorphous dust gesticulated and sinned; that what was dead, and had no shape, should usurp the offices of life. And this again, that that insurgent horror was knit to him closer than a wife, closer than an eye; lay caged in his flesh, where he heard it mutter and felt it struggle to be born; and at every hour of weakness, and in the confidence of slumber, prevailed against him, and deposed him out of life. The hatred of Hyde for Jekyll was of a different order. His terror of the gallows drove him continually to commit temporary suicide, and return to his subordinate station of a part instead of a person; but he loathed the necessity, he loathed the despondency into which Jekyll was now fallen, and he resented the dislike with which he was himself regarded. Hence the ape-like tricks that he would play me, scrawling in my own hand blasphemies on the pages of my books, burning the letters and destroying the portrait of my father; and indeed, had it not been for his fear of death, he would long ago have ruined himself in order to involve me in the ruin. But his love of life is wonderful; I go further: I, who sicken and freeze at the mere thought of him, when I recall the abjection and passion of this attachment, and when I know how he fears my power to cut him off by suicide, I find it in my heart to pity him.

It is useless, and the time awfully fails me, to prolong this description; no one has ever suffered such torments, let that suffice; and yet even to these, habit brought—no, not alleviation—but a certain callousness of soul, a certain acquiescence of despair; and my punishment might have gone on for years, but for the last calamity which has now fallen, and which has finally severed me from my own face and nature. My provision of the salt, which had never been renewed since the date of the first experiment, began to run low. I sent out for a fresh supply and mixed the draught; the ebullition followed, and the first change of colour, not the second; I drank it and it was without efficiency. You will learn from Poole how I have had London ransacked; it was in vain; and I am now persuaded that my first supply was impure, and that it was that unknown impurity which lent efficacy to the draught.

About a week has passed, and I am now finishing this statement under the influence of the last of the old powders. This, then, is the last time, short of a miracle, that Henry Jekyll can think his own thoughts or see his own face (now how sadly altered!) in the glass. Nor must I delay too long to bring my writing to an end; for if my narrative has hitherto escaped destruction, it has been by a combination of great prudence and great good luck. Should the throes of change take me in the act of writing it, Hyde will tear it in pieces; but if some time shall have elapsed after I have laid it by, his wonderful selfishness and circumscription to the moment will probably save it once again from the action of his ape-like spite. And indeed the doom that is closing on us both has already changed and crushed him. Half an hour from now, when I shall again and forever reindue that hated personality, I know how I shall sit shuddering and weeping in my chair, or continue, with the most strained and fearstruck ecstasy of listening, to pace up and down this room (my last earthly refuge) and give ear to every sound of menace. Will Hyde die upon the scaffold? or will he find courage to release himself at the last moment? God knows; I am careless; this is my true hour of death, and what is to follow concerns another than myself. Here then, as I lay down the pen and proceed to seal up my confession, I bring the life of that unhappy Henry Jekyll to an end.

STUDY QUESTIONS:

1. At what times of day or night do most of the events take place? Why is this a matter of importance so far as credibility is concerned?

2. How many scenes involve only two people? How does this number increase credibility?

3. Why is so much made of documents in this story; that is, letters, wills, and formal statements?

4. Stevenson is careful to establish several styles for his narrative, that of Mr. Utterson, that of Dr. Lanyon and that of Dr. Jekyll. What does this device add to the effect of the narrative?

5. Mr. Hyde's first crime is trampling down a little girl. Does this lead to the belief of the reader in the general incarnation of evil Hyde comes to represent? In what way?

6. Mr. Utterson is not directly involved in the main action until late in the tale; yet Stevenson goes to great pains to establish a particular character for him in the opening section. What do his characteristics add to the total impression made by the tale?

THE NIGHT
THE GHOST GOT IN

JAMES THURBER

When the great actor David Garrick (an actor brilliant in both tragedy *and* comedy) died, Dr. Samuel Johnson said that his death had eclipsed the gaiety of nations and impoverished the public stock of harmless pleasure. That was the way a great many literate Americans felt when they read of the death of James Thurber (1894–1962), who, handicapped by poor eyesight and eventual blindness, managed to amuse the world. He created with his pencil drawings a lunatic universe inhabited by people who look like un-baked sugar cookies, and in his prose he created an equally zany world in which the most preposterous events take place with simple and lucid insanity.

"The Night the Ghost Got In" is "Chapter Four" of a book entitled *My Life and Hard Times,* first published in 1933. The nine sketches that are labeled chapters and that make up the bulk of the volume are reminiscences of Thurber's life in Columbus, Ohio, where Thurber was born and where he attended Ohio State University. All students who have difficulty with science courses should read chapter eight, "University Days," in this book. In these sketches as in many other Thurber imperturbably fuses fact with fantasy, and the fantasy is presented with such obvious and worried sincerity that one cannot for a moment disbelieve it.

139

Technically, "The Night the Ghost Got In" is a sketch, not a short story. That is, it lacks a formal plot. Nevertheless it creates its own world. In Thurber's world people naturally yield to impulse, and with mathematical logic results follow. Thus the policeman takes Roy's zither and strums on it, and of course asks: "What is it?" Thurber on impulse tells him the truth: "It's an old zither our guinea pig used to sleep on." The result is a general impression of profound and harmless idiocy.

Thurber had vigorous views on the writing of English. He detested those who abused the language. In "The Night the Ghost Got In" one has an admirable example of colloquial language used precisely. Nothing is wasted and nothing seems forced.

The Ghost that got into our house on the night of November 17, 1915, raised such a hullabaloo of misundersandings that I am sorry I didn't just let it keep on walking, and go to bed. Its advent caused my mother to throw a shoe through a window of the house next door and ended up with my grandfather shooting a patrolman. I am sorry, therefore, that I ever paid any attention to the footsteps.

They began about a quarter past one o'clock in the morning, a rhythmic, quick-cadenced walking around the dining room table. My mother was asleep in one room upstairs, my brother Herman in another; grandfather was in the attic, in the old walnut bed, which, as you will remember, once fell on my father. I had just stepped out of the bathtub and was busily rubbing myself with a towel when I heard the steps. They were the steps of a man walking rapidly around the dining room table downstairs. The light from the bathroom shone down the back steps, which dropped directly into the dining-room; I could see the faint shine of plates on the plate rail; I couldn't see the table. The steps kept going round and round the table; at regular intervals a board creaked, when it was trod upon. I supposed at first that it was my father or my brother Roy, who had gone to Indianapolis but were expected home at any time. I suspected next that it was a burglar. It did not enter my mind until later that it was a ghost.

After the walking had gone on for perhaps three minutes, I tiptoed to Herman's room. "Psst!" I hissed, in the dark, shaking him. "Awp," he said, in the low, hopeless tone of a despondent beagle—he always half suspected that something would "get him" in the night. I told him who I was. "There's something downstairs!" I said. He got up and followed me to the head of the back staircase. We listened together. There was no sound. The steps had ceased. Herman looked at me in some alarm: I had only the bath towel around my waist. He wanted to go back to bed, but I gripped his arm, "There's something down there!" I said. Instantly the steps began again, circled the dining-room table like a man running, and started up the stairs toward us, heavily, two at a time. The light still shone palely down the stairs; we saw nothing coming; we only heard the steps. Herman rushed to his room and slammed the door. I slammed shut the door at the stairs top and held my knee against it. After a long minute, I slowly opened it again. There was nothing there. There was no sound. None of us ever heard the ghost again.

The slamming of the doors had aroused mother: she peered out of her room. "What on earth are you boys doing?" she demanded. Herman ventured out of his room. "Nothing," he said gruffy, but he was, in color, a light green. "What was all that running around downstairs?" said mother. So she had heard the steps, too! We just looked at her. "Burglars!" she shouted, intuitively. I tried to quiet her by starting lightly downstairs.

"Come on, Herman," I said.

"I'll stay with mother," he said. "She's all excited."

I stepped back onto the landing.

"Don't either of you go a step," said mother. "We'll call the police." Since the phone was downstairs, I didn't see how we were going to call the police—nor did I want the police—but mother made one of her quick, incomparable decisions. She flung up a window of her bedroom which faced the bedroom windows of the house of a neighbor, picked up a shoe, and whammed it through a pane of glass across the narrow space that separated the two houses. Glass tinkled into the bedroom occupied by a retired engraver named Bodwell and his wife. Bodwell had been for some years in rather a bad way and was subject to mild "attacks." Most everybody we knew or lived near had *some* kind of attacks.

It was now about two o'clock of a moonless night; clouds hung black and low. Bodwell was at the window in a minute, shouting, frothing a little, shaking his fist. "We'll sell the house and go back to Peoria," we could hear Mrs. Bodwell saying. It was some time before mother "got through" to Bodwell. "Burglars!" she shouted. "Burglars in the house!" Herman and I hadn't dared to tell her that it was not burglars but ghosts, for she was even more afraid of ghosts than of burglars. Bodwell at first thought that she meant there were burglars in his house, but finally he quieted down and called the police for us over an extension phone by his bed. After he had disappeared from the window, mother suddenly made as if to throw another shoe, not because there was further need of it but, as she later explained, because the thrill of heaving a shoe through a window glass had enormously taken her fancy. I prevented her.

The police were on hand in a commendably short time: a Ford sedan full of them, two on motorcycles, and a patrol wagon with about eight in it and a few reporters. They began banging at our front door. Flashlights shot streaks of gleam up and down the walls, across the yard, down the walk between our house and Bodwell's. "Open up!" cried a hoarse voice. "We're men from Headquarters!" I wanted to go down and let them in, since there they were, but mother wouldn't hear of it. "You haven't a stitch on," she pointed out. "You'd catch your death." I wound the towel around me again. Finally the cops put their shoulders to our big heavy front door with its thick beveled glass and broke it in: I could hear a rending of wood and a splash of glass on the floor of the hall. Their lights played all over the living-room and criss-crossed nervously in the dining-room, stabbed into hallways, shot up the front stairs and finally up the back. They caught me standing in my towel at the top. A heavy policeman bounded up the steps. "Who are you?" he demanded. "I live here," I said. "Well, whattsa matta, ya hot?" he asked. It was, as a matter of fact, cold; I went to my room and pulled on some trousers. On my way out, a cop stuck a gun into my ribs. "Whatta you doin' here?" he demanded. "I live here," I said.

The officer in charge reported to mother. "No sign of nobody, lady," he said. "Musta got away—what'd he look like?" "There were two or three of them," mother said, "whooping and carrying on and slamming doors." "Funny," said the cop. "All ya windows and doors was locked on the inside tight as a tick."

Downstairs, we could hear the tromping of the other police. Police were all over the place; doors were yanked open, drawers were yanked open, windows were shot up and pulled down, furniture fell with dull thumps. A half-dozen policemen emerged out of the darkness of the front hallway up-stairs. They began to ransack the floor: pulled beds away from walls, tore clothes off hooks in the closets, pulled suitcases and boxes off shelves. One of them found an old zither that Roy had won in a pool tournament. "Looky here, Joe," he said, strumming it with a big paw. The cop named Joe took it and turned it over. "What is it?" he asked me. "It's an old zither our guinea pig used to sleep on," I said. It was true that a pet guinea pig we once had would never sleep anywhere except on the zither, but I should never have said so. Joe and the other cop looked at me a long time. They put the zither back on a shelf.

"No sign o' nuthin'," said the cop who had first spoken to mother. "This guy," he explained to the others, jerking a thumb at me, "was nekked. The lady seems historical." They all nodded, but said nothing; just looked at me. In the small silence we all heard a creaking in the attic. Grandfather was turning over in bed. "What's 'at?" snapped Joe. Five or six cops sprang for the attic door before I could intervene or explain. I realized that it would be bad if they burst in on grandfather unannounced, or even announced. He was going through a phase in which he believed that General Meade's men under steady hammering by Stonewall Jackson, were beginning to retreat and even desert.

When I got to the attic, things were pretty confused. Grandfather had evidently jumped to the conclusion that the police were deserters from Meade's army, trying to hide away in his attic. He bounded out of bed wearing a long flannel nightgown over long woolen underwear, a nightcap, and a leather jacket around his chest. The cops must have realized at once that the indignant white-haired old man belonged in the house, but they had no chance to say so. "Back, ye cowardly dogs!" roared grandfather. "Back t' the lines, ye goddam lily-livered cattle!" With that, he fetched the officer who found the zither a flat-handed smack alongside his head that sent him sprawling. The others beat a retreat, but not fast enough; grandfather grabbed Zither's gun from its holster and let fly. The report seemed to crack the rafters; smoke filled the attic. A cop cursed and shot his hand to his shoulder. Somehow, we all finally got downstairs again and locked the door against the old gentleman. He fired once or twice more in the darkness and then went back to bed. "That was grandfather," I explained to Joe, out of breath. "He thinks you're deserters." "I'll say he does," said Joe.

The cops were reluctant to leave without getting their hands on somebody besides grandfather; the night had been distinctly a defeat for them. Furthermore, they obviously didn't like the "layout"; something looked— and I can see their viewpoint—phony. They began to poke into things again. A reporter, a thin-faced, wispy man, came up to me. I had put on one of mother's blouses, not being able to find anything else. The reporter looked at me with mingled suspicion and interest. "Just what the hell is the real low-down here, Bud?" he asked. I decided to be frank with him. "We had ghosts," I said. He gazed at me a long time as if I were a slot machine into which he had, without results, dropped a nickel. Then he walked away. The cops followed him, the one grandfather shot holding his now-bandaged arm, cursing and blaspheming. "I'm gonna get my gun back from that old bird," said the zither-cop. "Yeh," said Joe. "You—and who else?" I told them I would bring it to the station house the next day.

"What was the matter with that one policeman?" mother asked, after

they had gone. "Grandfather shot him," I said. "What for?" she demanded.
I told her he was a deserter. "Of all things!" said mother. "He was such a
nice-looking young man."

Grandfather was fresh as a daisy and full of jokes at breakfast next
morning. We thought at first he had forgotten all about what had happened,
but he hadn't. Over his third cup of coffee, he glared at Herman and me.
"What was the idee of all them cops tarryhootin' round the house last
night?" he demanded. He had us there.

STUDY QUESTIONS:

1. The story is farcical. Note, however, how naturally unexpected results
follow from such commonplace acts as taking a bath.

2. What is gained by equipping grandfather with an obsession about the
Civil War?

3. What is the difference between the prose in which events are narrated
and the prose given the characters to speak? What is the purpose of this difference?

4. The narrator relates events as he remembers them long after. What is
gained by looking at the story through a long tunnel of time? Is the credibility
of the story affected?

5. What functional connection is there between the first paragraph and the
last?

AN OCCURRENCE AT OWL CREEK BRIDGE

AMBROSE BIERCE

Ambrose Bierce, known as "Bitter Bierce" because of his acid prose and his cynical outlook, was born in a log cabin in Ohio in 1842 and disappeared in Mexico some time after 1913 or 1914. He served during the Civil War in an Indiana infantry regiment, saw both the romantic and the horrible aspects of battle, was wounded, and, finding peace-time service insupportable, took up journalism in San Francisco. Later, after rankling personal controversies, he was sent to Washington as a correspondent for Hearst's New York *American*. Typical book titles of Bierce's are *Cobwebs from an Empty Skull* and *The Devil's Dictionary*. The volume of Civil War stories which includes "An Occurrence at Owl Creek Bridge," known both as *In the Midst of Life* and *Tales of Soldiers and Civilians*, was published in this country by a friend of Bierce's in 1891, because no publishing house would bring out stories so grim and gruesome. Another notable collection, *Can Such Things Be?*, tales, for the most part, of supernatural horror, was published in 1893.

Bierce had no use for romantic war stories, and "An Occurrence at Owl Creek Bridge" is typical of his profound disgust with battle. It is of course a short story with a trick ending, but, unlike other trick endings, this

145

one does not suddenly reverse the central situation, it intensifies it. Note the casual quality of the title—the narrative is of a mere "occurrence" in war-time, not even a "case" as in the Stevenson story. The inference is that war is a dirty business full of casual cruelty. The dry, mechanical, precise prose hammers at the reader and creates a special, inhuman effect of its own. Bierce, who does not believe in emotions, deliberately reports everything as if this were a clinical experiment from which something scientific could be learned. He does not even bother to individualize speeches. His second-by-second account makes us feel that every event, every thought, every emotion follows inexorably on its predecessor, and so he creates a world in which human beings are helpless to be or do otherwise than as they do or are. Nobody is to blame for anything. Time in this story is like a wild machine out of control and running away until, all of a sudden, it is smashed in the last sentence. Such a style will do only for a few rather special effects. In Bierce there are virtually no human beings, but only human predicaments—and here is one of them.

A man stood upon a railroad bridge in northern Alabama, looking down into the swift water twenty feet below. The man's hands were behind his back, the wrists bound with a cord. A rope closely encircled his neck. It was attached to a stout cross-timber above his head and the slack fell to the level of his knees. Some loose boards laid upon the sleepers supporting the metals of the railway supplied a footing for him and his executioners—two private soldiers of the Federal army, directed by a sergeant who in civil life may have been a deputy sheriff. At a short remove upon the same temporary platform was an officer in the uniform of his rank, armed. He was a captain. A sentinel at each end of the bridge stood with his rifle in the position known as "support," that is to say, vertical in front of the left shoulder, the hammer resting on the forearm thrown straight across the chest—a formal and unnatural position, enforcing an erect carriage of the body. It did not appear to be the duty of these two men to know what was occurring at the center of the bridge; they merely blockaded the two ends of the foot planking that traversed it.

Beyond one of the sentinels nobody was in sight; the railroad ran straight away into a forest for a hundred yards, then, curving, was lost to view. Doubtless there was an outpost farther along. The other bank of the stream was open ground—a gentle acclivity topped with a stockade of vertical tree trunks, loopholed for rifles, with a single embrasure through which protruded the muzzle of a brass cannon commanding the bridge.

Midway of the slope between the bridge and fort were the spectators—a single company of infantry in line, at "parade rest," the butts of the rifles on the ground, the barrels inclining slightly backward against the right shoulder, the hands crossed upon the stock. A lieutenant stood at the right of the line, the point of his sword upon the ground, his left hand resting upon his right. Excepting the group of four at the center of the bridge, not a man moved. The company faced the bridge, staring stonily, motionless. The sentinels, facing the banks of the stream, might have been statues to adorn the bridge. The captain stood with folded arms, silent, observing the work of his subordinates, but making no sign. Death is a dignitary who when he comes announced is to be received with formal manifestations of respect, even by those most familiar with him. In the code of military etiquette silence and fixity are forms of deference.

The man who was engaged in being hanged was apparently about thirty-five years of age. He was a civilian, if one might judge from his habit, which was that of a planter. His features were good—a straight nose, firm mouth, broad forehead, from which his long, dark hair was combed straight back, falling behind his ears to the collar of his well-fitting frock coat. He wore a mustache and pointed beard, but no whiskers; his eyes were large and dark gray, and had a kindly expression which one would hardly have expected in one whose neck was in the hemp. Evidently this was no vulgar assassin. The liberal military code makes provision for hanging many kinds of persons, and gentlemen are not excluded.

The preparations being complete, the two private soldiers stepped aside and each drew away the plank upon which he had been standing. The sergeant turned to the captain, saluted and placed himself immediately behind that officer, who in turn moved apart one pace. These movements left the condemned man and the sergeant standing on the two ends of the same plank, which spanned three of the cross-ties of the bridge. The end upon which the civilian stood almost, but not quite, reached a fourth. This plank had been held in place by the weight of the captain; it was now held by that of the sergeant. At a signal from the former the latter would step aside, the plank would tilt and the condemned man go down between two ties. The arrangement commended itself to his judgment as simple and effective. His face had not been covered nor his eyes bandaged. He looked a moment at his "unsteadfast footing," then let his gaze wander to the swirling water of the stream racing madly beneath his feet. A piece of dancing driftwood caught his attention and his eyes followed it down the current. How slowly it appeared to move! What a sluggish stream!

He closed his eyes in order to fix his last thoughts upon his wife and children. The water, touched to gold by the early sun, the brooding mists under the banks at some distance down the stream, the fort, the soldiers, the piece of drift—all had distracted him. And now he became conscious of a new disturbance. Striking through the thought of his dear ones was a sound which he could neither ignore nor understand, a sharp, distinct, metallic percussion like the stroke of a blacksmith's hammer upon the anvil; it had the same ringing quality. He wondered what it was, and whether immeasurably distant or near by—it seemed both. Its recurrence was regular, but as slow as the tolling of a death knell. He awaited each stroke with impatience and—he knew not why—apprehension. The intervals of silence grew progressively longer; the delays became maddening. With their greater infrequency the sounds increased in strength and sharpness. They hurt his ear like the thrust of a knife; he feared he would shriek. What he heard was the ticking of his watch.

He unclosed his eyes and saw again the water below him. "If I could free my hands," he thought, "I might throw off the noose and spring into the stream. By diving I could evade the bullets and, swimming vigorously, reach the bank, take to the woods and get away home. My home, thank God, is as yet outside their lines; my wife and little ones are still beyond the invader's farthest advance."

As these thoughts, which have here to be set down in words, were flashed into the doomed man's brain rather than evolved from it the captain nodded to the sergeant. The sergeant stepped aside.

II

Peyton Farquhar was a well-to-do planter, of an old and highly respected Alabama family. Being a slave owner and like other slave owners a politician he was naturally an original secessionist and ardently devoted to the Southern cause. Circumstances of an imperious nature, which it is unnecessary to relate here, had prevented him from taking service with the gallant army that had fought the disastrous campaigns ending with the fall of Corinth, and he chafed under the inglorious restraint, longing for the release of his energies, the larger life of the soldier, the opportunity for distinction. That opportunity, he felt, would come, as it comes to all in war time. Meanwhile he did what he could. No service was too humble for him to perform in aid of the South, no adventure too perilous for him to undertake if consistent with the character of a civilian who was at heart a soldier, and who in good faith and without too much qualification assented to at least a part of the frankly villainous dictum that all is fair in love and war.

One evening while Farquhar and his wife were sitting on a rustic bench near the entrance to his grounds, a gray-clad soldier rode up to the gate and asked for a drink of water. Mrs. Farquhar was only too happy to serve him with her own white hands. While she was fetching the water her husband approached the dusty horseman and inquired eagerly for news from the front.

"The Yanks are repairing the railroads," said the man, "and are getting ready for another advance. They have reached the Owl Creek bridge, put it in order and built a stockade on the north bank. The commandant has issued an order, which is posted everywhere, declaring that any civilian caught interfering with the railroad, its bridges, tunnels or trains will be summarily hanged. I saw the order."

"How far is it to the Owl Creek bridge?" Farquhar asked.

"About thirty miles."

"Is there no force on this side the creek?"

"Only a picket post half a mile out, on the railroad, and a single sentinel at this end of the bridge."

"Suppose a man—a civilian and student of hanging—should elude the picket post and perhaps get the better of the sentinel," said Farquhar, smiling, "what could he accomplish?"

The soldier reflected. "I was there a month ago," he replied. "I observed that the flood of last winter had lodged a great quantity of driftwood against the wooden pier at this end of the bridge. It is now dry and would burn like tow."

The lady had now brought the water, which the soldier drank. He thanked her ceremoniously, bowed to her husband and rode away. An hour later, after nightfall, he repassed the plantation, going northward in the direction from which he had come. He was a Federal scout.

III

As Peyton Farquhar fell straight downward through the bridge he lost consciousness and was as one already dead. From this state he was awakened—ages later, it seemed to him—by the pain of a sharp pressure upon his throat, followed by a sense of suffocation. Keen, poignant agonies seemed to shoot from his neck downward through every fiber of his body and limbs. These pains appeared to flash along well-defined lines of ramification and to beat with an inconceivably rapid periodicity. They seemed like streams of pulsating fire heating him to an intolerable temperature. As to his head, he was conscious of nothing but a feeling of fulness—of congestion. These sensations were unaccompanied by thought. The intellectual part of his nature was already effaced; he had power only to feel, and feeling was torment. He was conscious of motion. Encompassed in a luminous cloud, of which he was now merely the fiery heart, without material substance he swung through unthinkable arcs of oscillation, like a vast pendulum. Then all at once, with terrible suddenness, the light about him shot upward with the noise of a loud plash; a frightful roaring was in his ears, and all was cold and dark. The power of thought was restored; he knew that the rope had broken and he had fallen into the stream. There was no additional strangulation; the noose about his neck was already suffocating him and kept the water from his lungs. To die of hanging at the bottom of a river!—the idea seemed to him ludicrous. He opened his eyes in the darkness and saw above him a gleam of light, but how distant, how inaccessible! He was still sinking, for the light became fainter and fainter until it was a mere glimmer. Then it began to grow and brighten, and he knew that he was rising toward the surface—knew it with reluctance, for he was now very comfortable. "To be hanged and drowned," he thought, "that is not so bad; but I do not wish to be shot. No; I will not be shot; that is not fair."

He was not conscious of an effort, but a sharp pain in his wrist apprised him that he was trying to free his hands. He gave the struggle his attention, as an idler might observe the feat of a juggler, without interest in the outcome. What spendid effort!—what magnificent, what superhuman strength! Ah, that was a fine endeavor! Bravo! The cord fell away; his arms parted and floated upward, the hands dimly seen on each side in the growing light. He watched them with a new interest as first one and then the other pounced upon the noose at his neck. They tore it away and thrust it fiercely aside, its undulations resembling those of a water snake. "Put it back, put it back!" He thought he shouted these words to his hands, for the undoing of the noose had been succeeded by the direst pang that he had yet experienced. His neck ached horribly; his brain was on fire; his heart, which had been fluttering faintly, gave a great leap, trying to force itself out at his mouth. His whole body was racked and wrenched with an insupportable anguish! But his disobedient hands gave no heed to the command. They beat the water vigorously with quick, downward strokes, forcing him to the surface. He felt his head emerge; his eyes were blinded by the sunlight; his chest expanded convulsively, and with a supreme and crowning agony his lungs engulfed a great draught of air, which instantly he expelled in a shriek!

He was now in full possession of his physical senses. They were, indeed, preternaturally keen and alert. Something in the awful disturbance of his organic system had so exalted and refined them that they made record of things never before perceived. He felt the ripples upon his face and heard their separate sounds as they struck. He looked at the forest on the bank of the stream, saw the individual trees, the leaves and the veining of each leaf—saw the very insects upon them: the locusts, the brilliant-bodied flies, the gray spiders stretching their webs from twig to twig. He noted the prismatic colors in all the dewdrops upon a million blades of grass. The humming of the gnats that danced above the eddies of the stream, the beating of the dragon flies' wings, the strokes of the waterspiders' legs, like oars which had lifted their boat—all these made audible music. A fish slid along beneath his eyes and he heard the rush of its body parting the water.

He had come to the surface facing down the stream; in a moment the visible world seemed to wheel slowly round, himself the pivotal point, and he saw the bridge, the fort, the soldiers upon the bridge, the captain, the sergeant, the two privates, his executioners. They were in silhouette against the blue sky. They shouted and gesticulated, pointing at him. The captain had drawn his pistol, but did not fire; the others were unarmed. Their movements were grotesque and horrible, their forms gigantic.

Suddenly he heard a sharp report and something struck the water smartly within a few inches of his head, spattering his face with spray. He heard a second report, and saw one of the sentinels with his rifle at his shoulder, a light cloud of blue smoke rising from the muzzle. The man in the water saw the eye of the man on the bridge gazing into his own through the sights of the rifle. He observed that it was a gray eye and remembered having read that gray eyes were keenest, and that all famous marksmen had them. Nevertheless, this one had missed.

A counter-swirl had caught Farquhar and turned him half round; he was again looking into the forest on the bank opposite the fort. The sound of a clear, high voice in a monotonous singsong now rang out behind him and came across the water with a distinctness that pierced and subdued all other sounds, even the beating of the ripples in his ears. Although no soldier, he had frequented camps enough to know the dread significance of that deliberate drawling, aspirated chant; the lieutenant on shore was taking a part in the morning's work. How coldly and pitilessly—with what an even, calm intonation, presaging, and enforcing tranquillity in the men—with what accurately measured intervals fell those cruel words:

"Attention, company! . . . Shoulder arms! . . . Ready! . . . Aim! . . . Fire!"

Farquhar dived—dived as deeply as he could. The water roared in his ears like the voice of Niagara, yet he heard the dulled thunder of the volley and, rising again toward the surface, met shining bits of metal, singularly flattened, oscillating slowly downward. Some of them touched him on the face and hands, then fell away, continuing their descent. One lodged between his collar and neck; it was uncomfortably warm and he snatched it out.

As he rose to the surface, gasping for breath, he saw that he had been a long time under water; he was perceptibly farther down stream—nearer to safety. The soldiers had almost finished reloading; the metal ramrods flashed all at once in the sunshine as they were drawn from the barrels, turned in the air, and thrust into their sockets. The two sentinels fired again, independently and ineffectually.

The hunted man saw all this over his shoulder; he was now swimming vigorously with the current. His brain was as energetic as his arms and legs; he thought with the rapidity of lightning.

"The officer," he reasoned, "will not make that martinet's error a second time. It is as easy to dodge a volley as a single shot. He had probably already given the command to fire at will. God help me, I cannot dodge them all!"

An appalling plash within two yards of him was followed by a loud, rushing sound, *diminuendo*, which seemed to travel back through the air to the fort and died in an explosion which stirred the very river to its deeps! A rising sheet of water curved over him, fell down upon him, blinded him, strangled him! The cannon had taken a hand in the game. As he shook his head free from the commotion of the smitten water he heard the deflected shot humming through the air ahead, and in an instant it was cracking and smashing the branches in the forest beyond.

"They will not do that again," he thought; "the next time they will use a charge of grape. I must keep my eye upon the gun; the smoke will apprise me—the report arrives too late; it lags behind the missle. That is a good gun."

Suddenly he felt himself whirled round and round—spinning like a top. The water, the banks, the forests, the now distant bridge, fort and men —all were commingled and blurred. Objects were represented by their colors only; circular horizontal streaks of color—that was all he saw. He had been caught in a vortex and was being whirled on with a velocity of advance and gyration that made him giddy and sick. In a few moments he was flung upon the gravel at the foot of the left bank of the stream—the southern bank—and behind a projecting point which concealed him from his enemies. The sudden arrest of his motion, the abrasion of one of his hands on the gravel, restored him, and he wept with delight. He dug his fingers into the sand, threw it over himself in handfuls and audibly blessed it. It looked like diamonds, rubies, emeralds; he could think of nothing beautiful which it did not resemble. The trees upon the bank were giant garden plants; he noted a definite order in their arrangement, inhaled the fragrance of their blooms. A strange, roseate light shone through the spaces among their trunks and the wind made in their branches the music of Æolian harps. He had no wish to perfect his escape — was content to remain in that enchanting spot until retaken.

A whiz and rattle of grapeshot among the branches high above his head roused him from his dream. The baffled cannoneer had fired him a random farewell. He sprang to his feet, rushed up the sloping bank, and plunged into the forest.

All that day he traveled, laying his course by the rounding sun. The forest seemed interminable; nowhere did he discover a break in it, not even a woodman's road. He had not known that he lived in so wild a region. There was something uncanny in the revelation.

By nightfall he was fatigued, footsore, famishing. The thought of his wife and children urged him on. At last he found a road which led him in what he knew to be the right direction. It was as wide and straight as a city street, yet it seemed untraveled. No fields bordered it, no dwelling anywhere. Not so much as the barking of a dog suggested human habitation. The black bodies of the trees formed a straight wall on both sides, terminating on the horizon in a point, like a diagram in a lesson in perspective. Overhead, as he looked up through this rift in the wood, shone great golden stars looking unfamiliar and grouped in strange constellations. He was sure they were arranged in some order which had a secret and malign significance. The wood on either side was full of singular noises, among which—once, twice, and again—he distinctly heard whispers in an unknown tongue.

His neck was in pain and lifting his hand to it found it horribly swollen. He knew that it had a circle of black where the rope had bruised it. His eyes felt congested; he could no longer close them. His tongue was swollen with thirst; he relieved its fever by thrusting it forward from between his teeth into the cold air. How softly the turf had carpeted the untraveled avenue—he could no longer feel the roadway beneath his feet!

Doubtless, despite his suffering, he had fallen asleep while walking, for now he sees another scene—perhaps he has merely recovered from a delirium. He stands at the gate of his own home. All is as he left it, and all bright and beautiful in the morning sunshine. He must have traveled the entire night. As he pushes open the gate and passes up the wide white walk,

he sees a flutter of female garments; his wife, looking fresh and cool and
sweet, steps down from the veranda to meet him. At the bottom of the steps
she stands waiting, with a smile of ineffable joy, an attitude of matchless
grace and dignity. Ah, how beautiful she is! He springs forward with extended arms. As he is about to clasp her he feels a stunning blow upon the
back of the neck; a blinding white light blazes all about him with a sound
like the shock of a cannon—then all is darkness and silence!

Peyton Farquhar was dead; his body, with a broken neck, swung
gently from side to side beneath the timbers of the Owl Creek bridge.

STUDY QUESTIONS:

1. In section I Bierce insists upon presenting the Federal soldiers as if
they were automata. Why?

2. What is the value to the story of the sentence (in section I): "The liberal
military code makes provision for hanging many kinds of persons, and gentlemen
are not excluded"?

3. In what sense does the plot hang on the last sentence in section II?

4. Why does Bierce detail at such length the efforts of the Federal soldiers
to shoot Farquhar?

5. What is the connection between the "kindly expression" on Farquhar's
face when he is first described, and the next to the last paragraph in the story?

HE

KATHERINE ANNE PORTER

Katherine Anne Porter (1894–) is another of the important Southern writers of our time. She was born in Indian Creek, Texas, and she has used the Texas farm country as the setting for a number of her stories. But she has written also about Germany, particularly about the difficult years before the coming of the Nazis, about Latin America, and about Mexico. Nearly all of her work has been done in the short story, and her published volumes include *Flowering Judas* (1930, 1935), *Pale Horse, Pale Rider* (1939), and *The Leaning Tower*, 1944. "He" is taken from *Flowering Judas.*

Miss Porter has been highly praised not only for the realistic accuracy of her stories and their shrewd analysis of human character but also for the simplicity and directness of her style. Because she is an extremely careful writer, she publishes very little, and the appearance of a new story by Katherine Anne Porter in a magazine is considered an event of literary importance. She makes occasional appearances at colleges and universities lecturing or reading from her work.

The problem of retarded children is an acute one, despite the progress our modern world has made in dealing with them. It is a particularly heart-breaking situation for the parents, who want the child to have as rich and full a life as other children but who are inevitably forced, as in this story, by the child's illness to accept a different fate for him.

The reader's interest in "He", however, is directed more at Mrs. Whipple, the mother of the boy, than at the boy himself. The boy is scarcely a character at all. It is Mrs. Whipple, in her terrible concern for appearances and in her sentimental self-pity, whom the author wants the reader to study. She is a universally recognizable human type, but she is something more, also. She is a weak, ineffectual woman whose lot is probably never going to improve, and her failures of perception are enormous. She is also caught in a predicament where the expression of normal mother love is impossible.

But, "He" is also a story about the troubles which afflict us all, and the reader who makes an automatic condemnation of Mrs. Whipple will have missed a large part of Miss Porter's very moving narrative.

"He" problem within family, within society, economy of family of society

Life was very hard for the Whipples. It was hard to feed all the hungry mouths, it was hard to keep the children in flannels during the winter, short as it was: "God knows what would become of us if we lived north," they would say: keeping them decently clean was hard. "It looks like our luck won't never let up on us," said Mr. Whipple, but Mrs. Whipple was all for taking what was sent and calling it good, anyhow when the neighbors were in earshot. "Don't ever let a soul hear us complain," she kept saying to her husband. She couldn't stand to be pitied. "No, not if it comes to it that we have to live in a wagon and pick cotton around the country," she said, "nobody's going to get a chance to look down on us."

Mrs. Whipple loved her second son, the simple-minded one, better than she loved the other two children put together. She was forever saying so, and when she talked with certain of her neighbors, she would even throw in her husband and her mother for good measure.

"You needn't keep on saying it around," said Mr. Whipple, "you'll make people think nobody else has any feelings about Him but you."

"It's natural for a mother," Mrs. Whipple would remind him. "You know yourself it's more natural for a mother to be that way. People don't expect so much of fathers, some way."

This didn't keep the neighbors from talking plainly among themselves. "A Lord's pure mercy if He should die," they said. "It's the sins of the fathers," they agreed among themselves. "There's bad blood and bad doings somewhere, you can bet on that." This behind the Whipples' backs.

To their faces everybody said, "He's not so bad off. He'll be all right yet. Look how He grows!"

Mrs. Whipple hated to talk about it, she tried to keep her mind off it, but every time anybody set foot in the house, the subject always came up, and she had to talk about Him first, before she could get on to anything else. It seemed to ease her mind. "I wouldn't have anything happen to Him for all the world, but it just looks like I can't keep Him out of mischief. He's so strong and active, He's always into everything; He was like that since He could walk. It's actually funny sometimes, the way He can do anything; it's laughable to see Him up to His tricks. Emly has more accidents; I'm forever tying up her bruises, and Adna can't fall a foot without cracking a bone. But He can do anything and not get a scratch. The preacher said such a nice thing once when he was here. He said, and I'll remember it to my dying day, 'The innocent walk with God—that's why He don't get hurt.'" Whenever Mrs. Whipple repeated these words, she always felt a warm pool spread in her breast, and the tears would fill her eyes, and then she could talk about something else.

He did grow and He never got hurt. A plank blew off the chicken house and struck Him on the head and He never seemed to know it. He had learned a few words, and after this He forgot them. He didn't whine for food as the other children did, but waited until it was given Him; He ate squatting in the corner, smacking and mumbling. Rolls of fat covered Him like an overcoat, and He could carry twice as much wood and water as Adna. Emly had a cold in the head most of the time—"she takes after me," said Mrs. Whipple—so in bad weather they gave her the extra blanket off His cot. He never seemed to mind the cold.

Just the same, Mrs. Whipple's life was a torment for fear something might happen to Him. He climbed the peach trees much better than Adna and went skittering along the branches like a monkey, just a regular monkey. "Oh, Mrs Whipple, you hadn't ought to let Him do that. He'll lose His balance sometime. He can't rightly know what He's doing."

Mrs. Whipple almost screamed out at the neighbor. "He *does* know what He's doing! He's as able as any other child! Come down out of there, you!" When He finally reached the ground she could hardly keep her hands off Him for acting like that before people, a grin all over His face and her worried sick about Him all the time.

"It's the neighbors." said Mrs. Whipple to her husband. "Oh, I do mortally wish they would keep out of our business. I can't afford to let Him do anything for fear they'll come nosing around about it.

Look at the bees, now. Adna can't handle them, they sting him up so; I haven't got time to do everything, and now I don't dare let Him. But if He gets a sting He don't really mind."

"It's just because He ain't got sense enough to be scared of anything." said Mr. Whipple.

"You ought to be ashamed of yourself," said Mrs. Whipple, "talking that way about your own child. Who's to take up for Him if we don't, I'd like to know? He sees a lot that goes on, He listens to things all the time. And anything I tell Him to do He does it. Don't never let anybody hear you say such things. They'd think you favored the other children over Him."

"Well, now I don't, and you know it, and what's the use of getting all worked up about it? You always think the worst of everything. Just let Him alone, He'll get along somehow. He gets plenty to eat and wear, don't He?" Mr. Whipple suddenly felt tired out. "Anyhow, it can't be helped now."

Mrs. Whipple felt tired too, she complained in a tired voice. "What's done can't never be undone, I know that good as anybody; but He's my child, and I'm not going to have people say anything. I get sick of people coming around saying things all the time."

In the early fall Mrs. Whipple got a letter from her brother saying he and his wife and two children were coming over for a little visit next Sunday week. "Put the big pot in the little one," he wrote at the end. Mrs. Whipple read this part out loud twice, she was so pleased. Her brother was a great one for saying funny things. "We'll just show him that's no joke," she said, "we'll just butcher one of the sucking pigs."

"It's a waste and I don't hold with waste the way we are now," said Mr. Whipple. "That pig'll be worth money by Christmas."

"It's a shame and a pity we can't have a decent meal's vittles once in a while when my own family comes to see us," said Mrs. Whipple. "I'd hate for his wife to go back and say there wasn't a thing in the house to eat. My God, it's better than buying up a great chance of meat in town. There's where you'd spend the money!"

"All right, do it yourself then," said Mr. Whipple. "Christamighty, no wonder we can't get ahead!"

The question was how to get the little pig away from his ma, a great fighter, worse than a Jersey cow. Adna wouldn't try it: "That sow'd rip my insides out all over the pen." "All right, old fraidy," said Mrs. Whipple, "*He's* not scared. Watch *Him* do it." And she laughed as though it was all a good joke and gave Him a little push towards the pen. He sneaked up and snatched the pig right away from the teat and galloped back and was over the fence with the sow raging at His heels. The little black squirming thing was screeching like a baby in a tantrum, stiffening its back and stretching its mouth to the ears. Mrs. Whipple took the pig with her face stiff and sliced its throat with one stroke. When He saw the blood He gave a great jolting breath and ran away. "But He'll forget and eat plenty, just the same," thought Mrs. Whipple. Whenever she was thinking, her lips moved making words. "He'd eat it all if I didn't stop Him. He'd eat up every mouthful from the other two if I'd let Him."

She felt badly about it. He was ten years old now and a third again as large as Adna, who was going on fourteen. "It's a shame, a shame," she kept saying under her breath, "and Adna with so much brains!"

She kept on feeling badly about all sorts of things. In the first place it was the man's work to butcher; the sight of the pig scraped pink and naked made her sick. He was too fat and soft and pitiful-looking. It was simply a shame the way things had to happen. By the time she had finished it up, she almost wished her brother would stay at home.

Early Sunday morning Mrs. Whipple dropped everything to get Him all cleaned up. In an hour He was dirty again, with crawling under fences after a possum, and straddling along the rafters of the barn looking for eggs in the hayloft. "My Lord, look at you now after all my trying! And here's Adna and Emly staying so quiet. I get tired trying to keep you decent. Get off that shirt and put on another, people will say I don't half dress you!" And she boxed Him on the ears, hard. He blinked and blinked and rubbed His head, and His face hurt Mrs. Whipple's feelings. Her knees began to tremble, she had to sit down while she buttoned His shirt. "I'm just all gone before the day starts."

The brother came with his plump healthy wife and two great roaring hungry boys. They had a grand dinner, with the pig roasted to a crackling in the middle of the table, full of dressing, a pickled peach in his mouth and plenty of gravy for the sweet potatoes.

"This looks like prosperity all right," said the brother; "you're going to have to roll me home like I was a barrel when I'm done."

Everybody laughed out loud; it was fine to hear them laughing all at once around the table. Mrs. Whipple felt warm and good about it. "Oh, we've got six more of these; I say it's as little as we can do when you come to see us so seldom."

He wouldn't come into the dining room, and Mrs. Whipple passed it off very well. "He's timider than my other two," she said, "He'll just have to get used to you. There isn't everybody He'll make up with, you know how it is with some children, even cousins." Nobody said anything out of the way.

"Just like my Alfy here," said the brother's wife. "I sometimes got to lick him to make him shake hands with his own grand-mammy."

So that was over, and Mrs. Whipple loaded up a big plate for Him first, before everybody. "I always say He ain't to be slighted, no matter who else goes without," she said, and carried it to Him herself.

"He can chin Himself on the top of the door," said Emly, helping along.

"That's fine, He's getting along fine," said the brother.

They went away after supper. Mrs. Whipple rounded up the dishes and sent the children to bed and sat down and unlaced her shoes. "You see?" she said to Mr. Whipple. "That's the way my whole family is. Nice and considerate about everything. No out-of-the-way remarks—they *have* got refinement. I get awfully sick of people's remarks. Wasn't that pig good?"

Mr. Whipple said, "Yes, we're out three hundred pounds of pork, that's all. It's easy to be polite when you come to eat. Who knows what they had in their minds all along?"

"Yes, that's like you," said Mrs. Whipple. "I don't expect anything else from you. You'll be telling me next that my own brother will be saying around that we made Him eat in the kitchen! Oh, my God!" She rocked her head in her hands, a hard pain started in the very middle of her forehead. "Now it's all spoiled, and everything was so nice and easy. All right, you don't like them and you never did—all right, they'll not come here again soon, never you mind! But they *can't* say He wasn't dressed every lick as good as Adna—oh, honest, sometimes I wish I was dead!"

"I wish you'd let up," said Mr. Whipple. "It's bad enough as it is."

It was a hard winter. It seemed to Mrs. Whipple that they hadn't ever known anything but hard times, and now to cap it all a winter like this. The crops were about half of what they had a right to expect; after the cotton was in it didn't do much more than cover the grocery bill. They swapped off one of the plow horses, and got cheated, for the new one died of the heaves. Mrs. Whipple kept thinking all the time it was terrible to have a man you couldn't depend on not to get cheated. They cut down on everything, but Mrs. Whipple kept saying there are things you can't cut down on, and they cost money. It took a lot of warm clothes for Adna and Emly, who walked four miles to school during the three-months session. "He sets around the fire a lot, He won't need so much," said Mr. Whipple. "That's so," said Mrs. Whipple, "and when He does the outdoor chores He can wear your tarpaullion coat. I can't do no better, that's all."

In February He was taken sick, and lay curled up under His blanket looking very blue in the face and acting as if He would choke. Mr. and Mrs. Whipple did everything they could for Him for two days, and then they were scared and sent for the doctor. The doctor told them they must keep Him warm and give Him plenty of milk and eggs. "He isn't as stout as He looks, I'm afraid," said the doctor. "You've got to watch them when they're like that. You must put more cover onto Him, too."

"I just took off His big blanket to wash," said Mrs. Whipple, ashamed. "I can't stand dirt."

"Well, you'd better put it back on the minute it's dry," said the doctor, "or He'll have pneumonia."

Mr. and Mrs. Whipple took a blanket off their own bed and put His cot in by the fire. "They can't say we didn't do everything for Him," she said, "even to sleeping cold ourselves on His account."

When the winter broke He seemed to be well again, but He walked as if His feet hurt Him. He was able to run a cotton planter during the season.

"I got it all fixed up with Jim Ferguson about breeding the cow next time," said Mr. Whipple. "I'll pasture the bull this summer and give Jim some fodder in the fall. That's better than paying out money when you haven't got it."

"I hope you didn't say such a thing before Jim Ferguson," said Mrs. Whipple. "You oughtn't to let him know we're so down as all that."

"Godamighty, that ain't saying we're down. A man is got to look ahead sometimes. *He* can lead the bull over today. I need Adna on the place."

At first Mrs. Whipple felt easy in her mind about sending Him for the bull. Adna was too jumpy and couldn't be trusted. You've got to be steady around animals. After He was gone she started thinking, and after a while she could hardly bear it any longer. She stood in the lane and watched for Him. It was nearly three miles to go and a hot day, but He oughtn't to be so long about it. She shaded her eyes and stared until colored bubbles floated in her eyeballs. It was just like everything else in life, she must always worry and never know a moment's peace about anything. After a long time she saw Him turn into the side lane, limping. He came on very slowly, leading the big hulk of an animal by a ring in the nose, twirling a little stick in His hand, never looking back or sideways, but coming on like a sleepwalker with His eyes half shut.

Mrs. Whipple was scared sick of bulls; she had heard awful stories about how they followed on quietly enough, and then suddenly pitched on with a bellow and pawed and gored a body to pieces. Any second now that black monster would come down on Him, my God, He'd never have sense enough to run.

She mustn't make a sound nor a move; she mustn't get the bull started. The bull heaved his head aside and horned the air at a fly. Her voice burst out of her in a shriek, and she screamed at Him to come on, for God's sake. He didn't seem to hear her clamor, but kept on twirling His switch and limping on, and the bull lumbered along behind him as gently as a calf. Mrs. Whipple stopped calling and ran towards the house, praying under her breath: "Lord, don't let anything happen to him. Lord, you *know* people will say we oughtn't to have sent Him. You *know* they'll say we didn't take care of Him. Oh, get Him home, safe home, safe home, and I'll look out for Him better! Amen."

She watched from the window while He led the beast in, and tied him up in the barn. It was no use trying to keep up, Mrs. Whipple couldn't bear another thing. She sat down and rocked and cried with her apron over her head.

From year to year the Whipples were growing poorer and poorer. The place just seemed to run down of itself, no matter how hard they worked. "We're losing our hold," said Mrs. Whipple. "Why can't we do like other people and watch for our best chances? They'll be calling us poor white trash next."

"When I get to be sixteen I'm going to leave," said Adna. "I'm going to get a job in Powell's grocery store. There's money in that. No more farm for me."

"I'm going to be a schoolteacher," said Emly. "But I've got to finish the eighth grade, anyhow. Then I can live in town. I don't see any chances here."

"Emly takes after my family," said Mrs. Whipple. "Ambitious every last one of them, and they don't take second place for anybody."

When fall came Emly got a chance to wait on table in the railroad eating-house in the town near by, and it seemed such a shame not to take it when the wages were good and she could get her food too, that Mrs. Whipple decided to let her take it, and not bother with school until the next session. "You've got plenty of time," she said. "You're young and smart as a whip."

With Adna gone too, Mr. Whipple tried to run the farm with just Him to help. He seemed to get along fine, doing His work and part of Adna's without noticing it. They did well enough until Christmas time, when one morning He slipped on the ice coming up from the barn. Instead of getting up He thrashed round and round, and when Mr. Whipple got to Him, He was having some sort of fit.

They brought Him inside and tried to make Him sit up, but He blub-bered and rolled, so they put Him to bed and Mr. Whipple rode to town for the doctor. All the way there and back he worried about where the money was to come from: it sure did look like he had about all the troubles he could carry.

From then on He stayed in bed. His legs swelled up double their size, and the fits kept coming back. After four months, the doctor said, "It's no use, I think you'd better put Him in the County Home for treatment right away. I'll see about it for you. He'll have good care there and be off your hands."

"We don't begrudge Him any care, and I won't let Him out of my sight," said Mrs. Whipple. "I won't have it said I sent my sick child off among strangers."

"I know how you feel," said the doctor. "You can't tell me anything about that, Mrs. Whipple. I've got a boy of my own. But you'd better listen to me. I can't do anything more for Him, that's the truth."

Mr. and Mrs. Whipple talked it over a long time that night after they went to bed. "It's just charity," said Mrs. Whipple, "that's what we've come to, charity! I certainly never looked for this."

"We pay taxes to help support the place just like everybody else," said Mr. Whipple, "and I don't call that taking charity. I think it would be fine to have Him where He'd get the best of everything . . . and besides, I can't keep up with these doctor bills any longer."

"Maybe that's why the doctor wants us to send Him—he's scared he won't get his money," said Mrs. Whipple.

"Don't talk like that," said Mr. Whipple, feeling pretty sick, "or we won't be able to send Him."

"Oh, but we won't keep Him there long," said Mrs. Whipple. "Soon's He's better, we'll bring Him right back home."

"The doctor has told you and told you time and again He can't ever get better, and you might as well stop talking," said Mr. Whipple.

"Doctor's don't know everything," said Mrs. Whipple, feeling almost happy. "But anyhow, in the summer Emly can come home for a vacation, and Adna can get down for Sundays: we'll all work together and get on our feet again, and the children will feel they've got a place to come to."

All at once she saw it full summer again, with the garden going fine, and new white roller shades up all over the house, and Adna and Emly home, so full of life, all of them happy together. Oh, it could happen, things would ease up on them.

They didn't talk before Him much, but they never knew just how much

He understood. Finally the doctor set the day and a neighbor who owned a double-seated carryall offered to drive them over. The hospital would have sent an ambulance, but Mrs. Whipple couldn't stand to see Him going away looking so sick as all that. They wrapped Him in blankets, and the neighbor and Mr. Whipple lifted Him into the back seat of the carryall beside Mrs. Whipple, who had on her black shirtwaist. She couldn't stand to go looking like charity.

"You'll be all right, I guess I'll stay behind," said Mr. Whipple. "It don't look like everybody ought to leave the place at once."

"Besides, it ain't as if He was going to stay forever," said Mrs. Whipple to the neighbor. "This is only for a little while."

They started away, Mrs. Whipple holding to the edges of the blankets to keep Him from sagging sideways. He sat there blinking and blinking. He worked His hands out and began rubbing His nose with His knuckles, and then with the end of the blanket. Mrs. Whipple couldn't believe what she saw; He was scrubbing away big tears that rolled out of the corners of His eyes. He sniveled and made a gulping noise. Mrs. Whipple kept saying, "Oh, honey, you don't feel so bad, do you? You don't feel so bad, do you?" for He seemed to be accusing her of something. Maybe He remembered that time she boxed His ears, maybe He had been scared that day with the bull, maybe He had slept cold and couldn't tell her about it; maybe He knew they were sending Him away for good and all because they were too poor to keep Him. Whatever it was, Mrs. Whipple couldn't bear to think of it. She began to cry, frightfully, and wrapped her arms tight around Him. His head rolled on her shoulder: she had loved Him as much as she possibly could, there were Adna and Emly who had to be thought of too, there was nothing she could do to make up to Him for His life. Oh, what a mortal pity He was ever born.

They came in sight of the hospital, with the neighbor driving very fast, not daring to look behind him.

STUDY QUESTIONS:

1. Why do you think Miss Porter uses the capital letter 'H' when referring to the boy? Generally, this practice is reserved only for references to the deity.

2. Characterize Mrs. Whipple. Why couldn't she "stand to be pitied"?

3. What differences are there between what Mrs. Whipple says and what

she does where her neighbors are concerned? What do the neighbors' comments about the boy indicate about their rather traditional attitudes toward the mentally retarded?

4. Did Mr. and Mrs. Whipple really "do everything for Him"? What, possibly, were their failures?

5. Miss Porter has been praised for the realistic accuracy of her dialogue. Point out several passages which seem especially true-to-life.

6. In the end, Mrs. Whipple makes the decision which she has for so long avoided. Write a paragraph of comment about the effective way in which the author builds up to and describes the final scene.

Mother is concerned about her own huberis

Ambivalence - uncertain
love, consideration, dislike, resentment
What Society says

THE CASK OF AMONTILLADO

EDGAR ALLAN POE

Edgar Allan Poe (1809–1849), who was born in Boston, who died mysteriously in Baltimore, and who presented himself to the world for a time as an aristocratic young Virginian, led an unhappy life in the America of pre-Civil War days. The country then had no assured place for a young man of talent who wanted to write for a living, and so Poe drifted from city to city, from job to job, from magazine to magazine, and from woman to woman, trying desperately to gain a foothold and to earn enough money for the support of his child bride, his mother-in-law, and himself. He wrote everything—"fillers" for newspapers, book notices, serious literary criticism, poetry, mere occasional verse, philosophy, and short narratives. He called himself a "magazinist," and he is remembered for his stories, some of his poetry, and his serious criticism. James Russell Lowell, a not unkindly man, characterized him as three-fifths genius and two-fifths sheer fudge. The world remembers the genius.

Poe's short stories are of four kinds—comic tales (modern readers do not find them funny), impressionistic sketches, detective stories, and "horror" stories—that is, stories of weird, wild atmospheric effects. He had a theory that every word in a story should be carefully chosen. He wrote that "if his very initial sentence tend not to the outbringing of this effect, then he (the author) has failed in his first step. In the whole composition there should be no word written, of which the tendency, direct or indirect, is not to the one pre-established design." "The Cask of Amontillado" is a perfect example of Poe's theory.

This is a story of revenge, and the conditions of the revenge are established in the first paragraph. Everything leads out of this, and everything leads back to it. We do not know, and care less, what were the thousand injuries that Fortunato had done to Montresor, the teller of the tale. We do not know where or when the story takes place except that we are in some Italian city during the carnival season when wearing masks is customary. With the clarity of a geometrical demonstration in which no word is wasted, Poe shows how Montresor, having thought through his problem, and having found Fortunato drunk enough not to be suspicious, carries out his plan by appealing to his victim's vanity. He has a perfect success. Or does he? Why does Poe insert, just before the end, the phrase, "my heart grew sick"? Why, in fact, does Montresor tell the story at all? He would be safer if he kept still.

The thousand injuries of Fortunato I had borne as I best could, but when he ventured upon insult I vowed revenge. You, who so well know the nature of my soul, will not suppose, however, that I gave utterance to a threat. *At length* I would be avenged; this was a point definitely settled— but the very definitiveness with which it was resolved precluded the idea of risk. I must not only punish but punish with impunity. A wrong is unredressed when retribution overtakes its redresser. It is equally unredressed when the avenger fails to make himself felt as such to him who has done the wrong.

It must be understood that neither by word nor deed had I given Fortunato cause to doubt my good will. I continued, as was my wont, to smile in his face, and he did not perceive that my smile *now* was at the thought of his immolation.

He had a weak point—this Fortunato—although in other regards he was a man to be respected and even feared. He prided himself on his connoisseurship in wine. Few Italians have the true virtuoso spirit. For the most part their enthusiasm is adopted to suit the time and opportunity, to practise imposture upon the British and Austrian *millionnaires*. In painting and gemmary, Fortunato, like his countrymen, was a quack, but in the matter of old wines he was sincere. In this respect I did not differ from him materially;—I was skilful in the Italian vintages myself, and bought largely whenever I could.

It was about dusk, one evening during the supreme madness of the carnival season, that I encountered my friend. He accosted me with excessive warmth, for he had been drinking much. The man wore motley. He had on a tight-fitting parti-striped dress, and his head was surmounted by the conical cap and bells. I was so pleased to see him that I thought I should never have done wringing his hand.

I said to him—"My dear Fortunato, you are luckily met. How remarkably well you are looking to-day. But I have received a pipe[1] of what passes for Amontillado, and I have my doubts."

"How?" said he. "Amontillado? A pipe? Impossible! And in the middle of the carnival!"

"I have my doubts," I replied; "and I was silly enough to pay the full Amontillado price without consulting you in the matter. You were not to be found, and I was fearful of losing a bargain."

"Amontillado!"

"I have my doubts."

"Amontillado!"

"And I must satisfy them."

"Amontillado!"

"As you are engaged, I am on my way to Luchresi. If any one has a critical turn, it is he. He will tell me——"

"Luchresi cannot tell Amontillado from Sherry."

"And yet some fools will have it that his taste is a match for your own."

"Come, let us go."

"Whither?"

"To your vaults."

"My friend, no; I will not impose upon your good nature. I perceive you have an engagement. Luchresi——"

"I have no engagement;—come."

"My friend, no. It is not the engagement, but the severe cold with which I perceive you are afflicted. The vaults are insufferably damp. They are encrusted with nitre."

---

[1] Pipe. A large cask of varying capacity.

"Let us go, nevertheless. The cold is merely nothing. Amontillado! You have been imposed upon. And as for Luchresi, he cannot distinguish Sherry from Amontillado."

Thus speaking, Fortunato possessed himself of my arm; and putting on a mask of black silk and drawing a *roquelaire*[2] closely about my person, I suffered him to hurry me to my palazzo.

There were no attendants at home; they had absconded to make merry in honour of the time. I had told them that I should not return until the morning, and had given them explicit orders not to stir from the house. These orders were sufficient, I well knew, to insure their immediate disappearance, one and all, as soon as my back was turned.

I took from their sconces two flambeaux, and giving one to Fortunato, bowed him through several suites of rooms to the arch way that led into the vaults. I passed down a long and winding staircase, requesting him to be cautious as he followed. We came at length to the foot of the descent, and stood together on the damp ground of the catacombs of the Montresors.

The gait of my friend was unsteady, and the bells upon his cap jingled as he strode.

"The pipe?" said he.

"It is farther on," said I; "but observe the white web-work which gleams from these cavern walls."

He turned towards me, and looked into my eyes with two filmy orbs that distilled the rheum of intoxication.

"Nitre?" he asked, at length.

"Nitre," I replied. "How long have you had that cough?"

"Ugh! ugh! ugh!—ugh! ugh! ugh!—ugh! ugh! ugh!—ugh! ugh! ugh!— ugh! ugh! ugh!"

My poor friend found it impossible to reply for many minutes.

"It is nothing," he said, at last.

"Come," I said, with decision, "we will go back; your health is precious. You are rich, respected, admired, beloved; you are happy, as once I was. You are a man to be missed. For me it is no matter. We will go back; you will be ill, and I cannot be responsible. Besides, there is Luchresi——"

"Enough," he said; "the cough is a mere nothing; it will not kill me. I shall not die of a cough."

"True—true," I replied; "and, indeed, I had no intention of alarming you unnecessarily—but you should use all proper caution. A draught of this Médoc will defend us from the damps."

[2] *Roquelaire.* A fancy cape.

Here I knocked off the neck of a bottle which I drew from a long row of its fellows that lay upon the mould.

"Drink," I said, presenting him the wine.

He raised it to his lips with a leer. He paused and nodded to me familiarly, while his bells jingled.

"I drink," he said, "to the buried that repose around us."

"And I to your long life."

He again took my arm, and we proceeded.

"These vaults," he said, "are extensive."

"The Montresors," I replied, "were a great and numerous family."

"I forget your arms."

"A huge human foot d'or, in a field azure; the foot crushes a serpent rampant whose fangs are imbedded in the heel."

"And the motto?"

"*Nemo me impune lacessit.*" [3]

"Good!" he said.

The wine sparkled in his eyes and the bells jingled. My own fancy grew warm with the Médoc. We had passed through long walls of piled skeletons, with casks and puncheons intermingling, into the inmost recesses of the catacombs. I paused again, and this time I made bold to seize Fortunato by an arm above the elbow.

"The nitre!" I said; "see, it increases. It hangs like moss upon the vaults. We are below the river's bed. The drops of moisture trickle among the bones. Come, we will go back ere it is too late. Your cough——"

"It is nothing," he said; "let us go on. But first, another draught of the Médoc."

I broke and reached him a flagon of De Grâve. He emptied it at a breath. His eyes flashed with a fierce light. He laughed and threw the bottle upward with a gesticulation I did not understand.

I looked at him in surprise. He repeated the movement—a grotesque one.

"You do not comprehend?" he said.

"Not I," I replied.

"Then you are not of the brotherhood."

"How?"

"You are not of the masons."

"Yes, yes," I said; "yes, yes."

[3] *Nemo me impune lacessit.* Latin: "No one harms me with impunity".

"You? Impossible! A mason?"

"A mason," I replied.

"A sign," he said, "a sign."

"It is this," I answered, producing from beneath the folds of my *roquelaire* a trowel.

"You jest," he exclaimed, recoiling a few paces. "But let us proceed to the Amontillado."

"Be it so," I said, replacing the tool beneath the cloak and again offering him my arm. He leaned upon it heavily. We continued our route in search of the Amontillado. We passed through a range of low arches, descended, passed on, and descending again, arrived at a deep crypt, in which the foulness of the air caused our flambeaux rather to glow than flame.

At the most remote end of the crypt there appeared another less spacious. Its walls had been lined with human remains, piled to the vault overhead, in the fashion of the great catacombs of Paris. Three sides of this interior crypt were still ornamented in this manner. From the fourth the bones had been thrown down, and lay promiscuously upon the earth, forming at one point a mound of some size. Within the wall thus exposed by the displacing of the bones, we perceived a still interior crypt or recess, in depth about four feet, in width three, in height six or seven. It seemed to have been constructed for no especial use within itself, but formed merely the interval between two of the colossal supports of the roof of the catacombs, and was backed by one of their circumscribing walls of solid granite.

It was in vain that Fortunato, uplifting his dull torch, endeavoured to pry into the depth of the recess. Its termination the feeble light did not enable us to see.

"Proceed," I said; "herein is the Amontillado. As for Luchresi——"

"He is an ignoramus," interrupted my friend, as he stepped unsteadily forward, while I followed immediately at his heels. In an instant he had reached the extremity of the niche, and finding his progress arrested by the rock, stood stupidly bewildered. A moment more and I had fettered him to the granite. In its surface were two iron staples, distant from each other about two feet, horizontally. From one of these depended a short chain, from the other a padlock. Throwing the links about his waist, it was but the work of a few seconds to secure it. He was too much astounded to resist. Withdrawing the key I stepped back from the recess.

"Pass your hand," I said, "over the wall; you cannot help feeling the nitre. Indeed it is *very* damp. Once more let me *implore* you to return. No? Then I must positively leave you. But I must first render you all the little attentions in my power."

"The Amontillado!" ejaculated my friend, not yet recovered from his astonishment.

"True," I replied; "the Amontillado."

As I said these words I busied myself among the pile of bones of which I have before spoken. Throwing them aside, I soon uncovered a quantity of building stone and mortar. With these materials and with the aid of my trowel, I began vigorously to wall up the entrance of the niche.

I had scarcely laid the first tier of the masonry when I discovered that the intoxication of Fortunato had in a great measure worn off. The earliest indication I had of this was a low moaning cry from the depth of the recess. It was *not* the cry of a drunken man. There was then a long and obstinate silence. I laid the second tier, and the third, and the fourth; and then I heard the furious vibrations of the chain. The noise lasted for several minutes, during which, that I might hearken to it with the more satisfaction, I ceased my labours and sat down upon the bones. When at last the clanking subsided, I resumed the trowel, and finished without interruption the fifth, the sixth, and the seventh tier. The wall was now nearly upon a level with my breast. I again paused, and holding the flambeaux over the mason-work, threw a few feeble rays upon the figure within.

A succession of loud and shrill screams, bursting suddenly from the throat of the chained form, seemed to thrust me violently back. For a brief moment I hesitated, I trembled. Unsheathing my rapier, I began to grope with it about the recess; but the thought of an instant reassured me. I placed my hand upon the solid fabric of the catacombs, and felt satisfied. I reapproached the wall. I replied to the yells of him who clamoured. I re-echoed, I aided, I surpassed them in volume and in strength. I did this, and the clamourer grew still.

It was now midnight, and my task was drawing to a close. I had completed the eighth, the ninth and the tenth tier. I had finished a portion of the last and the eleventh; there remained but a single stone to be fitted and plastered in. I struggled with its weight; I placed it partially in its destined position. But now there came from out the niche a low laugh that erected the hairs upon my head. It was succeeded by a sad voice, which I had difficulty in recognizing as that of the noble Fortunato. The voice said—

"Ha! ha! ha!—he! he! he!—a very good joke, indeed—an excellent jest.

We will have many a rich laugh about it at the palazzo—he! he! he!—over our wine—he! he! he!"

"The Amontillado!" I said.

"He! he! he!—he! he! he!—yes, the Amontillado. But is it not getting late? Will not they be awaiting us at the palazzo, the Lady Fortunato and the rest? Let us be gone."

"Yes," I said, "let us be gone."

"For the love of God, Montresor!"

"Yes," I said, "for the love of God!"

But to these words I hearkened in vain for a reply. I grew impatient. I called aloud—

"Fortunato!"

No answer. I called again—

"Fortunato!"

No answer still. I thrust a torch through the remaining aperture and let it fall within. There came forth in return only a jingling of the bells. My heart grew sick; on account of the dampness of the catacombs. I hastened to make an end of my labour. I forced the last stone into its position; I plastered it up. Against the new masonry I re-erected the old rampart of bones. For the half of a century no mortal has disturbed them. *In pace requiescat!*[4]

STUDY QUESTIONS:

1. Would this story be even more impressive if it were told impersonally rather than in the first person? State some reasons for your answer.

2. Why is so much of it told in dialogue between Montresor and Fortunato?

3. Does Fortunato die before the walling-up process is completed?

4. How old is the teller of the tale? Does his age have any important relation to the story, particularly to its ending?

---

[4] *In pace requiescat.* Latin: "May he rest in peace."

THE STANDARD
OF LIVING

DOROTHY PARKER

Dorothy Parker is possibly better known as a writer of verse than as a writer of the short story, though she has done distinguished work in both. Her collected poems are to be found in a volume titled *Not so Deep As A Well* (1936), and her stories in *Here Lies* (1939). But she has also written drama, drama criticism, autobiographical reminiscences, and motion picture scenarios. Some of the terse drama reviews she wrote about plays she did not like are still quoted for the sharpness of the wit. When she was on the staff of *The New Yorker* in the first years of that magazine's history, she became a legend because of the reputed quality of her wit, and many of the remarks she is supposed to have made (it is hard to believe she said them all) can be found in the book of a friend of hers, Alexander Woolcott, *While Rome Burns*.

While her verse is, for the most part, light, dealing with a limited number of themes (chiefly getting in and out of love), her short stories are another matter. In most of these Mrs. Parker is serious indeed; in "Clothe the Naked," "A Study in Black and White," "Big Blonde," "Soldiers of the Republic" and "The Standard of Living," she is dealing with some of the major problems of modern living. With admirable economy—not a word is wasted—she helps us to see the terror of a blind child in a hos-

174

tile world, the insensitivity of a rich society woman in the presence of a great Negro artist, the tawdriness of modern bad taste, and, with consummate poignancy, the childlike loneliness of men at war.

"The Standard of Living," like Joyce's "Clay" is another of those stories in which nothing much seems to happen. Two stenographers in New York play a little game of fantasy as they go to lunch each day. Then suddenly it seems to them that maybe one part of the fantasy could become real. They go into a store and price a necklace. The illusion is shattered, and in the story there are several moments of silence that act on the reader more devestatingly than anything the girls might have said. But the fantasy is persistent; within another moment they are back at the game.

Mrs. Parker has made her point. A number of critics have said that the most constant subject in American fiction is the conflict between illusion and reality, between what seems to be and what really is. Possibly we could go even further and say that this theme is at the heart of all great pieces of literature. At any rate, it forms the substance of this quiet but truly moving story about the dreams of present-day people in the huge commercialism of metropolitan life.

Annabel and Midge came out of the tea room with the arrogant slow gait of the leisured, for their Saturday afternoon stretched ahead of them. They had lunched, as was their wont, on sugar, starches, oils, and butterfats. Usually they ate sandwiches of spongy new white bread greased with butter and mayonnaise; they ate thick wedges of cake lying wet beneath ice cream and whipped cream and melted chocolate gritty with nuts. As alternates, they ate patties, sweating beads of inferior oil, containing bits of bland meat bogged in pale, stiffening sauce; they ate pastries, limber under rigid icing, filled with an indeterminate yellow sweet stuff, not still solid, not yet liquid, like salve that has been left in the sun. They chose no other sort of food, nor did they consider it. And their skin was like the petals of wood anemones, and their bellies were as flat and their flanks as lean as those of young Indian braves.

Annabel and Midge had been best friends almost from the day that Midge had found a job as stenographer with the firm that employed Annabel. By now, Annabel, two years longer in the stenographic department, had worked up to the wages of eighteen dollars and fifty cents a week; Midge was still at sixteen dollars. Each girl lived at home with her family and paid half her salary to its support.

The girls sat side by side at their desks, they lunched together every noon, together they set out for home at the end of the day's work. Many of their evenings and most of their Sundays were passed in each other's company. Often they were joined by two young men, but there was no steadiness to any such quartet; the two young men would give place, unlamented, to two other young men, and lament would have been inappropriate, really, since the newcomers were scarcely distinguishable from their predecessors. Invariably the girls spent the fine idle hours of their hot-weather Saturday afternoons together. Constant use had not worn ragged the fabric of their friendship.

They looked alike, though the resemblance did not lie in their features. It was in the shape of their bodies, their movements, their style, and their adornments. Annabel and Midge did, and completely, all that young office workers are besought not to do. They painted their lips and their nails, they darkened their lashes and lightened their hair, and scent seemed to shimmer from them. They wore thin, bright dresses, tight over their breasts and high on their legs, and tilted slippers, fancifully strapped. They looked conspicuous and cheap and charming.

Now, as they walked across to Fifth Avenue with their skirts swirled by the hot wind, they received audible admiration. Young men grouped lethargically about newsstands awarded them murmurs, exclamations, even —the ultimate tribute—whistles. Annabel and Midge passed without the condescension of hurrying their pace; they held their heads higher and set their feet with exquisite precision, as if they stepped over the necks of peasants.

Always the girls went to walk on Fifth Avenue on their free afternoons, for it was the ideal ground for their favorite game. The game could be played anywhere, and, indeed, was, but the great shop windows stimulated the two players to their best form.

Annabel had invented the game; or rather she had evolved it from an old one. Basically, it was no more than the ancient sport of what-would-you-do-if-you-had-a-million dollars? But Annabel had drawn a new set of rules for it, had narrowed it, pointed it, made it stricter. Like all games, it was the more absorbing for being more difficult.

Annabel's version went like this: You must suppose that somebody dies and leaves you a million dollars, cool. But there is a condition to the bequest. It is stated in the will that you must spend every nickel of the money on yourself.

There lay the hazard of the game. If, when playing it, you forgot, and listed among your expenditures the rental of a new apartment for your family, for example, you lost your turn to the other player. It was astonishing how many—and some of them among the experts, too—would forfeit all their innings by such slips.

It was essential, of course, that it be played in passionate seriousness. Each purchase must be carefully considered and, if necessary, supported by argument. There was no zest to playing wildly. Once Annabel had introduced the game to Sylvia, another girl who worked in the office. She explained the rules to Sylvia and then offered her the gambit "What would be the first thing you'd do?" Sylvia had not shown the decency of even a second of hesitation. "Well," she said, "the first thing I'd do, I'd go out and hire somebody to shoot Mrs. Gary Cooper, and then . . ." So it is to be seen that she was no fun.

But Annabel and Midge were surely born to be comrades, for Midge played the game like a master from the moment she learned it. It was she who added the touches that made the whole thing cozier. According to Midge's innovations, the eccentric who died and left you the money was not anybody you loved, or, for the matter of that, anybody you even knew. It was somebody who had seen you somewhere and had thought, "That girl ought to have lots of nice things. I'm going to leave her a million dollars when I die." And the death was to be neither untimely nor painful. Your benefactor, full of years and comfortably ready to depart, was to slip softly away during sleep and go right to heaven. These embroideries permitted Annabel and Midge to play their game in the luxury of peaceful consciences.

Midge played with a seriousness that was not only proper but extreme. The single strain on the girls' friendship had followed an announcement once made by Annabel that the first thing she would buy with her million dollars would be a silver-fox coat. It was as if she had struck Midge across the mouth. When Midge recovered her breath, she cried that she couldn't imagine how Annabel could do such a thing—silver-fox coats were common! Annabel defended her taste with the retort that they were not common, either. Midge then said that they were so. She added that everybody had a silver-fox coat. She went on, with perhaps a slight loss of head, to declare that she herself wouldn't be caught dead in silver fox.

For the next days, though the girls saw each other as constantly, their conversation was careful and infrequent, and they did not once play their game. Then one morning, as soon as Annabel entered the office, she came to Midge and said that she had changed her mind. She would not buy a silver-fox coat with any part of her million dollars. Immediately on receiving the legacy, she would select a coat of mink.

Midge smiled and her eyes shone. "I think," she said, "you're doing absolutely the right thing."

Now, as they walked along Fifth Avenue, they played the game anew. It was one of those days with which September is repeatedly cursed; hot and glaring, with slivers of dust in the wind. People drooped and shambled, but the girls carried themselves tall and walked a straight line, as befitted young heiresses on their afternoon promenade. There was no longer need for them to start the game at its formal opening. Annabel went direct to the heart of it.

"All right," she said. "So you've got this million dollars. So what would be the first thing you'd do?"

"Well, the first thing I'd do," Midge said, "I'd get a mink coat," But she said it mechanically, as if she were giving the memorized answer to an expected question.

"Yes," Annabel said, "I think you ought to. The terribly dark kind of mink." But she, too, spoke as if by rote. It was too hot; fur, no matter how dark and sleek and supple, was horrid to the thoughts.

They stepped along in silence for a while. Then Midge's eye was caught by a shop window. Cool, lovely gleamings were there set off by chaste and elegant darkness.

"No," Midge said, "I take it back. I wouldn't get a mink coat the first thing. Know what I'd do? I'd get a string of pearls. Real pearls."

Annabel's eyes turned to follow Midge's.

"Yes," she said, slowly. "I think that's a kind of a good idea. And it would make sense, too. Because you can wear pearls with anything."

Together they went over to the shop window and stood pressed against it. It contained but one object—a double row of great, even pearls clasped by a deep emerald around a little pink velvet throat.

"What do you suppose they cost?" Annabel said.

"Gee, I don't know," Midge said. "Plenty, I guess."

"Like a thousand dollars?" Annabel said.

"Oh, I guess like more," Midge said. "On account of the emerald."

"Well, like ten thousands dollars?" Annabel said.

"Gee, I wouldn't even know," Midge said.

The devil nudged Annabel in the ribs. "Dare you to go in and price them," she said.

"Like fun!" Midge said.

"Dare you," Annabel said.

"Why, a store like this wouldn't even be open this afternoon," Midge said.

"Yes, it is so, too," Annabel said. "People just came out. And there's a doorman on. Dare you."

"Well," Midge said. "But you've got to come too."

They tendered thanks, icily, to the doorman for ushering them into the shop. It was cool and quiet, a broad, gracious room with paneled walls and soft carpet. But the girls wore expressions of bitter disdain, as if they stood in a sty.

A slim, immaculate clerk came to them and bowed. His neat face showed no astonishment at their appearance.

"Good afternoon," he said. He implied that he would never forget it if they would grant him the favor of accepting his soft-spoken greeting.

"Good afternoon," Annabel and Midge said together, and in like freezing accents.

"Is there something—?" the clerk said.

"Oh, we're just looking," Annabel said. It was as if she flung the words down from a dais.

The clerk bowed.

"My friend and myself merely happened to be passing," Midge said, and stopped, seeming to listen to the phrase. "My friend here and myself," she went on, "merely happened to be wondering how much are those pearls you've got in your window."

"Ah, yes," the clerk said. "The double rope. That is two hundred and fifty thousand dollars, Madam."

"I see," Midge said.

The clerk bowed. "An exceptionally beautiful necklace," he said. "Would you care to look at it?"

"No, thank you," Annabel said.

"My friend and myself merely happened to be passing," Midge said.

They turned to go; to go, from their manner, where the tumbrel awaited them. The clerk sprang ahead and opened the door. He bowed as they swept by him.

The girls went on along the Avenue and disdain was still on their faces.

"Honestly!" Annabel said. "Can you imagine a thing like that?"

"Two hundred and fifty thousand dollars!" Midge said. "That's a quarter of a million dollars right there!"

"He's got his nerve!" Annabel said.

They walked on. Slowly the disdain went, slowly and completely as if drained from them, and with it went the regal carriage and tread. Their shoulders dropped and they dragged their feet; they bumped against each other, without notice or apology, and caromed away again. They were silent and their eyes were cloudy.

Suddenly Midge straightened her back, flung her head high, and spoke, clear and strong.

"Listen, Annabel," she said. "Look. Suppose there was this terribly rich person, see? You don't know this person, but this person has seen you somewhere and wants to do something for you. Well, it's a terribly old person, see? And so this person dies, just like going to sleep, and leaves you ten million dollars. Now, what would be the first thing you'd do?"

STUDY QUESTIONS:

1. How does the title apply to the story?
2. What is the point that the story wants to make? Are we merely to feel sorry for the two stenographers because they cannot afford the luxuries they talk about?
3. What is the significance of the one disagreement between the two girls?
4. Do you think the girls will continue to play the game in the future? Give reasons for your answer.
5. Mrs. Parker gives us very little character detail and no information about the kind of office in which the girls work, but in a story of this kind such detail is not necessary. Why not?

THE VALLEY
OF SPIDERS

H. G. WELLS

H. G. Wells (1866–1946) wrote an enormous amount. Trained as a biologist at London University, whence he was graduated in 1880 with a B.S. degree, he taught for a while, then discovered in himself a gift for fiction. He began by creating a wonderful world of science fiction, both in his novels and his short stories. "The Valley of Spiders" appeared in a collection of 1903 called *Twelve Stories and a Dream.* More and more aware of catastrophe approaching the Western world, he turned his novels and his expository writing to the question of how modern man could adjust to the immense problems created by technology, science, world wars, and socialism. Believing that knowledge should be widely available, he published an *Outline of History* (1920, rev. ed. 1931) and, with George Philip Wells and Julian Huxley, *The Science of Life* (1929–1930). These books, like Wells' later novels express his passionate concern that the moral order of modern life shall have a genuine relation to the social order.

"The Valley of Spiders" is science fiction. The successful science fiction writer usually assumes a single premise contrary to fact, then shrouds this premise in such a cloud of credible detail, develops his story with such logic and probability that the reader accepts the incredible. In "The Valley

181

of Spiders" one is asked to assume that in some barren region of the world—say, in South America—there are huge spiders floating in webbed balls of their own making, that the evening breeze will carry these cottony balls into a valley, and, depositing the spiders, leave them to feed on any living thing they can find. Considering the habits of land crabs and other voracious animals, one finds the supposition believable.

Such an idea, however striking, is not a story by itself. Wells unites with his gruesome invention a pursuit and escape narrative. He swings the reader's sympathy away from the pursuers, whom we see in detail (and an unlovely trio they are), to the pursued, whom we never see, though we know that among them is a young girl trying to escape from the evil genius who leads the pursuit. The trio fail, two of the pursuers are killed, and the third, baffled, rides away. We feel that justice is done. How Wells makes his spiders the instruments of justice is part of the cunning of the tale.

Towards midday the three pursuers came abruptly round a bend in the torrent bed upon the sight of a very broad and spacious valley. The difficult and winding trench of pebbles along which they had tracked the fugitives for so long, expanded to a broad slope, and with a common impulse the three men left the trail, and rode to a low eminence set with olive-dun trees, and there halted, the two others, as became them, a little behind the man with the silver-studded bridle.

For a space they scanned the great expanse below them with eager eyes. It spread remoter and remoter, with only a few clusters of sere thorn bushes here and there, and the dim suggestions of some now waterless ravine to break its desolation of yellow grass. Its purple distances melted at last into the bluish slopes of the further hills—hills it might be of a greener kind—and above them invisibly supported, and seeming indeed to hang in the blue, were the snow-clad summits of mountains—that grew larger and bolder to the north-westward as the sides of the valley grew together. And westward the valley opened until a distant darkness under the sky told where the forests began. But the three men looked neither east nor west, but only steadfastly across the valley.

The gaunt man with the scarred lip was the first to speak. "Nowhere," he said, with a sigh of disappointment in his voice. "But after all, they had a full day's start."

"They don't know we are after them," said the little man on the white horse.

"*She* would know," said the leader bitterly, as if speaking to himself.

"Even then they can't go fast. They've got no beast but the mule, and all to-day the girl's foot has been bleeding ——"

The man with the silver bridle flashed a quick intensity of rage on him. "Do you think I haven't seen that?" he snarled.

"It helps, anyhow," whispered the little man to himself.

The gaunt man with the scarred lip stared impassively. "They can't be over the valley," he said. "If we ride hard ——"

He glanced at the white horse and paused.

"Curse all white horses!" said the man with the silver bridle, and turned to scan the beast his curse included.

The little man looked down between the melancholy ears of his steed. "I did my best," he said.

The two others stared again across the valley for a space. The gaunt man passed the back of his hand across the scarred lip.

"Come up!" said the man who owned the silver bridle, suddenly. The little man started and jerked his rein, and the horse hoofs of the three made a multitudinous faint pattering upon the withered grass as they turned back towards the trail. . . .

They rode cautiously down the long slope before them, and so came through a waste of prickly twisted bushes and strange dry shapes of horny branches that grew amongst the rocks, into the level below. And there the trail grew faint, for the soil was scanty, and the only herbage was this scorched dead straw that lay upon the ground. Still, by hard scanning, by leaning beside the horse's necks and pausing ever and again, even these white men could contrive to follow after their prey.

There were trodden places, bent and broken blades of the coarse grass, and ever and again the sufficient intimation of a footmark. And once the leader saw a brown smear of blood where the half-caste girl may have trod. And at that under his breath he cursed her for a fool.

The gaunt man checked his leader's tracking, and the little man on the white horse rode behind, a man lost in a dream. They rode one after another, the man with the silver bridle led the way, and they spoke never a word. After a time it came to the little man on the white horse that the world was very still. He started out of his dream. Besides the minute noises of their horses and equipment, the whole great valley kept the brooding quiet of a painted scene.

Before him went his master and his fellow, each intently leaning forward to the left, each impassively moving with the paces of his horse; their shadows went before them—still, noiseless, tapering attendants; and nearer a crouched cool shape was his own. He looked about him. What was it had gone? Then he remembered the reverberation from the banks of the gorge and the perpetual accompaniment of shifting, jostling pebbles. And, more-over——? There was no breeze. That was it! What a vast, still place it was, a monotonous afternoon slumber. And the sky open and blank, except for a sombre veil of haze that had gathered in the upper valley.

He straightened his back, fretted with his bridle, puckered his lips to whistle, and simply sighed. He turned in his saddle for a time, and stared at the throat of the mountain gorge out of which they had come. Blank! Blank slopes on either side, with never a sign of a decent beast or tree—much less a man. What a land it was! What a wilderness! He dropped again into his former pose.

It filled him with a momentary pleasure to see a wry stick of purple black flash out into the form of a snake, and vanish amidst the brown. After all, the infernal valley *was* alive. And then, to rejoice him still more, came a breath across his face, a whisper that came and went, the faintest inclina-tion of a stiff black-antlered bush upon a crest, the first intimations of a pos-sible breeze. Idly he wetted his finger, and held it up.

He pulled up sharply to avoid a collision with the gaunt man, who had stopped at fault upon the trail. Just at that guilty moment he caught his mas-ter's eye looking towards him.

For a time he forced an interest in the tracking. Then, as they rode on again, he studied his master's shadow and hat and shoulder appearing and disappearing behind the gaunt man's nearer contours. They had ridden four days out of the very limits of the world into this desolate place, short of water, with nothing but a strip of dried meat under their saddles, over rocks and mountains, where surely none but these fugitives had ever been before —for *that!*

And all this was for a girl, a mere wilful child! And the man had whole cityfuls of people to do his basest bidding—girls, women! Why in the name of passionate folly *this* one in particular? asked the little man, and scowled at the world, and licked his parched lips with a blackened tongue. It was the way of the master, and that was all he knew. Just because she sought to evade him. . . .

His eye caught a whole row of high plumed canes bending in unison, and then the tails of silk that hung before his neck flapped and fell. The breeze was growing stronger. Somehow it took the stiff stillness out of things —and that was well.

"Hullo!" said the gaunt man.

All three stopped abruptly.

"What?" asked the master. "What?"

"Over there," said the gaunt man, pointing up the valley.

"What?"

"Something coming towards us."

And as he spoke a yellow animal crested a rise and came bearing down upon them. It was a big wild dog, coming before the wind, tongue out, at a steady pace, and running with such an intensity of purpose that he did not seem to see the horsemen he approached. He ran with his nose up, following, it was plain, neither scent nor quarry. As he drew nearer the little man felt his sword. "He's mad," said the gaunt rider.

"Shout!" said the little man and shouted.

The dog came on. Then when the little man's blade was already out, it swerved aside and went panting by them and past. The eyes of the little man followed its flight. "There was no foam," he said. For a space the man with the silver-studded bridle stared up the valley. "Oh, come on!" he cried at last. "What does it matter?" and jerked his horse into movement again.

The little man left the insoluble mystery of a dog that fled from nothing but the wind, and lapsed into profound musings on human character. "Come on!" he whispered to himself. "Why should it be given to one man to say 'Come on!' with that stupendous violence of effect. Always, all his life, the man with the silver bridle has been saying that. If *I* said it ——!" thought the little man. But people marvelled when the master was disobeyed even in the wildest things. This half-caste girl seemed to him, seemed to everyone, mad—blasphemous almost. The little man, by way of comparison, reflected on the gaunt rider with the scarred lip, as stalwart as his master, as brave and, indeed, perhaps braver, and yet for him there was obedience, nothing but to give obedience duly and stoutly . . . .

Certain sensations of the hands and knees called the little man back to more immediate things. He became aware of something. He rode up beside his gaunt fellow. "Do you notice the horses?" he said in an undertone.

The gaunt face looked interrogation.

"They don't like this wind," said the little man, and dropped behind as the man with the silver bridle turned upon him.

"It's all right," said the gaunt-faced man.

They rode on again for a space in silence. The foremost two rode downcast upon the trail, the hindmost man watched the haze that crept down the vastness of the valley, nearer and nearer, and noted how the wind grew in strength moment by moment. Far away on the left he saw a line of dark bulks—wild hog perhaps, galloping down the valley, but of that he said nothing, nor did he remark again upon the uneasiness of the horses.

And then he saw first one and then a second great white ball, a great shining white ball like a gigantic head of thistledown, that drove before the wind athwart the path. These balls soared high in the air, and dropped and rose again and caught for a moment, and hurried on and passed, but at the sight of them the restlessness of the horses increased.

Then presently he saw that more of these drifting globes—and then soon very many more—were hurrying towards him down the valley.

They became aware of a squealing. Athwart the path a huge boar rushed, turning his head but for one instant to glance at them, and then hurtling on down the valley again. And at that, all three stopped and sat in their saddles, staring into the thickening haze that was coming upon them.

"If it were not for this thistledown——" began the leader.

But now a big globe came drifting past within a score of yards of them. It was really not an even sphere at all, but a vast, soft, ragged, filmy thing, a sheet gathered by the corners, an aerial jelly-fish, as it were, but rolling over and over as it advanced, and trailing long, cobwebby threads and streamers that floated in its wake.

"It isn't thistledown," said the little man.

"I don't like the stuff," said the gaunt man.

And they looked at one another.

"Curse it!" cried the leader. "The air's full of it up there. If it keeps on at this pace long, it will stop us altogether."

An instinctive feeling, such as lines out a herd of deer at the approach of some ambiguous thing, prompted them to turn their horses to the wind, ride forward for a few paces, and stare at that advancing multitude of floating masses. They came on before the wind with a sort of smooth swiftness, rising and falling noiselessly, sinking to earth, rebounding high, soaring—all with a perfect unanimity, with a still, deliberate assurance.

Right and left of the horsemen the pioneers of this strange army passed. At one that rolled along the ground, breaking shapelessly and trailing out reluctantly into long grappling ribbons and bands, all three horses began to shy and dance. The master was seized with a sudden, unreasonable impatience. He cursed the drifting globes roundly. "Get on!" he cried; "get on! What do these things matter? How *can* they matter? Back to the trail!" He fell to swearing at his horse and sawed the bit across its mouth.

He shouted aloud with rage. "I will follow that trail, I tell you," he cried. "Where is the trail?"

He gripped the bridle of his prancing horse and searched amidst the grass. A long and clinging thread fell across his face, a grey streamer dropped about his bridle arm, some big, active thing with many legs ran down the back of his head. He looked up to discover one of those grey masses anchored as it were above him by these things and flapping out ends as a sail flaps when a boat comes about—but noiselessly.

He had an impression of many eyes, of a dense crew of squat bodies, of long, many-jointed limbs hauling at their mooring ropes to bring the thing down upon him. For a space he stared up, reining in his prancing horse with the instinct born of years of horsemanship. Then the flat of a sword smote his back, and a blade flashed overhead and cut the drifting balloon of spider-web free, and the whole mass lifted softly and drove clear and away.

"Spiders!" cried the voice of the gaunt man. "The things are full of big spiders! Look, my lord!"

The man with the silver bridle still followed the mass that drove away.

"Look, my lord!"

The master found himself staring down at a red smashed thing on the ground that, in spite of partial obliteration, could still wriggle unavailing legs. Then when the gaunt man pointed to another mass that bore down upon them, he drew his sword hastily. Up the valley now it was like a fog bank torn to rags. He tried to grasp the situation.

"Ride for it!" the little man was shouting. "Ride for it down the valley."

What happened then was like the confusion of a battle. The man with the silver bridle saw the little man go past him slashing furiously at imaginary cobwebs, saw him cannon into the horse of the gaunt man and hurl it and its rider to earth. His own horse went a dozen paces before he could rein it in. Then he looked up to avoid imaginary dangers, and then back again to see a horse rolling on the ground, the gaunt man standing and slashing over it at a rent and fluttering mass of grey that streamed and wrapped about them both. And thick and fast as thistledown on waste land on a windy day in July, the cobweb masses were coming on.

The little man had dismounted, but he dared not release his horse. He was endeavouring to lug the struggling brute back with the strength of one arm, while with the other he slashed aimlessly. The tentacles of a second grey mass had entangled themselves with the struggle, and this second grey mass came to its moorings, and slowly sank.

The master set his teeth, gripped his bridle, lowered his head, and spurred his horse forward. The horse on the ground rolled over, there was blood and moving shapes upon the flanks, and the gaunt man suddenly leaving it, ran forward towards his master, perhaps ten paces. His legs were

swathed and encumbered with grey; he made ineffectual movements with
his sword. Grey streamers waved from him; there was a thin veil of grey
across his face. With his left hand he beat at something on his body, and
suddenly he stumbled and fell. He struggled to rise, and fell again,
and suddenly, horribly, began to howl, "Oh—ohoo, ohooh!"

The master could see the great spiders upon him, and others upon
the ground.

As he strove to force his horse nearer to this gesticulating, screaming grey object that struggled up and down, there came a clatter of hoofs, and
the little man, in act of mounting, swordless, balanced on his belly athwart
the white horse, and clutching its mane, whirled past. And again a clinging
thread of grey gossamer swept across the master's face. All about him, and
over him, it seemed this drifting, noiseless cobweb circled and drew
nearer him. . . .

To the day of his death he never knew just how the event of
that moment happened. Did he, indeed, turn his horse or did it really of its
own accord stampede after its fellow? Suffice it that in another second he
was galloping full tilt down the valley with his sword whirling furiously overhead. And all about him on the quickening breeze, the spiders'
air-ships, their air bundles and air sheets, seemed to him to hurry in
a conscious pursuit.

Clatter, clatter, thud, thud—the man with the silver bridle rode, heedless of his direction, with his fearful face looking up now right, now left,
and his sword arm ready to slash. And a few hundred yards ahead of him,
with a tail of torn cobweb trailing behind him, rode the little man on the
white horse, still but imperfectly in the saddle. The reeds bent before them,
the wind blew fresh and strong, over his shoulder the master could see the
webs hurrying to overtake. . . .

He was so intent to escape the spiders' webs that only as his horse gathered together for a leap did he realise the ravine ahead. And then he
realised it only to misunderstand and interfere. He was leaning forward on
his horse's neck and sat up and back all too late.

But if in his excitement he had failed to leap, at any rate he had not
forgotten how to fall. He was horseman again in mid-air. He came off clear
with a mere bruise upon his shoulder, and his horse rolled, kicking
spasmodic legs, and lay still. But the master's sword drove its point into the
hard soil, and snapped clean across, as though Chance refused him any
longer as her Knight, and the splintered end missed his face by an inch or so.

He was on his feet in a moment, breathlessly scanning the onrushing spider-webs. For a moment he was minded to run, and then thought of the ravine, and turned back. He ran aside once to dodge one drifting terror, and then he was swiftly clambering down the precipitous sides, and out of the touch of the gale.

There under the lee of the dry torrent's steeper banks he might crouch, and watch these strange, grey masses pass and pass in safety till the wind fell, and it became possible to escape. And there for a long time he crouched, watching the strange, grey, ragged masses trail their streamers across his narrowed sky.

Once a stray spider fell into the ravine close beside him—a full foot it measured from leg to leg, and its body was half a man's hand—and after he had watched its monstrous alacrity of search and escape for a little while, and tempted it to bite his broken sword, he lifted up his iron heeled boot and smashed it into a pulp. He swore as he did so, and for a time sought up and down for another.

Then presently, when he was surer these spider swarms could not drop into the ravine, he found a place where he could sit down, and sat and fell into deep thought and began after his manner to gnaw his knuckles and bite his nails. And from this he was moved by the coming of the man with the white horse.

He heard him long before he saw him, as a clattering of hoofs, stumbling footsteps, and a reassuring voice. Then the little man appeared, a rueful figure, still with a tail of white cobweb trailing behind him. They approached each other without speaking, without a salutation. The little man was fatigued and shamed to the pitch of hopeless bitterness, and came to a stop at last, face to face with his seated master. The latter winced a little under his dependant's eye. "Well?" he said at last, with no pretence of authority.

"You left him?"

"My horse bolted."

"I know. So did mine."

He laughed at his master mirthlessly.

"I say my horse bolted," said the man who once had a silver-studded bridle.

"Cowards both," said the little man.

The other gnawed his knuckle through some meditative moments, with his eye on his inferior.

"Don't call me a coward," he said at length.

"You are a coward like myself."

"A coward possibly. There is a limit beyond which every man must fear. That I have learnt at last. But not like yourself. That is where the difference comes in."

"I never could have dreamt you would have left him. He saved your life two minutes before. . . . Why are you our lord?"

The master gnawed his knuckles again, and his countenance was dark.

"No man calls me a coward," he said. "No. . . . A broken sword is better than none. . . . One spavined white horse cannot be expected to carry two men a four days' journey. I hate white horses, but this time it cannot be helped. You begin to understand me? . . . I perceive that you are minded, on the strength of what you have seen and fancy, to taint my reputation. It is men of your sort who unmake kings. Besides which— I never liked you."

"My lord!" said the little man.

"No," said the master. "*No!*"

He stood up sharply as the little man moved. For a minute perhaps they faced one another. Overhead the spiders' balls went driving. There was a quick movement among the pebbles; a running of feet, a cry of despair, a gasp and a blow. . . .

Towards nightfall the wind fell. The sun set in a calm serenity, and the man who had once possessed the silver bridle came at last very cautiously and by an easy slope out of the ravine again; but now he led the white horse that once belonged to the little man. He would have gone back to his horse to get his silver-mounted bridle again, but he feared night and a quickening breeze might still find him in the valley, and besides he disliked greatly to think he might discover his horse all swathed in cobwebs and perhaps unpleasantly eaten.

And as he thought of those cobwebs and of all the dangers he had been through, and the manner in which he had been preserved that day, his hand sought a little reliquary that hung about his neck, and he clasped it for a moment with heartfelt gratitude. As he did so his eyes went across the valley.

"I was hot with passion," he said, "and now she has met her reward. They also, no doubt——"

And behold! Far away out of the wooded slopes across the valley, but in the clearness of the sunset distinct and unmistakable, he saw a little spire of smoke.

At that his expression of serene resignation changed to an amazed anger. Smoke? He turned the head of the white horse about, and hesitated.

And as he did so a little rustle of air went through the grass about him. Far away upon some reeds swayed a tattered sheet of grey. He looked at the cobwebs; he looked at the smoke.

"Perhaps, after all, it is not them," he said at last.

But he knew better.

After he had stared at the smoke for some time, he mounted the white horse.

As he rode, he picked his way amidst stranded masses of web. For some reason there were many dead spiders on the ground, and those that lived feasted guiltily on their fellows. At the sound of his horse's hoofs they fled.

Their time had passed. From the ground, without either a wind to carry them or a winding sheet ready, these things, for all their poison, could do him no evil.

He flicked with his belt at those he fancied came too near. Once, where a number ran together over a bare place, he was minded to dismount and trample them with his boots, but this impulse he overcame. Ever and again he turned in his saddle, and looked back at the smoke.

"Spiders," he muttered over and over again. "Spiders! Well, well. . . . The next time I must spin a web."

STUDY QUESTIONS:

1. Wells carefully refrains from giving a name to any of the characters in the story. Why?

2. What is gained by Wells' careful insistence upon the behavior of animal life (other than that of the spiders)?

3. What relation might there be between the repeated references to the silver bridle and the fact that the three pursuers are after a half-caste girl?

4. Why does Wells allow one of the men to live? Why should he especially be picked out for survival?

A WINTER NIGHT

Kay Boyle (1903–19   ), like various other American authors before her—Mark Twain, Henry James, Sinclair Lewis, Ernest Hemingway,
and F. Scott Fitzgerald—has spent much of her life abroad and has much
interest in the way Europe affects Americans. Actually, however, her
subject is much broader than this. It would probably be most accurate to
describe her as a citizen of the world. She was born in St. Paul, Minnesota,
and she makes her home in America now, but her vivid interest in
the social and political events of other nations, particularly France, Germany, and Austria is apparent in much that she writes, in her novels
(*Gentlemen, I Address You Privately*, 1933, and *Monday Night*, 1938, among
others) and as well as in her short stories. "A Winter Night" is from
Thirty Stories, published in 1946.

Many professional authors think of Kay Boyle as a "writer's writer,"
a term used to designate someone who thinks less of popular appeal than
of meticulous attention to the work itself. A writer's writer works long and
hard on the individual piece of writing; consequently, though he may not
turn out a great amount of work, what he does will be distinguished for
thoughtfulness, good taste, and careful revision. Indeed, some authors of

this variety never think of a particular story as finished, but go on revising it through the remainder of their careers.

"A Winter Night" is an excellent example both of the care that Miss Boyle takes with a short story and of her preoccupation with international events which have disturbed her in recent years. The woman who comes to sit with the American child whose mother must be away so often in the evenings has herself been through the horrors of a concentration camp, where she saw the systematic destruction of other people, including especially, another little girl like the one she now looks after. Beautifully the two come together, the child because she needs the affection which her busy mother is unable to supply, and the older woman because she needs something precious and real to which to attach herself. The story is not particularly eventful, but the whole tone of it has a twilight quality. It begins at the end of evening, and it moves into the serenity of sleep. Peace is achieved for both the old lady and the little girl.

There is a time of apprehension which begins with the beginning of darkness, and to which only the speech of love can lend security. It is there, in abeyance, at the end of every day, not urgent enough to be given the name of fear but rather of concern for how the hours are to be reprieved from fear, and those who have forgotten how it was when they were children can remember nothing of this. It may begin around five o'clock on a winter afternoon when the light outside is dying in the windows. At that hour the New York apartment in which Felicia lived was filled with shadows, and the little girl would wait alone in the living room, looking out at the winterstripped trees that stood black in the park against the isolated ovals of unclean snow. Now it was January, and the day had been a cold one; the water of the artificial lake was frozen fast, but because of the cold and the coming darkness, the skaters had ceased to move across its surface. The street that lay between the park and the apartment house was wide, and the two-way streams of cars and busses, some with their headlamps already shining, advanced and halted, halted and poured swiftly on to the tempo of the traffic signals' altering lights. The time of apprehension had set in, and Felicia, who was seven, stood at the window in the evening and waited before she asked the question. When the signals below would change from red to green again, or when the double-decker bus would turn the corner below, she would ask it. The words of it were already there, tentative in her mouth, when the answer came from the far end of the hall.

"Your mother," said the voice among the sound of kitchen things, "she telephoned up before you came in from nursery school. She won't be back in time for supper. I was to tell you a sitter was coming in from the sitting parents' place."

Felicia turned back from the window into the obscurity of the living room, and she looked toward the open door, and into the hall beyond it where the light from the kitchen fell in a clear yellow angle across the wall and onto the strip of carpet. Her hands were cold, and she put them in her jacket pockets as she walked carefully across the living-room rug and stopped at the edge of light.

"Will she be home late?" she said.

For a moment there was the sound of water running in the kitchen, a long way away, and then the sound of the water ceased, and the high, Southern voice went on:

"She'll come home when she gets ready to come home. That's all I have to say. If she wants to spend two dollars and fifty cents and ten cents' carfare on top of that three or four nights out of the week for a sitting parent to come in here and sit, it's her own business. It certainly ain't nothing to do with you or me. She makes her money, just like the rest of us does. She works all day down there in the office, or whatever it is, just like the rest of us works, and she's entitled to spend her money like she wants to spend it. There's no law in the world against buying your own freedom. Your mother and me, we're just buying our own freedom, that's all we're doing. And we're not doing nobody no harm."

"Do you know who she's having supper with?" said Felicia from the edge of the dark. There was one more step to take, and then she would be standing in the light that fell on the strip of carpet, but she did not take the step.

"Do I know who she's having supper with?" the voice cried out in what might have been derision, and there was the sound of dishes striking the metal ribs of the drainboard by the sink. "Maybe it's Mr. Van Johnson, or Mr. Frank Sinatra, or maybe it's just the Duke of Wincers for the evening. All I know is you're having soft-boiled egg and spinach and applesauce for supper, and you're going to have it quick now because the time is getting away."

The voice from the kitchen had no name. It was as variable as the faces and figures of the women who came and sat in the evenings. Month by month the voice in the kitchen altered to another voice, and the sitting parents were no more than lonely aunts of an evening or two who sometimes returned and sometimes did not to this apartment in which they had sat before. Nobody stayed anywhere very long any more, Felicia's mother told her. It was part of the time in which you lived, and part of the life of the city, but when the fathers came back, all this would be miraculously changed. Perhaps you would live in a house again, a small one, with fir trees on either side of the short brick walk, and Father would drive up every night from the station just after darkness set in. When Felicia thought of this, she stepped quickly into the clear angle of light, and she left the dark of the living room behind her and ran softly down the hall.

The drop-leaf table stood in the kitchen between the refrigerator and the sink, and Felicia sat down at the place that was set. The voice at the sink was speaking still, and while Felicia ate it did not cease to speak until the bell of the front door rang abruptly. The girl walked around the table and went down the hall, wiping her dark palms in her apron, and, from the drop-leaf table, Felicia watched her step from the angle of light into darkness and open the door.

"You put in an early appearance," the girl said, and the woman who had rung the bell came into the hall. The door closed behind her, and the girl showed her into the living room, and lit the lamp on the bookcase, and the shadows were suddenly bleached away. But when the girl turned, the woman turned from the living room too and followed her, humbly and in silence, to the threshold of the kitchen. "Sometimes they keep me standing around waiting after it's time for me to be getting on home, the sitting parents do," the girl said, and she picked up the last two dishes from the table and put them in the sink. The woman who stood in the doorway was a small woman, and when she undid the white silk scarf from around her head, Felicia saw that her hair was black. She wore it parted in the middle, and it had not been cut, but was drawn back loosely into a knot behind her head. She had very clean white gloves on, and her face was pale, and there was a look of sorrow in her soft black eyes. "Sometimes I have to stand out there in the hall with my hat and coat on, waiting for the sitting parents to turn up," the girl said, and, as she turned on the water in the sink, the contempt she had for them hung on the kitchen air. "But you're ahead of time," she said, and she held the dishes, first one and then the other, under the flow of steaming water.

The woman in the doorway wore a neat black coat, not a newlooking coat, and it had no fur on it, but it had a smooth velvet collar and velvet lapels. She did not move, or smile, and she gave no sign that she had heard the girl speaking above the sound of water at the sink. She simply stood looking at Felicia, who sat at the table with the milk in her glass not finished yet.

"Are you the child?" she said at last, and her voice was low, and the pronunciation of the words a little strange.

"Yes, this here's Felicia," the girl said, and the dark hands dried the dishes and put them away. "You drink up your milk quick now, Felicia, so's I can rinse your glass."

"I will wash the glass," said the woman. "I would like to wash the glass for her," and Felicia sat looking across the table at the face in the doorway that was filled with such unspoken grief. "I will wash the glass for her and clean off the table," the woman was saying quietly. "When the child is finished, she will show me where her night things are."

"The others, they wouldn't do anything like that," the girl said, and she hung the dishcloth over the rack. "They wouldn't put their hand to housework, the sitting parents. That's where they got the name for them," she said.

Whenever the front door closed behind the girl in the evening, it would usually be that the sitting parent who was there would take up a book of fairy stories and read aloud for a while to Felicia; or else would settle herself in the big chair in the living room and begin to tell the words of a story in drowsiness to her, while Felicia took off her clothes in the bedroom, and folded them, and put her pajamas on, and brushed her teeth, and did her hair. But this time, that was not the way it happened. Instead, the woman sat down on the other chair at the kitchen table, and she began at once to speak, not of good fairies or bad, or of animals endowed with human speech, but to speak quietly, in spite of the eagerness behind her words, of a thing that seemed of singular importance to her.

"It is strange that I should have been sent here tonight," she said, her eyes moving slowly from feature to feature of Felicia's face, "for you look like a child that I knew once, and this is the anniversary of that child."

"Did she have hair like mine?" Felicia asked quickly, and she did not keep her eyes fixed on the unfinished glass of milk in shyness any more.

"Yes, she did. She had hair like yours," said the woman, and her glance paused for a moment on the locks which fell straight and thick on the shoulders of Felicia's dress. It may have been that she thought to stretch out her hand and touch the ends of Felicia's hair, for her fingers stirred as they lay clasped together on the table, and then they relapsed into passivity again. "But it is not the hair alone, it is the delicacy of your face, too, and your eyes the same, filled with the same spring lilac color," the woman said, pronouncing the words carefully. "She had little coats of golden fur on her arms and legs," she said, "and when we were closed up there, the lot of us in the cold, I used to make her laugh when I told her that the fur that was so pretty, like a little fawn's skin on her arms, would always help to keep her warm."

"And did it keep her warm?" asked Felicia, and she gave a little jerk of laughter as she looked down at her own legs hanging under the table, with the bare calves thin and covered with a down of hair.

"It did not keep her warm enough," the woman said, and now the mask of grief had come back upon her face. "So we used to take everything we could spare from ourselves, and we would sew them into cloaks and other kinds of garments for her and for the other children. . . ."

"Was it a school?" said Felicia when the woman's voice had ceased to speak.

"No," said the woman softly, "it was not a school, but still there were a lot of children there. It was a camp—that was the name the place had; it was a camp. It was a place where they put people until they could decide what was to be done with them." She sat with her hands clasped, silent a moment, looking at Felicia. "That little dress you have on," she said, not saying the words to anybody, scarcely saying them aloud. "Oh, she would have liked that little dress, the little buttons shaped like hearts, and the white collar ———"

"I have four school dresses," Felicia said. "I'll show them to you. How many dresses did she have?"

"Well, there, you see, there in the camp," said the woman, "she did not have any dresses except the little skirt and the pullover. That was all she had. She had brought just a handkerchief of her belongings with her, like everybody else—just enough for three days away from home was what they told us, so she did not have enough to last the winter. But she had her ballet slippers," the woman said, and her clasped fingers did not move. "She had brought them because she thought during her three days away from home she would have the time to practice her ballet."

"I've been to the ballet," Felicia said suddenly, and she said it so eagerly that she stuttered a little as the words came out of her mouth. She slipped quickly down from the chair and went around the table to where the woman sat. Then she took one of the woman's hands away from the other that held it fast, and she pulled her toward the door. "Come into the living room and I'll do a pirouette for you," she said, and then she stopped speaking, her eyes halted on the woman's face. "Did she—did the little girl—could she do a pirouette very well?" she said.

"Yes, she could. At first she could," said the woman, and Felicia felt uneasy now at the sound of sorrow in her words. "But after that she was hungry. She was hungry all winter," she said in a low voice. "We were all hungry, but the children were the hungriest. Even now," she said, and her voice went suddenly savage, "when I see milk like that, clean, fresh milk standing in a glass, I want to cry out loud, I want to beat my hands on the table, because it did not have to be . . ." She had drawn her fingers abruptly away from Felicia now, and Felicia stood before her, cast off, forlorn, alone again in the time of apprehension. "That was three years ago," the woman was saying, and one hand was lifted, as in weariness, to shade her face. "It was somewhere else, it was in another country," she said, and behind her hand her eyes were turned upon the substance of a world in which Felicia had played no part.

"Did—did the little girl cry when she was hungry?" Felicia asked, and the woman shook her head.

"Sometimes she cried," she said, "but not very much. She was very quiet. One night when she heard the other children crying, she said to me, 'You know, they are not crying because they want something to eat. They are crying because their mothers have gone away.' "

"Did the mothers have to go out to supper?" Felicia asked, and she watched the woman's face for the answer.

"No," said the woman. She stood up from her chair, and now that she put her hand on the little girl's shoulder, Felicia was taken into the sphere of love and intimacy again. "Shall we go into the other room, and you will do your pirouette for me?" the woman said, and they went from the kitchen and down the strip of carpet on which the clear light fell. In the front room, they paused hand in hand in the glow of the shaded lamp, and the woman looked about her, at the books, the low tables with the magazines and ash trays on them, the vase of roses on the piano, looking with dark, scarcely seeing eyes at these things that had no reality at all. It was only when she saw the little white clock on the mantelpiece that she gave any sign, and then she said quickly: "What time does your mother put you to bed?"

Felicia waited a moment, and in the interval of waiting the woman lifted one hand and, as if in reverence, touched Felicia's hair.

"What time did the little girl you knew in the other place go to bed?" Felicia asked.

"Ah, God, I do not know, I do not remember," the woman said.

"Was she your little girl?" said Felicia softly, stubbornly.

"No," said the woman. "She was not mine. At least, at first she was not mine. She had a mother, a real mother, but the mother had to go away."

"Did she come back late?" asked Felicia.

"No, ah, no, she could not come back, she never came back," the woman said, and now she turned, her arm around Felicia's shoulders, and she sat down in the low soft chair. "Why am I saying all this to you, why am I doing it?" she cried out in grief, and she held Felicia close against her. "I had thought to speak of the anniversary to you, and that was all, and now I am saying these other things to you. Three years ago today, exactly, the little girl became my little girl because her mother went away. That is all there is to it. There is nothing more."

Felicia waited another moment, held close against the woman and listening to the swift, strong heartbeats in the woman's breast.

"But the mother," she said then in the small, persistent voice, "did she take a taxi when she went?"

"This is the way it used to happen," said the woman, speaking in hopelessness and bitterness in the softly lighted room. "Every week they used to come into the place where we were and they would read a list of names out. Sometimes it would be the names of children they would read out, and then a little later they would have to go away. And sometimes it would be the grown people's names, the names of the mothers or big sisters, or other women's names. The men were not with us. The fathers were somewhere else, in another place."

"Yes," Felicia said. "I know."

"We had been there only a little while, maybe ten days or maybe not so long," the woman went on, holding Felicia against her still, "when they read the name of the little girl's mother out, and that afternoon they took her away."

"What did the little girl do?" Felicia said.

"She wanted to think up the best way of getting out so that she could go find her mother," said the woman, "but she could not think of anything good enough until the third of fourth day. And then she tied her ballet slippers up in the handkerchief again, and she went up to the guard standing at the door." The woman's voice was gentle, controlled now. "She asked the guard please to open the door so that she could go out. 'This is Thursday,' she said, 'and every Tuesday and Thursday I have my ballet lessons. If I miss a ballet lesson, they do not count the money off, so my mother would just be paying for nothing, and she cannot afford to pay for nothing. I missed my ballet lesson on Tuesday,' she said to the guard, 'and I must not miss it again today.'"

Felicia lifted her head from the woman's shoulder, and she shook her hair back and looked in question and wonder at the woman's face.

"And did the man let her go?" she said.

"No, he did not. He could not do that," said the woman. "He was a
soldier and he had to do what he was told. So every evening after her
mother went, I used to brush the little girl's hair for her," the woman went
on saying. "And while I brushed it, I used to tell her the stories of the ballets.
Sometimes I would begin with *Narcissus*," the woman said, and she parted
Felicia's locks with her fingers, "so if you will go and get your brush now,
I will tell it while I brush your hair."

"Oh, yes," said Felicia, and she made two whirls as she went quickly
to the bedroom. On the way back, she stopped and held on to the piano
with the fingers of one hand while she went up on her toes. "Did you see
me? Did you see me standing on my toes?" she called to the woman, and
the woman sat smiling in love and contentment at her.

"Yes, wonderful, really wonderful," she said. "I am sure I have
never seen anyone do it so well." Felicia came spinning toward her,
whirling in pirouette after pirouette, and she flung herself down in the chair
close to her, with her thin bones pressed against the woman's soft, wide
hip. The woman took the silver-backed, monogrammed brush and the
tortoise-shell comb in her hands, and now she began to brush Felicia's hair.
"We did not have any soap at all and not very much water to wash in, so
I never could fix her as nicely and prettily as I wanted to," she said
and the brush stroked regularly, carefully down, caressing the shape of
Felicia's head.

"If there wasn't very much water, then how did she do her teeth?"
Felicia said.

"She did not do her teeth," said the woman, and she drew the comb
through Felicia's hair. "There were not any toothbrushes or tooth paste,
or anything like that."

Felicia waited a moment, constructing the unfamiliar scene of it in
silence, and then she asked the tentative question.

"Do I have to do my teeth tonight?" she said.

"No," said the woman, and she was thinking of something else, "you
do not have to do your teeth."

"If I am your little girl tonight, can I pretend there isn't enough
water to wash?" said Felicia.

"Yes," said the woman, "you can pretend that if you like. You do not
have to wash," she said, and the comb passed lightly through Felicia's hair.

"Will you tell me the story of the ballet?" said Felicia, and the rhythm
of the brushing was like the soft, slow rocking of sleep.

"Yes," said the woman. "In the first one, the place is a forest glade with
little pale birches growing in it, and they have green veils over their faces

and green veils drifting from their fingers, because it is the springtime. There is the music of a flute," said the woman's voice softly, softly, "and creatures of the wood are dancing———"

"But the mother," Felicia said as suddenly as if she had been awaked from sleep. "What did the little girl's mother say when she didn't do her teeth and didn't wash at night?"

"The mother was not there, you remember," said the woman, and the brush moved steadily in her hand. "But she did send one little letter back. Sometimes the people who went away were able to do that. The mother wrote it in a train, standing up in a car that had no seats," she said, and she might have been telling the story of the ballet still, for her voice was gentle and the brush did not falter on Felicia's hair. "There were perhaps a great many other people standing up in the train with her, perhaps all trying to write their little letters on the bits of paper they had managed to hide on them, or that they had found in forgotten corners as they traveled. When they had written their letters, then they must try to slip them out through the boards of the car in which they journeyed, standing up," said the woman, "and these letters fell down on the tracks under the train, or they were blown into the fields or onto the country roads, and if it was a kind person who picked them up, he would seal them in envelopes and send them to where they were addressed to go. So a letter came back like this from the little girl's mother," the woman said, and the brush followed the comb, the comb the brush in steady pursuit through Felicia's hair. "It said good-by to the little girl, and it said please to take care of her. It said: 'Whoever reads this letter in the camp, please take good care of my little girl for me, and please have her tonsils looked at by a doctor if this is possible to do.' "

"And then," said Felicia softly, persistently, "what happened to the little girl?"

"I do not know. I cannot say," the woman said. But now the brush and comb had ceased to move, and in the silence Felicia turned her thin, small body on the chair, and she and the woman suddenly put their arms around each other. "They must all be asleep now, all of them," the woman said, and in the silence that fell on them again, they held each other closer. "They must be quietly asleep somewhere, and not crying all night because they are hungry and because they are cold. For three years I have been saying 'They must all be asleep, and the cold and the hunger and the seasons or night or day or nothing matters to them———' "

It was after midnight when Felicia's mother put her key in the lock of the front door, and pushed it open, and stepped into the hallway. She walked quickly to the living room, and just across the threshold she slipped the three blue foxskins from her shoulders and dropped them, with her little velvet bag, upon the chair. The room was quiet, so quiet that she could hear the sound of breathing in it, and no one spoke to her in greeting as she crossed toward the bedroom door. And then, as startling as a slap across her delicately tinted face, she saw the woman lying sleeping on the divan, and Felicia, in her school dress still, asleep within the woman's arms.

STUDY QUESTIONS:

1. Why do you think the sitter of this story is more thoughtful and considerate of the servant than the other sitters have been?

2. Where did the sitter's meeting with the other little girl she tells about take place? What was her possible relationship to that child?

3. Felicia seems almost like a doll rather than a flesh-and-blood child. What in her life and background would help to account for this doll-like quality?

4, What possible objections to the sitter's telling Felicia of the other little girl can you think of?

5. The principal part of this story is largely straight narration. How does the author manage to keep the reader's interest during this section?

XINGU

EDITH WHARTON

When Edith Wharton (1862–1937) wrote her first novel at the age of eleven, she submitted the manuscript to her mother. It began: "Oh, how do you do, Mrs. Brown?" said Mrs. Tompkins. "If only I had known you were going to call I should have tidied up the drawing-room." Her mother handed her back the manuscript saying briefly: "Drawing-rooms are always tidy."

Edith Wharton lived in a world (New York, Newport, London, Paris, and the Riviera) in which drawing-rooms were always tidy. So was language. So likewise was art, including literature, which must always be precisely and clearly written. Inevitably the structure of the stories she wrote took on a kind of elegance. She published a superb tragic novel of New England farm life, *Ethan Frome* (1911), but her more characteristic books like *The House of Mirth* (1905) and *The Age of Innocence* (1920) have to do with the life of the well-born or of the wealthy or of both. She valued highly an inherited social and cultural tradition, she wrote from that point of view, and she detested sham.

"Xingu" (from *Xingu and Other Stories*, 1916) is a comic expression of this detestation, and is an entirely feminine story. Female pretenders to

culture have been the subjects of satire since the days of the Greek and
Roman poets. Shakespeare, Molière, Thackeray, and Sinclair Lewis have
portrayed them. But despite these attacks, amused or angry, the type lives
on, one supposes because, like other human types, it is eternal.

There has been no more adroit job done on culture fakers than
is done in "Xingu." After reading it, one imagines that Mrs. Wharton had
been exposed to too many literary "functions" and was now enjoying
a long-time revenge. The formula she uses is an ancient one: the story of
the person who turns the tables on her tormentors. Mrs. Roby has been
snubbed so many times that she finally resolves quietly to strike back. The
result is exposure. Since the fun of the story lies in the situation rather
than in individual characterizations, it is sufficient that the ladies of the
Lunch Club should remain mere sketches, as does, for that matter, both
Osric Dane (what a literary name!) and Mrs. Roby. But what more does
any one need to get the point?

I

Mrs. Ballinger is one of the ladies who pursue Culture in bands, as
though it were dangerous to meet alone. To this end she had founded the
Lunch Club, an association composed of herself and several other indomi-
table huntresses of erudition. The Lunch Club, after three or four winters of
lunching and debate, had acquired such local distinction that the entertainment of distinguished strangers became one of its accepted functions; in
recognition of which it duly extended to the celebrated "Osric Dane," on
the day of her arrival in Hillbridge, an invitation to be present at the next
meeting.

The club was to meet at Mrs. Ballinger's. The other members, behind
her back, were of one voice in deploring her unwillingness to cede her
rights in favor of Mrs. Plinth, whose house made a more impressive setting
for the entertainment of celebrities; while, as Mrs. Leveret observed, there
was always the picture-gallery to fall back on.

Mrs. Plinth made no secret of sharing this view. She had always
regarded it as one of her obligations to entertain the Lunch Club's
distinguished guests. Mrs. Plinth was almost as proud of her obligations as
she was of her picture-gallery; she was in fact fond of implying that the one
possession implied the other, and that only a woman of her wealth could
afford to live up to a standard as high as that which she had set herself. An
all-round sense of duty, roughly adaptable to various ends, was, in her

opinion, all that Providence exacted of the more humbly stationed; but the power which had predestined Mrs. Plinth to keep a footman clearly intended her to maintain an equally specialized staff of responsibilities. It was the more to be regretted that Mrs. Ballinger, whose obligations to society were bounded by the narrow scope of two parlour-maids, should have been so tenacious of the right to entertain Osric Dane.

The question of that lady's reception had for a month past profoundly moved the members of the Lunch Club. It was not that they felt themselves unequal to the task, but that their sense of the opportunity plunged them into the agreeable uncertainty of the lady who weighs the alternatives of a well-stocked wardrobe. If such subsidiary members as Mrs. Leveret were fluttered by the thought of exchanging ideas with the author of "The Wings of Death," no forebodings disturbed the conscious adequacy of Mrs. Plinth, Mrs. Ballinger and Miss Van Vluyck. "The Wings of Death" had, in fact, at Miss Van Vluyck's suggestion, been chosen as the subject of discussion at the last club meeting, and each member had thus been enabled to express her own opinion or to appropriate whatever sounded well in the comments of the others.

Mrs. Roby alone had abstained from profiting by the opportunity; but it was now openly recognised that, as a member of the Lunch Club, Mrs. Roby was a failure. "It all comes," as Miss Van Vluyck put it, "of accepting a woman on a man's estimation." Mrs. Roby, returning to Hillbridge from a prolonged sojourn in exotic lands—the other ladies no longer took the trouble to remember where—had been heralded by the distinguished biologist, Professor Foreland, as the most agreeable woman he had ever met; and the members of the Lunch Club, impressed by an encomium that carried the weight of a diploma, and rashly assuming that the Professor's social sympathies would follow the line of his professional bent, had seized the chance of annexing a biological member. Their disillusionment was complete. At Miss Van Vluyck's first off-hand mention of the pterodactyl Mrs. Roby had confusedly murmured: "I know so little about metres—" and after that painful betrayal of incompetence she had prudently withdrawn from farther participation in the mental gymnastics of the club.

"I suppose she flattered him," Miss Van Vluyck summed up—"or else it's the way she does her hair."

The dimensions of Miss Van Vluyck's dining-room having restricted the membership of the club to six, the non-conductiveness of one member was a serious obstacle to the exchange of ideas, and some wonder had already been expressed that Mrs. Roby should care to live, as it were, on

the intellectual bounty of the others. This feeling was increased by the discovery that she had not yet read "The Wings of Death." She owned to having heard the name of Osric Dane; but that—incredible as it appeared—
was the extent of her acquaintance with the celebrated novelist. The ladies
could not conceal their surprise; but Mrs. Ballinger, whose pride in the club
made her wish to put even Mrs. Roby in the best possible light, gently in-
sinuated that, though she had not had time to acquaint herself with "The
Wings of Death," she must at least be familiar with its equally remarkable
predecessor, "The Supreme Instant."

Mrs. Roby wrinkled her sunny brows in a conscientious effort of
memory, as a result of which she recalled that, oh, yes, she *had* seen the
book at her brother's, when she was staying with him in Brazil, and had
even carried it off to read one day on a boating party; but they had all got
to shying things at each other in the boat, and the book had gone
overboard, so she had never had the chance—

The picture evoked by this anecdote did not increase Mrs. Roby's
credit with the club, and there was a painful pause, which was broken by
Mrs. Plinth's remarking: "I can understand that, with all your other pur-
suits, you should not find much time for reading; but I should have thought
you might at least have *got up* 'The Wings of Death' before Osric
Dane's arrival."

Mrs. Roby took this rebuke good-humouredly. She had meant, she
owned, to glance through the book; but she had been so absorbed in a novel
of Trollope's that—

"No one reads Trollope now," Mrs. Ballinger interrupted.

Mrs. Roby looked pained. "I'm only just beginning," she confessed.

"And does he interest you?" Mrs. Plinth enquired.

"He amuses me."

"Amusement," said Mrs. Plinth, "is hardly what I look for in my
choice of books."

"Oh, certainly, 'The Wings of Death' is not amusing," ventured Mrs.
Leveret, whose manner of putting forth an opinion was like that of an obliging salesman with a variety of other styles to submit if his first selection does
not suit.

"Was it *meant* to be?" enquired Mrs. Plinth, who was fond of asking
questions that she permitted no one but herself to answer. "Assuredly not."

"Assuredly not—that is what I was going to say," assented Mrs.
Leveret, hastily rolling up her opinion and reaching for another. "It was
meant to—to elevate."

Miss Van Vluyck adjusted her spectacles as though they were the black cap of condemmation. "I hardly see," she interposed, "how a book steeped in the bitterest pessimism can be said to elevate, however much it may instruct."

"I meant of course, to instruct," said Mrs. Leveret, flurried by the unexpected distinction between two terms which she had supposed to be synonymous. Mrs. Leveret's enjoyment of the Lunch Club was frequently marred by such surprises; and not knowing her own value to the other ladies as a mirror for their mental complacency she was sometimes troubled by a doubt of her worthiness to join in their debates. It was only the fact of having a dull sister who thought her clever that saved her from a sense of hopeless inferiority.

"Do they get married in the end?" Mrs. Roby interposed.

"They—who?" the Lunch Club collectively exclaimed.

"Why, the girl and man. It's a novel, isn't it? I always think that's the one thing that matters. If they're parted it spoils my dinner."

Mrs. Plinth and Mrs. Ballinger exchanged scandalised glances, and the latter said: "I should hardly advise you to read 'The Wings of Death' in that spirit. For my part, when there are so many books one *has* to read, I wonder how any one can find time for those that are merely amusing."

"The beautiful part of it," Laura Glyde murmured, "is surely just this —that no one can tell *how* 'The Wings of Death' ends. Osric Dane, overcome by the awful significance of her own meaning, has mercifully veiled it —perhaps even from herself—as Apelles, in representing the sacrifice of Iphigenia, veiled the face of Agamemnon."

"What's that? Is it poetry?" whispered Mrs. Leveret to Mrs. Plinth, who, disdaining a definite reply, said coldly: "You should look it up. I always make it a point to look things up." Her tone added—"though I might easily have it done for me by the footman."

"I was about to say," Miss Van Vluyck resumed, "that it must always be a question whether a book *can* instruct unless it elevates."

"Oh—" murmured Mrs. Leveret, now feeling herself hopelessly astray.

"I don't know," said Mrs. Ballinger, scenting in Miss Van Vluyck's tone a tendency to depreciate the coveted distinction of entertaining Osric Dane; "I don't know that such a question can seriously be raised as to a book which has attracted more attention among thoughtful people than any novel since 'Robert Elsmere.' "

"Oh, but don't you see," exclaimed Laura Glyde, "that it's just the dark hopelessness of it all—the wonderful tone-scheme of black on black—

that makes it such an artistic achievement? It reminded me when I read it
of Prince Rupert's *manière noire* . . . the book is etched, not painted, yet
one feels the colour-values so intensely. . . ."

"Who is *he?*" Mrs. Leveret whispered to her neighbour "Some one
she's met abroad?"

"The wonderful part of the book," Mrs. Ballinger conceded, "is that
it may be looked at from so many points of view. I hear that as a study of
determinism Professor Lupton ranks it with 'The Data of Ethics.' "

"I'm told that Osric Dane spent ten years in preparatory studies before
beginning to write it," said Mrs. Plinth. "She looks up everything—verifies
everything. It has always been my principle, as you know. Nothing would
induce me, now, to put aside a book before I'd finished it, just because I
can buy as many more as I want."

"And what do *you* think of 'The Wings of Death'?" Mrs. Roby
abruptly asked her.

It was the kind of question that might be termed out of order, and the
ladies glanced at each other as though disclaiming any share in such a
breach of discipline. They all knew there was nothing Mrs. Plinth so much
disliked as being asked her opinion of a book. Books were written to read;
if one read them what more could be expected? To be questioned in detail
regarding the contents of a volume seemed to her as great an outrage
as being searched for smuggled laces at the Custom House. The club had
always respected this idiosyncrasy of Mrs. Plinth's. Such opinions as she
had were imposing and substantial: her mind, like her house, was furnished
with monumental "pieces" that were not meant to be disarranged; and it
was one of the unwritten rules of the Lunch Club that, within her own
province, each member's habits of thought should be respected. The meeting therefore closed with an increased sense, on the part of the other ladies,
of Mrs. Roby's hopeless unfitness to be one of them.

II

Mrs. Leveret, on the eventful day, arrived early at Mrs. Ballinger's, her
volume of Appropriate Allusions in her pocket.

It always flustered Mrs. Leveret to be late at the Lunch Club: she
liked to collect her thoughts and gather a hint, as the others assembled, of
the turn the conversation was likely to take. Today, however, she felt herself completely at a loss; and even the familiar contact of Appropriate
Allusions, which stuck into her as she sat down, failed to give her any reassurance. It was an admirable little volume, compiled to meet all the social

emergencies; so that, whether on the occasion of Anniversaries, joyful or melancholy (as the classification ran), of Banquets, social or municipal, or of Baptisms, Church of England or sectarian, its student need never be at a loss for a pertinent reference. Mrs. Leveret, though she had for years devoutly conned its pages, valued it, however, rather for its moral support than for its practical services; for though in the privacy of her own room she commanded an army of quotations, these invariably deserted her at the critical moment, and the only phrase she retained—*Canst thou draw out leviathan with a hook?*—was one she had never yet found occasion to apply.

To-day she felt that even the complete mastery of the volume would hardly have insured her self-possession; for she thought it probable that, even if she *did,* in some miraculous way, remember an Allusion, it would be only to find that Osric Dane used a different volume (Mrs. Leveret was convinced that literary people always carried them), and would consequently not recognise her quotations.

Mrs. Leveret's sense of being adrift was intensified by the appearance of Mrs. Ballinger's drawing-room. To a careless eye its aspect was unchanged; but those acquainted with Mrs. Ballinger's way of arranging her books would instantly have detected the marks of recent perturbation. Mrs. Ballinger's province, as a member of the Lunch Club, was the Book of the Day. On that, whatever it was, from a novel to a treatise on experimental psychology, she was confidently, authoritatively "up." What became of last year's books, or last week's even; what she did with the "subjects" she had previously professed with equal authority; no one had ever yet discovered. Her mind was an hotel where facts came and went like transient lodgers, without leaving their address behind, and frequently without paying for their board. It was Mrs. Ballinger's boast that she was "abreast with the Thought of the Day," and her pride that this advanced position should be expressed by the books on her table. These volumes, frequently renewed, and almost always damp from the press, bore names generally unfamiliar to Mrs. Leveret, and giving her, as she furtively scanned them, a disheartened glimpse of new fields of knowledge to be breathlessly traversed in Mrs. Ballinger's wake. But to-day a number of maturer-looking volumes were adroitly mingled with the *primeurs* of the press—Karl Marx jostled Professor Bergson, and the "Confessions of St. Augustine" lay beside the last work on "Mendelism"; so that even to Mrs. Leveret's fluttered perceptions it was clear that Mrs. Ballinger didn't in the least know what Osric Dane was likely to talk about, and had taken measures to be prepared for anything. Mrs. Leveret felt like a passenger on an ocean steamer who

is told that there is no immediate danger, but that she had better put
on her life-belt.

It was a relief to be roused from these forebodings by Miss Van
Vluyck's arrival.

"Well, my dear," the new-comer briskly asked her hostess, "what
subjects are we to discuss to-day?"

Mrs. Ballinger was furtively replacing a volume of Wordsworth by a
copy of Verlaine. "I hardly know," she said, somewhat nervously. "Perhaps
we had better leave that to circumstances."

"Circumstances?" said Miss Van Vluyck drily. "That means, I suppose,
that Laura Glyde will take the floor as usual, and we shall be deluged with
literature."

Philanthropy and statistics were Miss Van Vluyck's province, and she
resented any tendency to divert their guest's attention from these topics.

Mrs. Plinth at this moment appeared.

"Literature?" she protested in a tone of remonstrance. "But this
is perfectly unexpected. I understood we were to talk of Orsic Dane's novel."

Mrs. Ballinger winced at the discrimination, but let it pass. "We hardly
make that our chief subject—at least not *too* intentionally," she suggested. "Of course we can let our talk *drift* in that direction, but we ought
to have some other topic as an introduction, and that is what I wanted to
consult you about. The fact is, we know so little of Osric Dane's tastes and
interests that it is difficult to make any special preparation."

"It may be difficult," said Mrs. Plinth with decision, "but it is necessary. I know what that happy-go-lucky principle leads to. As I told one of
my nieces the other day, there are certain emergencies for which a
lady should always be prepared. It's in shocking taste to wear colours when
one pays a visit of condolence, or a last year's dress when there are reports
that one's husband is on the wrong side of the market; and so it is
with conversation. All I ask is that I should know beforehand what is to be
talked about; then I feel sure of being able to say the proper thing."

"I quite agree with you," Mrs. Ballinger assented: "but—"

And at that instant, heralded by the fluttered parlour-maid, Osric Dane
appeared upon the threshold.

Mrs. Leveret told her sister afterward that she had known at a glance
what was coming. She saw that Osric Dane was not going to meet them half
way. That distinguished personage had indeed entered with an air of com-
pulsion not calculated to promote the easy exercise of hospitality. She
looked as though she were about to be photographed for a new edition of
her books.

The desire to propitiate a divinity is generally in inverse ratio to its responsiveness, and the sense of discouragement produced by Osric Dane's entrance visibly increased the Lunch Club's eagerness to please her. Any lingering idea that she might consider herself under an obligation to her entertainers was at once dispelled by her manner: as Mrs. Leveret said afterward to her sister, she had a way of looking at you that made you feel as if there was something wrong with your hat. This evidence of greatness produced such an immediate impression on the ladies that a shudder of awe ran through them when Mrs. Roby, as their hostess led the great personage into the dining-room, turned back to whisper to the others: "What a brute she is!"

The hour about the table did not tend to revise this verdict. It was passed by Osric Dane in the silent deglutition of Mrs. Ballinger's menu, and by the members of the club in the emission of tentative platitudes which their guest seemed to swallow as perfunctorily as the successive courses of the luncheon.

Mrs. Ballinger's reluctance to fix a topic had thrown the club into a mental disarray which increased with the return to the drawing-room, where the actual business of discussion was to open. Each lady waited for the other to speak; and there was a general shock of disappointment when their hostess opened the conversation by the painfully commonplace enquiry: "Is this your first visit to Hillbridge?"

Even Mrs. Leveret was conscious that this was a bad beginning; and a vague impulse of deprecation made Miss Glyde interject: "It is a very small place indeed."

Mrs. Plinth bristled. "We have a great many representative people," she said, in the tone of one who speaks for her order.

Osric Dane turned to her. "What do they represent?" she asked.

Mrs. Plinth's constitutional dislike to being questioned was intensified by her sense of unpreparedness; and her reproachful glance passed the question on to Mrs. Ballinger.

"Why," said that lady, glancing in turn at the other members, "as a community I hope it is not too much to say that we stand for culture."

"For art—" Miss Glyde interjected.

"For art and literature," Mrs. Ballinger emended.

"And for sociology, I trust," snapped Miss Van Vluyck.

"We have a standard," said Mrs. Plinth, feeling herself suddenly secure on the vast expanse of a generalisation; and Mrs. Leveret, thinking there must be room for more than one on so broad a statement, took courage to murmur: "Oh, certainly; we have a standard."

"The object of our little club," Mrs. Ballinger continued, "is to concentrate the highest tendencies of Hillbridge—to centralise and focus its intellectual effort."

This was felt to be so happy that the ladies drew an almost audible breath of relief.

"We aspire," the President went on, "to be in touch with whatever is highest in art, literature and ethics."

Osric Dane again turned to her. "What ethics?" she asked.

A tremor of apprehension encircled the room. None of the ladies required any preparation to pronounce on a question of morals; but when they were called ethics it was different. The club, when fresh from the "Encyclopaedia Britannica," the "Reader's Handbook" or Smith's "Classical Dictionary," could deal confidently with any subject; but when taken unawares it had been known to define agnosticism as a heresy of the Early Church and Professor Froude as a distinguished histologist; and such minor members as Mrs. Leveret still secretly regarded ethics as something vaguely pagan.

Even to Mrs. Ballinger, Osric Dane's question was unsettling, and there was a general sense of gratitude when Laura Glyde leaned forward to say, with her most sympathetic accent: "You must excuse us, Mrs. Dane, for not being able, just at present, to talk of anything but 'The Wings of Death.' "

"Yes," said Miss Van Vluyck, with a sudden resolve to carry the war into the enemy's camp. "We are so anxious to know the exact purpose you had in mind in writing your wonderful book."

"You will find," Mrs. Plinth interposed, "that we are not superficial readers."

"We are eager to hear from you," Miss Van Vluyck continued, "if the pessimistic tendency of the book is an expression of your own convictions or—"

"Or merely," Miss Glyde thrust in, "a sombre background brushed in to throw your figures into more vivid relief. *Are* you not primarily plastic?"

"*I* have always maintained," Mrs. Ballinger interposed, "that you represent the purely objective method—"

Osric Dane helped herself critically to coffee. "How do you define objective?" she then enquired.

There was a flurried pause before Laura Glyde intensely murmured: "In reading *you* we don't define, we feel."

Osric Dane smiled. "The cerebellum," she remarked, "is not infrequently the seat of the literary emotions." And she took a second lump of sugar.

The sting that this remark was vaguely felt to conceal was almost neutralised by the satisfaction of being addressed in such technical language.

"Ah, the cerebellum," said Miss Van Vluyck complacently. "The club took a course in psychology last winter."

"Which psychology?" asked Osric Dane.

There was an agonising pause, during which each member of the club secretly deplored the distressing inefficiency of the others. Only Mrs. Roby went on placidly sipping her chartreuse. At last Mrs. Ballinger said, with an attempt at a high tone: "Well, really, you know, it was last year that we took psychology, and this winter we have been so absorbed in—"

She broke off, nervously trying to recall some of the club's discussions; but her faculties seemed to be paralysed by the petrifying stare of Osric Dane. What *had* the club been absorbed in? Mrs. Ballinger, with a vague purpose of gaining time, repeated slowly: "We've been so intensely absorbed in—"

Mrs. Roby put down her liqueur glass and drew near the group with a smile.

"In Xingu?" she gently prompted.

A thrill ran through the other members. They exchanged confused glances, and then, with one accord, turned a gaze of mingled relief and interrogation on their rescuer. The expression of each denoted a different phase of the same emotion. Mrs. Plinth was the first to compose her features to an air of reassurance: after a moment's hasty adjustment her look almost implied that it was she who had given the word to Mrs. Ballinger.

"Xingu, of course!" exclaimed the latter with her accustomed promptness, while Miss Van Vluyck and Laura Glyde seemed to be plumbing the depths of memory, and Mrs. Leveret, feeling apprehensively for Appropriate Allusions, was somehow reassured by the uncomfortable pressure of its bulk against her person.

Osric Dane's change of countenance was no less striking than that of her entertainers. She too put down her coffee-cup, but with a look of distinct annoyance; she too wore, for a brief moment, what Mrs. Roby afterward described as the look of feeling for something in the back of her head; and before she could dissemble these momentary signs of weakness, Mrs. Roby, turning to her with a deferential smile, had said: "And we've been so hoping that to-day you would tell us just what you think of it."

Osric Dane received the homage of the smile as a matter of course; but the accompanying question obviously embarrassed her, and it became clear to her observers that she was not quick at shifting her facial scenery. It was as though her countenance had so long been set in an expression of unchallenged superiority that the muscles had stiffened, and refused to obey her orders.

"Xingu—" she said, as if seeking in her turn to gain time.

Mrs. Roby continued to press her. "Knowing how engrossing the subject is, you will understand how it happens that the club has let everything else go to the wall for the moment. Since we took up Xingu I might almost say—were it not for your books—that nothing else seems to us worth remembering."

Osric Dane's stern features were darkened rather than lit up by an uneasy smile. "I am glad to hear that you make one exception," she gave out between narrowed lips.

"Oh, of course," Mrs. Roby said prettily; "but as you have shown us that—so very naturally!—you don't care to talk of your own things, we really can't let you off from telling us exactly what you think about Xingu; especially," she added, with a still more persuasive smile, "as some people say that one of your last books was saturated with it."

It was an *it*, then—the assurance sped like fire through the parched minds of the other members. In their eagerness to gain the least little clue to Xingu they almost forgot the joy of assisting at the discomfiture of Mrs. Dane.

The latter reddened nervously under her antagonist's challenge. "May I ask," she faltered out, "to which of my books you refer?"

Mrs. Roby did not falter. "That's just what I want you to tell us; because, though I was present, I didn't actually take part."

"Present at what?" Mrs. Dane took her up; and for an instant the trembling members of the Lunch Club thought that the champion Providence had raised up for them had lost a point. But Mrs. Roby explained herself gaily: "At the discussion, of course. And so we're dreadfully anxious to know just how it was that you went into the Xingu."

There was a portentous pause, a silence so big with incalculable dangers that the members with one accord checked the words on their lips, like soldiers dropping their arms to watch a single combat between their leaders. Then Mrs. Dane gave expression to their inmost dread by saying sharply: "Ah—you say *the* Xingu, do you?"

Mrs. Roby smiled undauntedly. "It *is* a shade pedantic, isn't it? Personally, I always drop the article; but I don't know how the other members feel about it."

The other members looked as though they would willingly have dis-
pensed with this appeal to their opinion, and Mrs. Roby, after a bright glance
about the group, went on: "They probably think, as I do, that nothing really
matters except the thing itself—except Xingu."

No immediate reply seemed to occur to Mrs. Dane, and Mrs. Ballinger
gathered courage to say: "Surely every one must feel that about Xingu."

Mrs. Plinth came to her support with a heavy murmur of assent, and
Laura Glyde sighed out emotionally: "I have known cases where it has
changed a whole life."

"It has done me worlds of good," Mrs. Leveret interjected, seeming to
herself to remember that she had either taken it or read it the winter before.

"Of course," Mrs. Roby admitted,. "the difficulty is that one must give
up so much time to it. It's very long."

"I can't imagine," said Miss Van Vluyck, "grudging the time given to
such a subject."

"And deep in places," Mrs. Roby pursued; (so then it was a book!)
"And it isn't easy to skip."

"I never skip," said Mrs. Plinth dogmatically.

"Ah, it's dangerous to, in Xingu. Even at the start there are places
where one can't. One must just wade through."

"I should hardly call it *wading*," said Mrs. Ballinger sarcastically.

Mrs. Roby sent her a look of interest. "Ah—you always found it
went swimming?"

Mrs. Ballinger hesitated. "Of course there are difficult passages,"
she conceded.

"Yes; some are not at all clear—even," Mrs. Roby added, "if one is
familiar with the original."

"As I suppose you are?" Osric Dane interposed, suddenly fixing her
with a look of challange.

Mrs. Roby met it by a deprecating gesture. "Oh, it's really not difficult
up to a certain point; though some of the branches are very little known, and
it's almost impossible to get at the source."

"Have you ever tried?" Mrs. Plinth enquired, still distrustful of Mrs.
Roby's thoroughness.

Mrs. Roby was silent for a moment; then she replied with lowered
lids: "No—but a friend of mine did; a very brilliant man; and he told me
it was best for women—not to. . . ."

A shudder ran around the room. Mrs. Leveret coughed so that
the parlour-maid, who was handing the cigarettes, should not hear; Miss Van

Vluyck's face took on a nauseated expression, and Mrs. Plinth looked as if she were passing some one she did not care to bow to. But the most remarkable result of Mrs. Roby's words was the effect they produced on the Lunch Club's distinguished guest. Osric Dane's impassive features suddenly softened to an expression of the warmest human sympathy, and edging her chair toward Mrs. Roby's she asked: "Did he really? And—did you find he was right?"

Mrs. Ballinger, in whom annoyance at Mrs. Roby's unwonted assumption of prominence was beginning to displace gratitude for the aid she had rendered, could not consent to her being allowed by such dubious means, to monopolise the attention of their guest. If Osric Dane had not enough self-respect to resent Mrs. Roby's flippancy, at least the Lunch Club would do so in the person of its President.

Mrs. Ballinger laid her hand on Mrs. Roby's arm. "We must not forget," she said with a frigid amiability, "that absorbing as Xingu is to *us*, it may be less interesting to—"

"Oh, no, on the contrary, I assure you," Osric Dane intervened.

"—to others," Mrs. Ballinger finished firmly; "and we must not allow our little meeting to end without persuading Mrs. Dane to say a few words to us on a subject which, to-day, is much more present in all our thoughts. I refer, of course, to 'The Wings of Death.' "

The other members, animated by various degrees of the same sentiment, and encouraged by the humanised mien of their redoubtable guest, repeated after Mrs. Ballinger: "Oh, yes, you really *must* talk to us a little about your book."

Osric Dane's expression became as bored, though not as haughty, as when her work had been previously mentioned. But before she could respond to Mrs. Ballinger's request, Mrs. Roby had risen from her seat, and was pulling down her veil over her frivolous nose.

"I'm so sorry," she said, advancing toward her hostess with outstretched hand, "but before Mrs. Dane begins I think I'd better run away. Unluckily, as you know, I haven't read her books, so I should be at a terrible disadvantage among you all, and besides, I've an engagement to play bridge."

If Mrs. Roby had simply pleaded her ignorance of Osric Dane's works as a reason for withdrawing, the Lunch Club, in view of her recent prowess, might have approved such evidence of discretion; but to couple this excuse with the brazen announcement that she was foregoing the privilege for the purpose of joining a bridge-party was only one more instance of her deplorable lack of discrimination.

The ladies were disposed, however, to feel that her departure—now that she had performed the sole service she was ever likely to render them—would probably make for greater order and dignity in the impending discussion, besides relieving them of the sense of self-distrust which her presence always mysteriously produced. Mrs. Ballinger therefore restricted herself to a formal murmur of regret, and the other members were just grouping themselves comfortably about Osric Dane when the latter, to their dismay, started up from the sofa on which she had been seated.

"Oh wait—do wait, and I'll go with you!" she called out to Mrs. Roby; and, seizing the hands of the disconcerted members, she administered a series of farewell pressures with the mechanical haste of a railway-conductor punching tickets.

"I'm so sorry—I'd quite forgotten—" she flung back at them from the threshold; and as she joined Mrs. Roby, who had turned in surprise at her appeal, the other ladies had the mortification of hearing her say, in a voice which she did not take the pains to lower: "If you'll let me walk a little way with you, I should so like to ask you a few more questions about Xingu . . . "

III

The incident had been so rapid that the door closed on the departing pair before the other members had time to understand what was happening. Then a sense of the indignity put upon them by Osric Dane's unceremonious desertion began to contend with the confused feeling that they had been cheated out of their due without exactly knowing how or why.

There was a silence, during which Mrs. Ballinger, with a perfunctory hand, rearranged the skilfully grouped literature at which her distinguished guest had not so much as glanced; then Miss Van Vluyck tartly pronounced: "Well, I can't say that I consider Osric Dane's departure a great loss."

This confession crystallised the resentment of the other members, and Mrs. Leveret exclaimed: "I do believe she came on purpose to be nasty!"

It was Mrs. Plinth's private opinion that Osric Dane's attitude toward the Lunch Club might have been very different had it welcomed her in the majestic setting of the Plinth drawing-rooms; but not liking to reflect on the inadequacy of Mrs. Ballinger's establishment she sought a roundabout satisfaction in depreciating her lack of foresight.

"I said from the first that we ought to have had a subject ready. It's what always happens when you're unprepared. Now if we'd only got up Xingu—"

The slowness of Mrs. Plinth's mental processes was always allowed for by the club; but this instance of it was too much for Mrs. Ballinger's equanimity.

"Xingu!" she scoffed. "Why, it was the fact of our knowing so much more about it than she did—unprepared though we were—that made Osric Dane so furious. I should have thought that was plain enough to everybody!"

This retort impressed even Mrs. Plinth, and Laura Glyde, moved by an impulse of generosity, said: "Yes, we really ought to be grateful to Mrs. Roby for introducing the topic. It may have made Osric Dane furious, but at least it made her civil."

"I am glad we were able to show her," added Miss Van Vluyck, "that a broad and up-to-date culture is not confined to the great intellectual centres."

This increased the satisfaction of the other members, and they began to forget their wrath against Osric Dane in the pleasure of having contributed to her discomfiture.

Miss Van Vluyck thoughtfully rubbed her spectacles. "What surprised me most," she continued, "was that Fanny Roby should be so up on Xingu."

This remark threw a slight chill on the company, but Mrs. Ballinger said with an air of indulgent irony: "Mrs. Roby always has the knack of making a little go a long way; still, we certainly owe her a debt for happening to remember that she'd heard of Xingu." And this was felt by the other members to be a graceful way of cancelling once for all the club's obligation to Mrs. Roby.

Even Mrs. Leveret took courage to speed a timid shaft of irony. "I fancy Osric Dane hardly expected to take a lesson in Xingu at Hillbridge!"

Mrs. Ballinger smiled. "When she asked me what we represented—do you remember?—I wish I'd simply said we represented Xingu!"

All the ladies laughed appreciatively at this sally, except Mrs. Plinth, who said, after a moment's deliberation: "I'm not sure it would have been wise to do so."

Mrs. Ballinger, who was already beginning to feel as if she had launched at Osric Dane the retort which had just occurred to her, turned ironically on Mrs. Plinth. "May I ask why?" she enquired.

Mrs. Plinth looked grave. "Surely," she said, "I understood from Mrs. Roby herself that the subject was one it was as well not to go into too deeply?"

Miss Van Vluyck rejoined with precision: "I think that applied only to an investigation of the origin of the—of the—"; and suddenly she found that her usually accurate memory had failed her. "It's a part of the subject I never studied myself," she concluded.

"Nor I," said Mrs. Ballinger.

Laura Glyde bent toward them with widened eyes. "And yet it seems—doesn't it?—the part that is fullest of an esoteric fascination?"

"I don't know on what you base that," said Miss Van Vluyck argumentatively.

"Well, didn't you notice how intensely interested Osric Dane became as soon as she heard what the brilliant foreigner—he *was* a foreigner, wasn't he?—had told Mrs. Roby about the origin—the origin of the rite—or whatever you call it?"

Mrs. Plinth looked disapproving, and Mrs. Ballinger visibly wavered. Then she said: "It may not be desirable to touch on the—on that part of the subject in general conversation; but, from the importance it evidently has to a woman of Osric Dane's distinction, I feel as if we ought not to be afraid to discuss it among ourselves—without gloves—though with closed doors, if necessary."

"I'm quite of your opinion," Miss Van Vluyck came briskly to her support; "on condition, that is, that all grossness of language is avoided."

"Oh, I'm sure we shall understand without that," Mrs. Leverett tittered; and Laura Glyde added significantly: "I fancy we can read between the lines," while Mrs. Ballinger rose to assure herself that the doors were really closed.

Mrs. Plinth had not yet given her adhesion. "I hardly see," she began, "what benefit is to be derived from investigating such peculiar customs—"

But Mrs. Ballinger's patience had reached the extreme limit of tension. "This at least," she returned; "that we shall not be placed again in the humiliating position of finding ourselves less up on our own subjects than Fanny Roby!"

Even to Mrs. Plinth this argument was conclusive. She peered furtively about the room and lowered her commanding tones to ask: "Have you got a copy?"

"A—a copy?" stammered Mrs. Ballinger. She was aware that the other members were looking at her expectantly, and that this answer was inadequate, so she supported it by asking another question. "A copy of what?"

Her companions bent their expectant gaze on Mrs. Plinth, who, in turn, appeared less sure of herself than usual. "Why, of—of—the book," she explained.

"What book?" snapped Miss Van Vluyck, almost as sharply as Osric Dane.

Mrs. Ballinger looked at Laura Glyde, whose eyes were interrogatively fixed on Mrs. Leveret. The fact of being deferred to was so new to the latter that it filled her with an insane temerity. "Why, Xingu, of course!" she exclaimed.

A profound silence followed this challenge to the resources of Mrs. Ballinger's library, and the latter, after glancing nervously toward the Books of the Day, returned with dignity: "It's not a thing one cares to leave about."

"I should think *not!*" exclaimed Mrs. Plinth.

"It *is* a book, then?" said Miss Van Vluyck.

This again threw the company into disarray, and Mrs. Ballinger, with an impatient sigh, rejoined: "Why—there *is* a book—naturally. . . ."

"Then why did Miss Glyde call it a religion?"

Laura Glyde started up. "A religion? I never—"

"Yes, you did," Miss Van Vluyck insisted; "you spoke of rites; and Mrs. Plinth said it was a custom."

Miss Glyde was evidently making a desperate effort to recall her statement; but accuracy of detail was not her strongest point. At length she began in a deep murmur: "Surely they used to do something of the kind at the Eleusinian mysteries—"

"Oh—" said Miss Van Vluyck, on the verge of disapproval; and Mrs. Plinth protested: "I understood there was to be no indelicacy!"

Mrs. Ballinger could not control her irritation. "Really, it is too bad that we should not be able to talk the matter over quietly among ourselves. Personally, I think that if one goes into Xingu at all—"

"Oh, so do I!" cried Miss Glyde.

"And I don't see how one can avoid doing so, if one wishes to keep up with the Thought of the Day—"

Mrs. Leveret uttered an exclamation of relief. "There—that's it!" she interposed.

"What's it?" the President took her up.

"Why—it's a—a Thought: I mean a philosophy."

This seemed to bring a certain relief to Mrs. Ballinger and Laura Glyde, but Miss Van Vluyck said: "Excuse me if I tell you that you're all mistaken. Xingu happens to be a language."

"A language!" the Lunch Club cried.

"Certainly. Don't you remember Fanny Roby's saying that there were several branches, and that some were hard to trace? What could that apply to but dialects?"

Mrs. Ballinger could no longer restrain a contemptuous laugh. "Really, if the Lunch Club has reached such a pass that it has to go to Fanny Roby for instruction on a subject like Xingu, it had almost better cease to exist!"

"It's really her fault for not being clearer," Laura Glyde put in.

"Oh, clearness and Fanny Roby!" Mrs. Ballinger shrugged. "I daresay we shall find she was mistaken on almost every point."

"Why not look it up?" said Mrs. Plinth.

As a rule this recurrent suggestion of Mrs. Plinth's was ignored in the heat of discussion, and only resorted to afterward in the privacy of each member's home. But on the present occasion the desire to ascribe their own confusion of thought to the vague and contradictory nature of Mrs. Roby's statements caused the members of the Lunch Club to utter a collective demand for a book of reference.

At this point the production of her treasured volume gave Mrs. Leveret, for a moment, the unusual experience of occupying the centre front; but she was not able to hold it long, for Appropriate Allusions contained no mention of Xingu.

"Oh, that's not the kind of thing we want!" exclaimed Miss Van Vluyck. She cast a disparaging glance over Mrs. Ballinger's assortment of literature, and added impatiently: "Haven't you any useful books?"

"Oh course I have," replied Mrs. Ballinger indignantly; "I keep them in my husband's dressing-room."

From this region, after some difficulty and delay, the parlourmaid produced the W-Z volume of an Encyclopædia and, in deference to that fact that the demand for it had come from Miss Van Vluyck, laid the ponderous tome before her.

There was a moment of painful suspense while Miss Van Vluyck rubbed her spectacles, adjusted them, and turned to Z; and a murmur of surprise when she said: "It isn't here."

"I suppose," said Mrs. Plinth, "it's not fit to be put in a book of reference."

"Oh, nonsense!" exclaimed Mrs. Ballinger. "Try X."

Miss Van Vluyck turned back through the volume, peering shortsightedly up and down the pages, till she came to a stop and remained motionless, like a dog on a point.

"Well, have you found it?" Mrs. Ballinger enquired after a considerable delay.

"Yes. I've found it," said Miss Van Vluyck in a queer voice.

Mrs. Plinth hastily interposed: "I beg you won't read it aloud if there's anything offensive."

Miss Van Vluyck, without answering, continued her silent scrutiny.

"Well, what *is* it?" exclaimed Laura Glyde excitedly.

"*Do* tell us!" urged Mrs. Leveret, feeling that she would have something awful to tell her sister.

Miss Van Vluyck pushed the volume aside and turned slowly toward the expectant group.

"It's a river."

"A *river?*"

"Yes: in Brazil. Isn't that where she's been living?"

"Who? Fanny Roby? Oh, but you must be mistaken. You've been reading the wrong thing," Mrs. Ballinger exclaimed, leaning over her to seize the volume.

"It's the only *Xingu* in the Encyclopædia; and she *has* been living in Brazil," Miss Van Vluyck persisted.

"Yes: her brother has a consulship there," Mrs. Leveret interposed.

"But it's too ridiculous! I—we—why we *all* remember studying Xingu last year—or the year before last," Mrs. Ballinger stammered.

"I thought I did when *you* said so," Laura Glyde avowed.

"*I* said so?" cried Mrs. Ballinger.

"Yes. You said it had crowded everything else out of your mind."

"Well *you* said it had changed your whole life!"

"For that matter, Miss Van Vluyck said she had never grudged the time she'd given it."

Mrs. Plinth interposed: "I made it clear that I knew nothing whatever of the original."

Mrs. Ballinger broke off the dispute with a groan. "Oh, what does it all matter if she's been making fools of us? I believe Miss Van Vluyck's right —she was talking of the river all the while!"

"How could she? It's too preposterous," Miss Glyde exclaimed.

"Listen." Miss Van Vluyck had repossessed herself of the Encyclopædia, and restored her spectacles to a nose reddened by excitement. " 'The Xingu, one of the principal rivers of Brazil, rises on the plateau of Mato Grosso, and flows in a northerly direction for a length of no less than one thousand one hundred and eighteen miles, entering the Amazon near the mouth of the latter river. The upper course of the Xingu is auriferous and fed by numerous branches. Its source was first discovered in 1884 by the German explorer von den Steinen, after a difficult and dangerous expedition through a region inhabited by tribes still in the Stone Age of culture.' "

The ladies received this communication in a state of stupefied silence from which Mrs. Leveret was the first to rally. "She certainly *did* speak of its having branches."

The word seemed to snap the last thread of their incredulity. "And of its great length," gasped Mrs. Ballinger.

"She said it was awfully deep, and you couldn't skip—you just had to wade through," Miss Glyde added.

The idea worked its way more slowly through Mrs. Plinth's compact resistances. "How could there be anything improper about a river?" she enquired.

"Improper?"

"Why, what she said about the source—that it was corrupt?"

"Not corrupt, but hard to get at," Laura Glyde corrected. "Some one who'd been there had told her so. I daresay it was the explorer himself— doesn't it say the expedition was dangerous?"

" 'Difficult and dangerous,' " read Miss Van Vluyck.

Mrs. Ballinger pressed her hands to her throbbing temples. "There's nothing she said that wouldn't apply to a river—to this river!" She swung about excitedly to the other members. "Why, do you remember her telling us that she hadn't read 'The Supreme Instant' because she'd taken it on a boating party while she was staying with her brother, and some one had 'shied' it overboard—'shied' of course was her own expression."

The ladies breathlessly signified that the expression had not escaped them.

"Well—and then didn't she tell Osric Dane that one of her books was simply saturated with Xingu? Of course it was, if one of Mrs. Roby's rowdy friends had thrown it into the river!"

This surprising reconstruction of the scene in which they had just participated left the members of the Lunch Club inarticulate. At length, Mrs. Plinth, after visibly labouring with the problem, said in a heavy tone: "Osric Dane was taken in too."

Mrs. Leveret took courage at this. "Perhaps that's what Mrs. Roby did it for. She said Osric Dane was a brute, and she may have wanted to give her a lesson."

Miss Van Vluyck frowned. "It was hardly worth while to do it at our expense."

"At least," said Miss Glyde with a touch of bitterness, "she succeeded in interesting her, which was more than we did."

"What chance had we?" rejoined Mrs. Ballinger. "Mrs. Roby monopolished her from the first. And *that*, I've no doubt, was her purpose—to give Osric Dane a false impression of her own standing in the club. She would hesitate at nothing to attract attention: we all know how she took in poor Professor Foreland."

"She actually makes him give bridge-teas every Thursday," Mrs. Leveret piped up.

Laura Glyde struck her hands together. "Why, this is Thursday, and it's *there* she's gone, of course; and taken Osric with her!"

"And they're shrieking over us at this moment," said Mrs. Ballinger between her teeth.

This possibility seemed too preposterous to be admitted. "She would hardly dare," said Miss Van Vluyck, "confess the imposture to Osric Dane."

"I'm not so sure: I thought I saw her make a sign as she left. If she hadn't made a sign, why should Osric Dane have rushed out after her?"

"Well, you know, we'd all been telling her how wonderful Xingu was, and she said she wanted to find out more about it," Mrs. Leveret said, with a tardy impulse of justice to the absent.

This reminder, far from mitigating the wrath of the other members, gave it a stronger impetus.

"Yes—and that's exactly what they're both laughing over now," said Laura Glyde ironically.

Mrs. Plinth stood up and gathered her expensive furs about her monumental form. "I have no wish to criticise," she said; "but unless the Lunch Club can protect its members against the recurrence of such—such unbecoming scenes, I for one—"

"Oh, so do I!" agreed Miss Glyde, rising also.

Miss Van Vluyck closed the Encyclopædia and proceeded to button herself into her jacket. "My time is really too valuable—" she began.

"I fancy we are all of one mind," said Mrs. Ballinger, looking searchingly at Mrs. Leveret, who looked at the others.

"I always deprecate anything like a scandal—" Mrs. Plinth continued.

"She has been the cause of one to-day!" exclaimed Miss Glyde.

Mrs. Leveret moaned: "I don't see how she *could!*" and Miss Van Vluyck said, picking up her note-book: "Some women stop at nothing."

"—but if," Mrs. Plinth took up her argument impressively, "anything of the kind had happened in *my* house" (it never would have, her tone implied), "I should have felt that I owed it to myself either to ask for Mrs. Roby's resignation—or to offer mine."

"Oh, Mrs. Plinth—" gasped the Lunch Club.

"Fortunately for me," Mrs. Plinth continued with an awful magnanimity, "the matter was taken out of my hands by our President's decision that the right to entertain distinguished guests was a privilege vested in her office; and I think the other members will agree that, as she was alone in this opinion, she ought to be alone in deciding on the best way of effacing its—its really deplorable consequences."

A deep silence followed this outbreak of Mrs. Plinth's longstored resentment.

"I don't see why *I* should be expected to ask her to resign—" Mrs. Ballinger at length began; but Laura Glyde turned back to remind her: "You know she made you say that you'd got on swimmingly in Xingu."

An ill-timed giggle escaped from Mrs. Leveret, and Mrs. Ballinger energetically continued "—but you needn't think for a moment that I'm afraid to!"

The door of the drawing-room closed on the retreating backs of the Lunch Club, and the President of that distinguished association, seating herself at her writing-table, and pushing away a copy of "The Wings of Death" to make room for her elbow, drew forth a sheet of the club's note-paper, on which she began to write: "My dear Mrs. Roby—"

STUDY QUESTIONS:

1. Each member of the Lunch Club is given a good many lines of dialogue, yet Mrs. Wharton dwells most upon the responses of the group as a whole both to Osric Dane and to Xingu. Why?

2. Does Osric Dane understand that Mrs. Roby is spoofing the whole show when she leaves, or is her exit merely a means of getting out of a situation that bores her beyond expression? What are your reasons for your opinion?

3. How is it appropriate that Osric Dane has written a novel called "The Wings of Death"?

4. What did Mrs. Ballinger say in her note, and how did she say it?

AFTER YOU,
MY DEAR ALPHONSE

Shirley Jackson (1920–19   ) is probably best known for her long
short story "The Lottery," which first appeared in *The New Yorker* in 1948.
It is a terrifying piece of fiction which leaves readers guessing. Not a
mystery story in any of the traditional ways, it is modeled somewhat on the
nightmarish tales of the Austrian writer Franz Kafka, whose strangely
allegorical novels *The Trial* and *The Castle* have had an appeal for many
modern readers.

Miss Jackson was born in California but received her higher education
at Syracuse University. She is now married to Stanley Edgar Hyman,
a literary critic, who has been at the center of much critical controversy in
recent years. Mr. and Mrs. Hyman have three children.

"After You, My Dear Alphonse" is not at all like "The Lottery," but
it has its own way of surprising, perhaps even frightening, the unsuspecting
reader. In a matter-of-fact way, it tells about the relationship between two
little boys. Nothing could be more natural than the relationship that exists
between Johnny and Boyd; in every sense—culturally, intellectually, and
economically—they are equals. However, the story is not just about Johnny
and Boyd, but, more specifically, about Mrs. Wilson and her understanding,
or misunderstanding, of their relationship. One must be fair to Mrs. Wilson;

226

she means well and has good motives. But, the story seems to pose a question for us. Is it enough to be well-intentioned and to have good motives? Do we not have an obligation to understand that the world has changed and that sentimental or charitable tolerance is no longer valid?

Readers of the story should note Miss Jackson's superb economy. There is really nothing here but dialog and not very much of that. The author is completely missing; the reader sees and hears and makes his own interpretations and judgments. This is a technique much favored by modern writers. They believe that the reader is capable of doing his own work. It is to Miss Jackson's credit that she has written her story in such a way that new insights keep occurring with our additional readings. A study of how the meanings multiply as an observer looks carefully at the dialog will teach much about how authors of judgment and intelligence work.

Mother is stereotyped

Mrs. Wilson was just taking the gingerbread out of the oven when she heard Johnny outside talking to someone. *(from comic strip)*

"Johnny," she called, "you're late. Come in and get your lunch."

"Just a minute, Mother," Johnny said. "After you, my dear Alphonse."

"After *you*, my dear Alphonse," another voice said.

"No, after *you*, my dear Alphonse," Johnny said.

Mrs. Wilson opened the door. "Johnny," she said, "you come in this minute and get your lunch. You can play after you've eaten."

Johnny came in after her, slowly. "Mother," he said. "I brought Boyd home for lunch with me."

"Boyd?" Mrs. Wilson thought for a moment. "I don't believe I've met Boyd. Bring him in, dear, since you've invited him. Lunch is ready."

"Boyd!" Johnny yelled. "Hey, Boyd, come on in!"

"I'm coming. Just got to unload this stuff."

"Well, hurry, or my mother'll be sore."

"Johnny, that's not very polite to either your friend or your mother," Mrs. Wilson said. "Come sit down, Boyd."

As she turned to show Boyd where to sit, she saw he was a Negro boy, smaller than Johnny but about the same age. His arms were loaded with split kindling wood. "Where'll I put this stuff, Johnny?" he asked.

Mrs. Wilson turned to Johnny. "Johnny," she said, "what did you make Boyd do? What is that wood?"

"Dead Japanese," Johnny said mildly. "We stand them in the ground and run over them with tanks."

"How do you do, Mrs. Wilson?" Boyd said.

"How do you do, Boyd? You shouldn't let Johnny make you carry all that wood. Sit down now and eat lunch, both of you."

"Why shouldn't he carry the wood, Mother? It's his wood. We got it at his place."

"Johnny," Mrs. Wilson said, "go on and eat your lunch."

"Sure," Johnny said. He held out the dish of scrambled eggs to Boyd. "After you, my dear Alphonse.'

"After *you*, my dear Alphonse," Boyd said.

"After *you*, my dear Alphonse," Johnny said. They began to giggle.

"Are you hungry, Boyd?" Mrs Wilson asked.

"Yes, Mrs. Wilson."

"Well, don't you let Johnny stop you. He always fusses about eating, so you just see that you get a good lunch. There's plenty of food here for you to have all you want."

"Thank you, Mrs. Wilson."

"Come on, Alphonse," Johnny said. He pushed half the scrambled eggs on to Boyd's plate. Boyd watched while Mrs. Wilson put a dish of stewed tomatoes beside his plate.

"Boyd don't eat tomatoes, do you, Boyd?" Johnny said.

"*Doesn't* eat tomatoes, Johnny. And just because you don't like them, don't say that about Boyd. Boyd will eat *anything*."

"Bet he won't" Johnny said, attacking his scrambled eggs.

"Boyd wants to grow up and be a big strong man so he can work hard," Mrs. Wilson said. "I'll bet Boyd's father eats stewed tomatoes."

"My father eats anything he wants to," Boyd said.

"So does mine," Johnny said. "Sometimes he doesn't eat hardly anything. He's a little guy, though. Wouldn't hurt a flea."

"Mine's a little guy too," Boyd said.

"I'll bet he's strong, though," Mrs. Wilson said. She hesitated. "Does he . . . work?"

"Sure," Johnny said. "Boyd's father works in a factory."

"There, you see?" Mrs. Wilson said. "And he certainly has to be strong to do that—all that lifting and carrying at a factory."

"Boyd's father doesn't have to," Johnny said. "He's a foreman."

Mrs. Wilson felt defeated. "What does your mother do, Boyd?"

"My mother?" Boyd was surprised. "She takes care of us kids."

"Oh. She doesn't work, then?"

"Why should she?" Johnny said through a mouthful of eggs. "You don't work."

"You really don't want any stewed tomatoes, Boyd?"

"No, thank you, Mrs. Wilson," Boyd said.

"No, thank you, Mrs. Wilson, no, thank you, Mrs Wilson, no, thank you, Mrs. Wilson," Johnny said. "Boyd's sister's going to work, though. She's going to be a teacher."

"That's a very fine attitude for her to have, Boyd." Mrs. Wilson restrained an impulse to pat Boyd on the head. "I imagine you're all very proud of her?"

"I guess so," Boyd said.

"What about all your other brothers and sisters? I guess all of you want to make just as much of yourselves as you can."

"There's only me and Jean," Boyd said. "I don't know yet what I want to be when I grow up."

"We're going to be tank drivers, Boyd and me," Johnny said. "Zoom." Mrs. Wilson caught Boyd's glass of milk as Johnny's napkin ring, suddenly transformed into a tank, plowed heavily across the table.

"Look, Johnny," Boyd said. "Here's a foxhole. I'm shooting at you."

Mrs. Wilson, with the speed born of long experience, took the gingerbread off the shelf and placed it carefully between the tank and the foxhole.

"Now eat as much as you want to, Boyd," she said. "I want to see you get filled up."

"Boyd eats a lot, but not as much as I do," Johnny said. "I'm bigger than he is."

"You're not much bigger," Boyd said. "I can beat you running."

Mrs. Wilson took a deep breath. "Boyd," she said. Both boys turned to her. "Boyd, Johnny has some suits that are a little too small for him, and a winter coat. It's not new, of course, but there's lots of wear in it still. And I have a few dresses that your mother or sister could probably use. Your mother can make them over into lots of things for all of you, and I'd be very happy to give them to you. Suppose before you leave I make up a big bundle and then you and Johnny can take it over to your mother right away . . ." Her voice trailed off as she saw Boyd's puzzled expression.

"But I have plenty of clothes, thank you," he said. "And I don't think my mother knows how to sew very well, and anyway I guess we buy about everything we need. Thank you very much, though."

"We don't have time to carry that old stuff around, Mother," Johnny said. "We got to play tanks with the kids today."

Mrs. Wilson lifted the plate of gingerbread off the table as Boyd was about to take another piece. "There are many little boys like you, Boyd, who would be very grateful for the clothes someone was kind enough to give them."

"Boyd will take them if you want him to, Mother," Johnny said.

"I didn't mean to make you mad, Mrs. Wilson," Boyd said.

"Don't think I'm angry, Boyd. I'm just disappointed in you, that's all. Now let's not say anything more about it."

She began clearing the plates off the table, and Johnny took Boyd's hand and pulled him to the door. "Bye, Mother," Johnny said. Boyd stood for a minute, staring at Mrs. Wilson's back.

"After you, my dear Alphonse," Johnny said, holding the door open.

"Is your mother still mad?" Mrs. Wilson heard Boyd ask in a low voice.

"I don't know," Johnny said. "She's screwy sometimes."

"So's mine," Boyd said. He hesitated. "After *you*, my dear Alphonse."

STUDY QUESTIONS:

1. This story is almost nothing but dialogue. What are the advantages for this particular subject?

2. What is the importance of the fact that there are no really significant character differences between Johnny and Boyd?

3. What does this sentence tell you about Mrs. Wilson? "Mrs. Wilson lifted the plate of gingerbread off the table as Boyd was about to take another piece."

4. Comment on the ending of the story, particularly on Boyd's saying "Is your mother still mad?"

TWO SOLDIERS

WILLIAM FAULKNER

Readers familiar only with the novels of William Faulkner (1897–
1962) will probably read a delightful story like "Two Soldiers" with some
surprise, because it gives a different picture of this author's work from the
one to which the public is accustomed. But this picture is not altogether accurate. William Faulkner has been one of the most prolific writers of
modern American literature, and as one commentator on his work has put
it, each new story has been an experiment. Some of these are, to be sure,
brutally naturalistic stories about degraded people, stories to which many
serious readers of fiction take violent exception. But there are stories of
honor and heroism, too, lyrically presented in a prose style which, though
often difficult, is always fascinating. Many readers have trouble with
Faulkner, as with Henry James, because they begin at the wrong place.
They first read *The Sound and the Fury* or *Absalom, Absalom!*, and the result
is that they become discouraged, often for more reasons than one. The
beginning reader of Faulkner should go first to pieces like "The Bear" or
to his fine novel about the Civil War, *The Unvanquished*, or, possibly, to
Sartoris or to any one of a number of excellent short stories, now published
as *Collected Stories of William Faulkner*. An especially effective way to ap-

proach him and to see the whole design of his work is to read, from beginning to end, *The Viking Portable Faulkner*, edited by Malcolm Cowley.

The systematic approach is valuable because Faulkner's work is all one
vast design, an attempt to present the full record of a Southern community,
Yoknapatawpha County, from the Indian days down to the present. Thus all
of his stories (there are a few minor exceptions) take place within the same
scene, and we meet a number of the characters more than once. It is a tremendously ambitious undertaking, "unequaled," says Robert Penn Warren,
"by anyone else in our time." Probably no one in present-day American
literature has a higher reputation among critics and other writers than
William Faulkner. He is one of five American authors to have won
the Nobel Prize.

"Two Soldiers" is an everyday kind of story. All of us know anecdotes
about younger brothers who want to do whatever their older brothers do.
And the appeal for the younger boy is likely to be much stronger when the
matter concerned is that of doing something glamorous like going off to
war. Faulkner's story is a superbly true one, and it is not hard for the
reader to understand the bafflement of all the people who have to face the
stubborn resistance of the boy when they want to return him to his home.
It is perhaps even easier for the reader to understand the boy. "Two
Soldiers" is a story of great fun but also of great tenderness.

Me and Pete would go down to Old Man Killegrew's and listen to his
radio. We would wait until after supper, after dark, and we would stand outside Old Man Killegrew's parlor window, and we could hear it because Old
Man Killegrew's wife was deaf, and so he run the radio as loud as it would
run, and so me and Pete could hear it plain as Old Man Killegrew's wife
could, I reckon, even standing outside with the window closed.

And that night I said, "What? Japanese? What's a pearl harbor?" and
Pete said, "Hush."

And so we stood there, it was cold, listening to the fellow in the radio
talking, only I couldn't make no heads nor tails out of it. Then the fellow
said that woud be all for a while, and me and Pete walked back up the road
to home, and Pete told me what it was. Because he was nigh twenty and he
had done finished the Consolidated last June and he knowed a heap: about
them Japanese dropping bombs on Pearl Harbor and that Pearl Habor was
across the water.

"Across what water?" I said. "Across that Government reservoy
up at Oxford?"

"Naw," Pete said. "Across the big water. The Pacific Ocean."

We went home. Maw and pap was already asleep and me and Pete laid in bed, and I still couldn't understand where it was, and Pete told me again —the Pacific Ocean.

"What's the matter with you?" Pete said. "You're going on nine year old. You been in school now ever since September. Ain't you learned nothing yet?"

"I reckon we ain't got as fer as the Pacific Ocean yet," I said.

We was still sowing the vetch then that ought to been all finished by the fifteenth of November, because pap was still behind, just like he had been ever since me and Pete had knowed him. And we had firewood to git in, too, but every night me and Pete would go down to Old Man Killegrew's and stand outside his parlor window in the cold and listen to his radio; then we would come back home and lay in bed and Pete would tell me what it was. That is, he would tell me for awhile. Then he wouldn't tell me. It was like he didn't want to talk about it no more. He would tell me to shut up because he wanted to go to sleep, but he never wanted to go to sleep.

He would lay there, a heap stiller than if he was asleep, and it would be something, I could feel it coming out of him, like he was mad at me, or like he was worried about something, and it wasn't that neither, because he never had nothing to worry about. He never got behind like pap, let alone stayed behind. Pap give him ten acres when he graduated from the Consolidated, and me and Pete both reckoned pap was durn glad to get shut of at least ten acres less to have to worry about himself; and Pete had them ten acres all sowed to vetch and busted out and bedded for the winter, and so it wasn't that. But it was something. And still we would go down to Old Man Killegrew's every night and listen to his radio, and they was at it in the Philippines now, but General MacArthur was holding um. Then we would come back home and lay in the bed, and Pete wouldn't tell me nothing or talk at all. He would just lay there still as an ambush and when I would touch him, his side or his leg would feel hard and still as iron, until after a while and I would go to sleep.

Then one night—it was the first time he had said nothing to me except to jump on me about not chopping enough wood at the wood tree where he was cutting—he said, "I got to go."

"Go where?" I said.

"To that war," Pete said.

"Before we even finish gettin' in the firewood?"

"Firewood, heck," Pete said.

"All right," I said. "When we going to start?"

But he wasn't even listening. He laid there, hard and still as iron in the dark. "I got to go," he said. "I jest ain't going to put up with no folks treating the Unity States that way."

"Yes, I said. "Firewood or no firewood, I reckon we got to go."

This time he heard me. He laid still again, but it was a different kind of still.

"You?" he said. "To a war?"

"You'll whup the big uns and I'll whup the little uns," I said.

Then he told me I couldn't go. At first I thought he just never wanted me tagging after him, like he wouldn't leave me go with him when he went sparking them girls of Tull's. Then he told me the Army wouldn't leave me go because I was too little, and then I knowed he really meant it and that I couldn't go nohow noways. And somehow I hadn't believed until then that he was going himself, but now I knowed he was and that he wasn't going to leave me go with him a-tall.

"I'll chop the wood and tote the water for you-all then!" I said. "You got to have wood and water!"

Anyway, he was listening to me now. He wasn't like iron now.

He turned onto his side and put his hand on my chest because it was me that was laying straight and hard on my back now.

"No," he said. "You got to stay here and help pap."

"Help him what?" I said. "He ain't never caught up nohow. He can't get no further behind. He can sholy take care of this little shirttail of a farm while me and you are whupping them Japanese. I got to go too. If you got to go, then so have I."

"No," Pete said. "Hush now. Hush." And he meant it. and I knowed he did. Only I made sho from his own mouth. I quit.

"So I just can't go then," I said.

"No," Pete said. "You just can't go. You're too little, in the first place, and in the second place—"

"All right," I said. "Then shut up and leave me to go to sleep."

So he hushed then and laid back. And I laid there like I was already asleep, and pretty soon he was asleep and I knowed it was the wanting to go to the war that had worried him and kept him awake, and now that he had decided to go, he wasn't worried any more.

The next morning he told maw and pap. Maw was all right. She cried.

"No," she said, crying, "I don't want him to go. I would rather go myself in his place, if I could. I don't want to save the country. Them Japanese could take it all and keep it, so long as they left me and my family and my children alone. But I remember my brother Marsh in that other war. He had to go to that one when he wasn't but nineteen and our mother couldn't understand it then any more than I can now. But she told Marsh if he had to go, he had to go. And so, if Pete's got to go to this one, he's got to go to it. Jest don't ask me to understand why."

But pap was the one. He was the feller. "To the war?" he said. "Why I don't see a bit of use in that. You ain't old enough for the draft, and the country ain't being invaded. Our President in Washington, D.C., is watching the conditions and he will notify us. Besides, in that other war your ma just mentioned, I was drafted and sent clean to Texas and was held there nigh eight months until they finally quit fighting. It seems to me that that, along with your Uncle Marsh who received a actual wound on the battlefields of France, is enough for me and mine to have to do to protect the country, at least in my lifetime. Besides, what'll I do for help on the farm with you gone? It seems to me I'll get mighty far behind."

"You been behind as long as I can remember," Pete said. "Anyway I'm going. I got to."

"Of course he's got to go," I said. "Them Japanese—"

"You hush your mouth!" maw said, crying. "Nobody's talking to you! Go and get Ma a armful of wood! That's what you can do!"

So I got the wood. And all the next day, while me and Pete and pap was getting in as much wood as we could in that time because Pete said how pap's idea of plenty of wood was one more stick laying against the wall that maw ain't put on the fire yet, maw was getting Pete ready to go. She washed and mended his clothes and cooked him a shoe box of vittles. And that night me and Pete laid in the bed and listened to her packing his grip and crying, until after a while Pete got up in his nightshirt and went back there, and I could hear them talking, until at last maw said, "You ought to go, and so I want you to go. But I don't understand it, and I won't never, and so don't expect me to." And Pete come back and got into bed again and laid again still and hard as iron on his back, and then he said, and he wasn't talking to me, he wasn't talking to nobody: "I got to go. I just got to."

"Sho you got to," I said. "Them Japanese—" He turned over hard, he kind of surged over onto his side, looking at me in the dark.

"Anyway, you're all right," he said. "I expected to have more trouble with you than with all the rest of them put together."

"I reckon I can't help it neither," I said. "But maybe it will run a few years longer and I can get there. Maybe someday I will jest walk in on you."

"I hope not," Pete said. "Folks don't go to wars for fun. A man don't leave his maw crying just for fun."

"Then why are you going?" I said.

"I got to," he said. "I just go to. Now you go on to sleep. I got to ketch that early bus in the morning."

"All right," I said, "I hear tell Memphis is a big place. How will you find where the Army's at?"

"I'll ask somebody where to go to join it," Pete said. "Go on to sleep now."

"Is that what you'll ask for? Where to join the Army?" I said.

"Yes," Pete said. He turned onto his back again. "Shut up and go to sleep."

We went to sleep. The next morning we et breakfast by lamplight because the bus would pass at six o'clock. Maw wasn't crying now. She just looked grim and busy, putting breakfast on the table while we et it. Then she finished packing Pete's grip, except he never wanted to take no grip to the war, but maw said decent folks never went nowhere, not even to a war, without change of clothes and something to tote them in. She put in the shoe box of fried chicken and biscuits and she put the Bible in, too, and then it was time to go. We didn't know until then that maw wasn't going to the bus. She jest brought Pete's cap and overcoat, and still she didn't cry no more, she jest stood with her hands on Pete's shoulders and she didn't move, but somehow, and just holding Pete's shoulders, she looked as hard and fierce as when Pete had turned toward me in the bed last night and tole me that anyway I was all right.

"They could take the country and keep the country, as long as they never bothered me and mine," she said. Then she said, "Don't never forget who you are. You ain't rich and the rest of the world outside of Frenchman's Bend never heard of you. But your blood is good as any blood anywhere, and don't you never forget it."

Then she kissed him, and then we was out of the house, with pap toting Pete's grip whether Pete wanted him to or not. There wasn't no dawn even yet, not even after we had stood on the highway by the mailbox, awhile. Then we seen the lights of the bus coming and I was watching the bus until it come up and Pete flagged it, and then, sho enough, there was daylight—it had started while I wasn't watching. And now me and Pete

expected pap to say something else foolish, like he done before, about how
Uncle Marsh getting wounded in France and that trip to Texas pap
had taken in 1918 ought to be enough to save the Unity States in 1942, but
he never. He done all right too. He jest said, "Good-by, son. Always
remember what your ma told you and write her whenever you find the
time." Then he shaken Pete's hand, and Pete looked at me a minute and
put his hand on my head and rubbed my head durn nigh hard enough to
wring my neck off and jumped into the bus, and the feller wound the door
shut and the bus begun to hum; then it was moving, humming and grinding
and whining louder and louder; it was going fast, with two little red lights
behind it that never seemed to get no littler, but jest seemed to be running
together until pretty soon they would touch and jest be one light. But they
never did, and then the bus was gone, and even like it was, I could have
pretty nigh busted out crying, nigh to nine years old and all.

Me and pap went back to the house. All that day we worked at
the wood tree, and so I never had no good chance until about middle of the
afternoon. Then I taken my slingshot and I would have liked to took all my
bird eggs, too, because Pete had give me his collection and he holp me with
mine, and he would like to git the box out and look at them as good as I
would, even if he was nigh twenty years old. But the box was too big to tote
a long ways and have to worry with, so I just taken the shikepoke egg, because it was the best un, and wropped it up good into a matchbox and hid
it and the slingshot under the corner of the barn. Then we et supper and
went to bed, and I thought then how if I would 'a' had to stayed in that
room and that bed like that even for one more night, I jest couldn't 'a'
stood it. Then I could hear pap snoring, but I never heard no sound from
maw, whether she was asleep or not, and I don't reckon she was. So I taken
my shoes and drapped them out the window, and then I clumb out like I
used to watch Pete do when he was still jest seventeen and pap wouldn't
leave him out, and I put on my shoes and went to the barn and got
the slingshot and the shikepoke egg and went to the highway.

It wasn't cold, it was jest durn confounded dark, and that highway
stretched on in front of me like, without nobody using it, it had stretched
out half again as fer just like a man does when he lays down, so that for a
time it looked like full sun was going to ketch me before I had finished
them twenty-two miles to Jefferson. But it didn't. Daybreak was jest starting
when I walked up the hill into town. I could smell breakfast cooking in the
cabins and I wished I had thought to brought me a cold biscuit, but that
was too late now. And Pete had told me Memphis was a piece beyond

Jefferson, but I never knowed it was no eighty miles. So I stood there on that empty square, with daylight coming and coming and the street lights still burning and that Law looking down at me, and me still eighty miles from Memphis, and it had took me all night to walk jest twenty-two miles, and so, by the time I got to Memphis at that rate, Pete would 'a' done already started for Pearl Harbor.

"Where do you come from?" the Law said. And I told him again. "I got to git to Memphis. My brother's there."

"You mean you ain't got any folks around here?" the Law said. "Nobody but that brother? What are you doing way off down here and your brother in Memphis?"

And I told him again, "I got to git to Memphis. I ain't got no time to waste talking about it and I ain't got time to walk it. I got to git there today."

"Come on here," the Law said.

We went down another street. And there was the bus, jest like when Pete got into it yestiddy morning, except there wasn't no lights on it now and it was empty. There was a regular bus dee-po like a railroad dee-po, with a ticket counter and a feller behind it, and the Law said, "Set down over there," and I set down on the bench, and the Law said, "I want to use your telephone," and he talked into the telephone a minute and put it down and said to the feller behind the ticket counter, "Keep your eye on him. I'll be back as soon as Mrs. Habersham can arrange to get herself up and dressed." He went out. I got up and went to the ticket counter.

"I want to go to Memphis," I said.

"You bet," the feller said. "You set down on the bench now. Mr. Foote will be back in a minute."

"I don't know no Mr. Foote," I said. "I want to ride that bus to Memphis."

"You got some money?" he said. "It'll cost seventy-two cents."

I taken out the matchbox and unwropped the shikepoke egg. "I'll swap you this for a ticket to Memphis," I said.

"What's that?" he said.

"It's a shikepoke egg," I said. "You never seen one before. It's worth a dollar. I'll take seventy-two cents fer it."

"No," he said, " the fellers that own that bus insist on a cash basis. If I started swapping tickets for bird eggs and livestock and such, they would fire me. You go set down on the bench now, like Mr. Foote—"

I started for the door, but he caught me, he put one hand on the ticket counter and jumped over it and caught up with me and reached his hand out to ketch my shirt.

"You put a hand on me and I'll cut it off," I said.

I tried to dodge him and run at the door, but he could move quicker than any grown man I ever see, quick as Pete almost. He cut me off and stood with his back against the door and one foot raised a little, and there wasn't no other way to get out. "Get back on that bench and stay there," he said.

And there wasn't no other way out. And he stood against the door. So I went back to the bench. And then it seemed like to me that dee-po was full of folks. There was that Law again, and there was two ladies in fur coats and their faces already painted. But they still looked like they had got up in a hurry and they still never liked it, a old one and a young one, looking down at me.

"He hasn't got an overcoat!" the old one said. "How in the world did he ever get down here by himself?"

"I ask you," the Law said. "I couldn't get nothing out of him except his brother is in Memphis and he wants to get back up there."

"That's right," I said. "I got to git to Memphis today."

"Of course you must," the old one said. "Are you sure you can find your brother when you get to Memphis?"

"I reckon I can," I said. "I ain't got but one and I have knowed him all my life. I reckon I will know him again when I see him."

The old one looked at me. "Somehow he doesn't look like he lives in Memphis," she said.

"He probably don't," the Law said. "You can't tell though. He might live anywhere, overhalls or not. This day and time they get scattered overnight from hope to breakfast; boys and girls, too, almost before they can walk good. He might have been in Missouri or Texas either yestiddy, for all we know. But he don't seem to have any doubt his brother is in Memphis. All I know to do is send him up there and leave him look."

"Yes," the old one said.

The young one set down on the bench by me and opened a hand satchel and taken out a artermatic writing pen and some papers.

"Now, honey," the old one said. "we're going to see that you find your brother, but we must have a case history for our files first. We want to know your name and your brother's name and where you were born and when your parents died."

"I don't need no case history neither," I said. "All I want is to git to Memphis. I got to git there today."

"You see?" the Law said. He said it almost like he enjoyed it. "That's what I told you."

"You're lucky, at that, Mrs. Habersham," the bus feller said. "I don't
think he's got a gun on him, but he can open that knife fast enough to suit
any man."

But the old one just stood there looking at me.

"Well," she said. "Well. I really don't know what to do."

"I do," the bus feller said. "I'm going to give him a ticket out of my
own pocket, as a measure of protecting the company against riot and blood-
shed. And when Mr. Foote tells the city board about it, it will be a civic
matter and they will give me a medal too. Hey, Mr. Foote?"

But nobody paid him no mind. The old one still stood looking down at
me. She said, "Well," again. Then she taken a dollar from her purse and
give it to the bus feller. "I suppose he will travel on a child's ticket,
won't he?"

"Wellum," the bus feller said, "I just don't know what the regulations
would be. Likely I will be fired for not crating him and marking the crate
Poison. But I'll risk it."

Then they were gone. Then the Law come back with a sandwich and
give it to me.

"You're sure you can find that brother?" he said.

"I ain't yet convinced why not," I said. "If I don't see Pete first, he'll
see me. He knows me too."

Then the Law went out for good, too, and I et the sandwich. Then
more folks come in and bought tickets, and then the bus feller said it was
time to go, and I got into the bus just like Pete done, and we were gone.

I seen all the towns. I seen all of them. When the bus got to going
good, I found out I was jest about wore out for sleep. But there was too
much I hadn't never saw before. We run out of Jefferson and run past fields
and woods, then we would run into another town and out of that un and
past fields and woods again, and then into another town with stores and gins
and water tanks, and we run along by the railroad for a spell and I seen the
signal arm move, and then some more towns, and I was jest about plumb
wore out for sleep, but I couldn't resk it. Then Memphis begun. It seemed
like, to me, it went on for miles. We would pass a patch of stores and I
would think that was sholy it and the bus would even stop. But it wouldn't
be Memphis yet and we would go on again past water tanks and smokestacks
on top of the mills, and if they was gins and sawmills, I never knowed there
was that many and I never seen any that big, and where they got enough
cotton and logs to run um I don't know.

Then I seen Memphis. I knowed I was right this time. It was standing up into the air. It looked like about a dozen whole towns bigger than Jefferson was set up on one edge in a field, standing up into the air higher than ara hill in all Yoknapatawpha County. Then we was in it, with the bus stopping every few feet, it seemed like to me, and cars rushing past on both sides of it and the streets crowded with folks from ever'where in town that day, until I didn't see how there could 'a' been nobody left in Mis'sippi a-tall to even sell me a bus ticket, let alone write out no case histories. Then the bus stopped. It was another bus dee-po, a heap bigger than the one in Jefferson. And I said, "All right. Where do folks join the Army?"

"What?" the bus feller said.

And I said it again, "Where do folks join the Army?"

"Oh," he said. Then he told me how to get there. I was afraid at first I wouldn't ketch on how to do in a town as big as Memphis. But I caught on all right. I never had to ask but twice more. Then I was there, and I was durn glad to git out of all them rushing cars and shoving folks and all that racket for a spell, and I thought, it won't be long now, and I thought how if there was any kind of a crowd there that had done already joined the Army, too, Pete would likely see me before I seen him. And so I walked into the room. And Pete wasn't there.

He wasn't even there. There was a soldier with a big arrerhead on his sleeve, writing, and two fellers standing in front of him, and there was some more folks there, I reckon. It seems to me I remember some more folks there.

I went to the table where the soldier was writing, and I said, "Where's Pete?" and he looked up and I said, "My brother. Pete Grier. Where is he?"

"What?" the soldier said. "Who?"

And I told him again. "He joined the Army yestiddy. He's going to Pearl Harbor. So am I. I want to ketch him. Where you all got him?" Now they were all looking at me, but I never paid them no mind. "Come on," I said. "Where is he?"

The soldier had quit writing. He had both hands spraddled out on the table. "Oh," he said. "You're going, too, hah?"

"Yes," I said. "They got to have wood and water. I can chop it and tote it. Come on. Where's Pete?"

The soldier stood up. "Who let you in here?" he said. "Go on. Beat it."

"Durn that," I said. "You tell me where Pete—"

I be dog if he couldn't move faster than the bus feller even. He never come over the table, he come around it, he was on me almost before I knowed it, so that I jest had time to jump back and whup out my pocket-knife and snap it open. He hollared and jumped back and grabbed one hand with the other and stood there cussing and hollering.

One of the other fellers grabbed me from behind, and I hit at him, but I couldn't reach him.

Then both of the fellers had me from behind, and then another soldier come out of a door at the back. He had on a belt with a britching strop over one shoulder.

"What's this?" he said.

"That little guy tried to knife me!" the first soldier hollared. Both them fellers was holding me, two against one, and the soldier with the backing strop said. "Here, here. Put your knife up, feller. None of us are armed. A man don't knife-fight folks that are bare-handed." I could begin to hear him then. He sounded jest like Pete talked to me. "Let him go," he said. They let me go. "Now what's all the trouble about?" And I told him. "I see," he said. "And you come up to see if he was all right before he left."

"No," I said. "I came to—"

But he had already turned to the first soldier.

"Have you got him?" he said. The first soldier went back to the table and looked at some papers.

"Here he is," he said. "He enlisted yestiddy. He's in a detachment leaving this morning for Little Rock." He had a watch stropped on his arm. He looked at it. "The train leaves in about fifty minutes. If I know country boys, they're probably all down there at the station right now."

"Get him up here," the one with the backing strop said. "Phone the station. Tell the porter to get him a cab. And you come with me," he said.

It was another office behind that un, with jest a table and some chairs. We set there while the soldier smoked, and it wasn't long; I knowed Pete's feet soon as I heard them. Then the first soldier opened the door and Pete come in. He never had no soldier clothes on. He looked just like he did when he got on the bus yestiddy morning, except it seemed to me like it was at least a week, so much had happened, and I had done had to do so much traveling. He come in and there he was, looking at me like he hadn't never left home, except that here he was in Memphis, on the way to Pearl Harbor.

"What in durnation are you doing here?" he said.

And I told him, "You got to have wood and water to cook with. I can chop it and tote it for you-all."

"No," Pete said. "You're going back home."

"No, Pete," I said. "I got to go too. I got to. It hurts my heart, Pete."

"No," Pete said. He looked at the soldier. "I jest don't know what could have happened to him, lootenant," he said. "He never drawed a knife on anybody before in his life."

He looked at me. "What did you do it for?"

"I don't know," I said. "I jest had to. I jest had to git here. I jest had to find you."

"Well, don't you never do it again, you hear?" Pete said. "You put that knife in your pocket and you keep it there. If I ever again hear of you drawing it on anybody, I'm coming back from wherever I am at and whup the fire out of you. You hear me?"

"I would pure cut a throat if it would bring you back to stay," I said. "Pete," I said. "Pete."

"No," Pete said. Now his voice wasn't hard and quick no more, it was almost quiet, and I knowed now I wouldn't never change him. "You must go home. You must look after maw, and I am depending on you to look after my ten acres. I want you to go back home. Today. Do you hear?"

"I hear," I said.

"Can he get back home by himself?" the soldier said.

"He come up here by himself," Pete said.

"I can get back, I reckon," I said "I don't live in but one place. I don't reckon it's moved."

Pete taken a dollar out of his pocket and give it to me. "That'll buy your bus ticket right to our mailbox," he said. "I want you to mind the lootenant. He'll send you to the bus. And you go back home and you take care of maw and look after my ten acres and keep that durn knife in your pocket. You hear me?"

"Yes, Pete," I said.

"All right," Pete said. "Now I got to go." He put his hand on my head again. But this time he never wrung my neck. He just laid his hand on my head a minute. And then I be dog if he didn't lean down and kiss me, and I heard his feet and then the door, and I never looked up and that was all, me setting there, rubbing the place where Pete kissed me and the soldier throwed back in his chair, looking out the window and coughing. He reached into his pocket and handed something to me without looking around. It was a piece of chewing gum.

"Much obliged," I said. "Well, I reckon I might as well start back. I got a right fer piece to go."

"Wait," the soldier said. Then he telephoned again and I said again I better start back, and he said again. "Wait. Remember what Pete told you."

So we waited, and then another lady come in, old, too, in a fur coat, too, but she smelled all right, she never had no artermatic writing pen nor no case history neither. She come in and the soldier got up, and she looked around quick until she saw me, and come and put her hand on my shoulder light and quick and easy as maw herself might 'a' done it.

"Come on." she said. "Let's go home to dinner."

"Nome," I said. "I got to ketch the bus to Jefferson."

"I know. There's plenty of time. We'll go home and eat dinner first."

She had a car. And now we was right down in the middle of all them other cars. We was almost under the busses, and all them crowds of people on the street close enough to where I could have talked to them if I had knowed who they was. After a while she stopped the car. "Here we are," she said, and I looked at it, and if all that was her house, she sho had a big family. But all of it wasn't. We crossed a hall with trees growing in it and went into a little room without nothing in it but a man dressed up in a uniform a heap shinier than them soldiers had, and the man shut the door, and then I hollered, "Look out!" and grabbed, but it was all right; that whole little room jest went right on up and stopped and the door opened and we was in another hall, and the lady unlocked a door and we went in, and there was another soldier, and old feller, with a britching strop, too, and a silver-colored bird on each shoulder.

"Here we are," the lady said, "This is Colonel McKellogg. Now, what would you like for dinner?"

"I reckon I'll jest have some ham and eggs and coffee," I said.

She had done started to pick up the telephone. She stopped. "Coffee?" she said. "When did you start drinking coffee?"

"I don't know," I said. "I reckon it was before I could remember."

"You're about eight, aren't you?" she said.

"Nome," I said. "I'm eight and ten months. Going on eleven months."

She telephoned then. Then we set there and I told them how Pete had jest left that morning for Pearl Harbor and I had aimed to go with him, but I would have to go back home to take care of maw and look after Pete's ten acres, and she said how they had a little boy about my size, too, in a school in the East. Then a man, another one, in a short kind of shirttail coat, rolled a kind of wheelbarrer in. It had my ham and eggs and a glass of milk and a piece of pie, too, and I thought I was hungry. But when I taken the first bite I found out I couldn't swallow it, and I got up quick.

"I got to go," I said.

"Wait," she said.

"I got to go," I said.

"Just a minute," she said. "I've already telephoned for the car. It won't be but a minute now. Can't you drink the milk even? Or maybe some of your coffee?"

"Nome," I said. "I ain't hungry. I'll eat when I git home." Then the telephone rung. She never even answered it.

"There," she said. "There's the car." And we went back down in that 'ere little moving room with the dressed-up man. This time it was a big car with a soldier driving it. I got into the front with him. She give the soldier a dollar. "He might get hungry," she said. "Try to find a decent place for him."

"O.K., Mrs. McKellogg," the soldier said.

Then we was gone again. And now I could see Memphis good, bright in the sunshine, while we was swinging around it. And the first thing I knowed, we was back on the same highway the bus run on this morning— the patches of stores and them big gins and sawmills, and Memphis running on for miles, it seemed like to me, before it begun to give out. Then we was running again between the fields and woods, running fast now, and except for that soldier, it was like I hadn't never been to Memphis a-tall. We was going fast now. At this rate, before I knowed it we would be home again, and I thought about me riding up to Frenchman's Bend in this here big car with a soldier running it, and all of a sudden I began to cry. I never knowed I was fixing to, and I couldn't stop it. I set there by that soldier, crying. We was going fast.

STUDY QUESTIONS:

1. A story like this one, in some ways not very believable perhaps, nevertheless tells an important kind of truth because it deals with human characteristics which readers like to think are part of the American spirit. Which of these characteristics are particularly emphasized in the story?

2. Some of the boy's dealings are with people whose official or philanthropic functions he cannot identify because of his age and limited experience. How does Faulkner make their identity known to the reader without violating the boy's point of view?

3. Write a paragraph commenting on the relationship between the two brothers.

4. Notice how much the effectiveness of the story depends on dialect. What are some of the unusual dialect words? How does Faulkner manage to keep dialect under control so that the narrator does not sound like a comic strip character?

A VILLAGE LEAR

MARY E. WILKINS FREEMAN

Mary E. Wilkins (1852–1930), who married Dr. Charles M. Freeman in 1902, was born in Massachusetts, educated in Vermont and at Mount Holyoke "Female Seminary," as the college was once known, and wrote about farm and village life in eastern Massachusetts even after she removed to New Jersey upon her marriage. She wrote novels, but none of them was as successful as her best stories, of which the first to be published was "A Humble Romance" (1884). She wrote too much, for she took to imitating herself, and try as she would, she could never master the material necessary for fiction that was not "local color" in origin. But her great stories are unparalleled in technique and in truth. One of them is "A Village Lear," collected into *A New England Nun and Other Stories* (1891). This story is one of the great modern re-tellings of the story of King Lear and his ungrateful daughters, two others being *Père Goriot* by the French novelist Balzac, and another, *A Lear of the Steppes* by the equally famous Russian novelist, Turgeniev.

"A Village Lear" parallels Shakespeare's tragedy in the relation of Barney Swan to his two ungrateful daughters, Malvina and Ellen. The place of Cordelia, however, is taken by Sarah Arnold, who is not a member of

the family, a fact that makes Barney's dependence upon her for understanding and sympathy all the more heart-rending. Shakespeare, of course,
has no Willy and in a sense no Annie, although Annie's shallow indifference to her grandfather is like the indifference of the courtiers to the plight
of the deposed king. Barney disposes of his property much after the manner of King Lear, and the sacrifice of his watch to buy the despised gold
brooch is a vague echo of some of Lear's behavior in the drama. But to
have made the story a mechanical equivalent of the tragedy would have
spoiled Miss Wilkins' narrative, since the point is a recurrent human
situation and not literary imitativeness.

If the title suggests the pity for old age, part of the strength of the
story is that "A Village Lear" is by somebody who understands villages.
As such the tale is a local color story. The action of any local color story
is confined within the limits of some small area—in this case a New
England small town. Local dialect is sympathetically overheard and recorded. Village customs, village morals, and village traditions, as in this
story, or those of a farm, a mountain "cove," a Western mining camp, a
Southern plantation, or any other smaller social unit are dramatized. If "A
Village Lear" is told from an omniscient point of view, most readers will
agree that the author is filled with sympathy and compassion both for un-
loved old age and for short-sighted selfishness. The tradition of local color,
of which Miss Wilkins is a classic representative, continues into our own
time, the stories of William Faulkner being examples of Southern local color.

"Jest wait a minute, Sary." The old man made a sly backward motion
of his hand; his voice was a cautious whisper.

Sarah Arnold stood back and waited. She was a large, fair young
woman in a brown calico dress. She held a plate of tapioca pudding that she
had brought for the old man's dinner, and she was impatient to give it to
him and be off; but she said nothing. The old man stood in the shop door;
he had in one hand a stick of red-and-white peppermint candy, and he held
it out enticingly towards a little boy in a white frock. The little boy had a
sweet, rosy face, and his glossy, fair hair was carefully curled. He stood out
in the green yard, and there were dandelions blooming around his feet. It
was May, and the air was sweet and warm; over on one side of the yard
there was some linen laid out to bleach in the sun.

The little boy looked at the old man and frowned, yet he seemed
fascinated.

The old man held out the stick of candy, and coaxed, in his soft, cracked voice. "Jest look a-here, Willy!" said he; "jest look a-here! See what gran'pa's got: a whole stick of candy! He brought it down to the store on purpose for Willy, an' he can have it if he'll jest come here an' give gran'pa a kiss. Does Willy want it?" The old man took a step forward.

But the child drew back, and shook his head violently, while the frown deepened. "No, no," said he, with baby vehemence.

The old man stepped back and began again. It was as if he were enticing a bird. "Now, Willy," said he, "jest look a-here! Don't Willy like candy?"

The child did not nod, but his blue, solemn eyes were riveted on the candy.

"Well," the grandfather went on, "here's a whole stick of candy come from the store, real nice pep'mint candy, an' Willy shall have it if he'll jest come here an' give gran'pa a kiss."

The child reached out a desperate hand. "Gimme!" he cried imperatively.

"Yes, Willy shall have it jest as soon as he gives gran'pa a kiss." The old man waved the stick of candy; his sunken mouth was curved in a sly smile. "Jest look at it! Willy, see it! Red-an'-white candy, real sweet an' nice, with pep'mint in it. An' it's all twisted! Willy want it?"

The child began to take almost imperceptible steps forward, his eyes still fixed on the candy. His grandfather stood motionless, while his smile deepened. Once he rolled his eyes delightedly around at Sarah. The child advanced with frequent halts.

Suddenly the old man made a spring forward. "Now I've got ye!" he cried. He threw his arms around the boy and hugged him tight.

The child struggled. "Lemme go!——lemme go!" he half sobbed.

"Yes, Willy shall go jest as soon as he gives gran'pa the kiss," said the old man. "Give gran'pa the kiss, and then he shall have the candy an' go."

The child put up his pretty rosy face and pursed his lips sulkily. The grandfather bent down and gave an ecstatic kiss.

"There! Now Willy shall have the candy, 'cause he's kissed gran'pa. He's a good boy, an' gran'pa 'll let him have the candy right off. He sha'n't wait no longer."

The child snatched the candy and fled across the yard.

The old man laughed, and his laugh was a shrill, rapturous cackle, like the high notes of an old parrot. He turned to the young woman. "I knowed I could toll him in," he said; "I knowed I could. The little fellar likes candy, I tell ye."

Sarah smiled sympathetically and extended the plate of pudding. "I brought you over a little of our pudding," said she. "Mother thought you might relish it."

The old man took it quite eagerly. "Brought a spoon in't, didn't ye?"

"Yes; I thought maybe you'd like to eat it out here."

"Well, I guess I may jest as well eat it out here, an' not carry it into the house. Viny might kinder git the notion that it would clutter up some. I'll jest set down here an' eat this, an' then I won't want no dinner in the house. I guess they're goin' to have beef, an' I don't relish beef much lately. I'd ruther have soft victuals; but Viny she don't cook much soft victuals; the folks in the house don't care much about 'em."

The old man held the plate of pudding, but did not at once begin to eat; his eyes still followed the little boy, who stood aloof under a blooming apple-tree and sucked his candy.

"Jest look at him," he said, admiringly. "I tell ye what 'tis, Sary, that little fellar does like candy. I can allers toll him in with a stick of candy. He's dreadful kind o' bashful. I s'pose Ellen she don't jest like to have him round in the shop here much. She dresses him up real nice an' clean in them little white frocks, an' she's afeared he'll get somethin' on 'em; so I guess she tells him he must keep away, an' it makes him kind of afeard. I s'pose she thinks I ain't none too clean nuther to be a-handlin' of him, an' I dun know as I be, but I allers wash my hands real pertickler afore I tech him. I've got my tin wash-dish there on the bench, an' I'm real pertickler 'bout it."

The old man waved his hand towards a rusty tin wash-basin on the old shoemaker's bench under the window. There was a smoky curtain over the window; the plastered walls and the ceiling were dark with smoke; the place was full of brown lights. Sarah, in her brown dress, with her fair rosy face, stood waiting until the old man should finish talking.

"Well, I must go now," said she. "I haven't been to dinner myself."

"You jest wait a minute," whispered the old man, with a mysterious air. In the little shop, beside the old shoemaker's bench, was a table that was brown and dark with age and dirt, and it was heaped with litter. There was a drawer in it, and this the old man opened with an effort; it stuck a little. "Look a-here," he whispered—"look a-here, Sary."

Sarah came close, and peered around his elbow.

The old man took a little parcel from the midst of the leather chips and waxed threads and pegs that half filled the drawer. He unrolled it carefully. "Look a-here," he said again, with a chuckle. He held up a stick of pink candy. "There," he went on, winking an old blue eye at Sarah, "I ain't

goin' to give that to him till to-morrer. To-morrer I'll jest toll him in with
that, don't ye see? Hey?"

"That's checkerberry, ain't it?"

"Yes, that's checkerberry, an' the tother was pep'mint. I got two
sticks of candy down to the store this mornin', one checkerberry an'
the tother pep'mint. Ye see, I put a patch on a shoe for the Briggs boy last
week, an' he give me ten cents for't. I'd kinder calkilated to lay it out in
terbacker——I ain't had none lately——but the more I thought 'bout it
the more I thought I'd git a leetle candy. Ye never see sech a chap fer candy
as he is; he'll hang off, an' hang off, but he can't stan' it to lose the candy
nohow. I dun know but the Old Nick could toll him in with a stick of candy,
he's in such a takin' for't; never see sech a fellar fer candy." The old man
raised his cackling laugh again, and Sarah laughed, too, going out the back
door of the shop. "I'm real obleeged to your mother, Sary; you tell her,"
he called after her.

He replaced the candy in the drawer, still chuckling to himself; then
he sat down to his pudding. He sat on his shoemaker's bench, well
back from the door, and ate. He smacked his lips loudly; he liked this soft,
sweet food.

Barney Swan was a small, frail old man; he stooped weakly, and did
not look much larger than a child, sitting there on his bench. His face, too,
was like a child's; his sunken mouth had an innocent, infantile expression,
and his eyes had that blank, fixed gaze, with an occasional twinkle of shrewdness, that babies' eyes have. His thin white hair hung to his shoulders, and
he had no beard. He owned only one decent coat, and that he kept for Sundays: he always went to meeting. On week-days he wore his brown calico
shirt sleeves and his old sagging vest. His bagging, brownish black trousers
were hauled around his waist, and his ankles showed like a little boy's.

Old Barney Swan had sat upon that shoemaker's bench the greater part
of his time for sixty years. His father before him had been a shoemaker and
cobbler; he had learned the trade when a child, and been faithful to it all
his life. Now not only his own powers had failed, but hand shoemaking and
cobbling were at a discount. There were two thriving boot and shoe factories
in the town, and the new boots and shoes were finer to see than the old
coarsely cobbled ones. Old Barney was too old to go to work in the shoe factory, but it is doubtful if he would have done so in any case. He had always
had a vein of childish obstinacy in spite of his mildness, and it had not de-
creased with age. "If folks want to wear them manufactured shoes, they can,"
he would say, with a sudden stiffening of his bent back: "old shackly things!

You'd orter seen them shoes the Briggs boy brought in here t'other day; they wa'n't wuth treein' up, an' they never had been."

Although now old Barney's revenue was derived from the Briggs boy and sundry other sturdy, stubbed urchins, whose shoe-leather demanded the cheapest and most thorough repairs to be had, he had accumulated quite a little property through his faithful toil on that leathern seat on the end of that old bench. But it had seemed easier for him to accumulate property than to care for it. His greatest talent was for patient, unremitting labor and economy; his financial conceptions were limited to them. Ten years before, he had made a misadventure and lost a few hundred dollars, and was so humbled and dejected over it that he had made his property over to his daughters on consideration of a life support. They had long been urging him to make such an arrangement. He had two daughters, Malvina and Ellen. His wife had died when they were about twenty. The wife had been a delicate, feeble woman, yet with a certain spirit of her own. In her day the daughters had struggled hard for the mastery of the little household, but with only partial success; after her death they were entirely victorious. Barney had always thought his daughters perfect; they had their own way in everything, with the exception of the money. He clung to that for a while. He was childishly fond of the few dollars he had earned all by himself and stowed away in his house and acres of green meadow-land and the village savings-bank. He was fond of the dollars for themselves; the sense of treasure pleased him. He did not care to spend for himself; there were few things that he wished for except a decent meeting-coat and a little tobacco. The tobacco was one point upon which he displayed his obstinacy; his daughters had never been able entirely to do away with that, although they waged constant war upon it. He would still occasionally have his little comforting pipe, and chew in spite of all berating and disgust. But the tobacco was sadly curtailed since the property had changed hands; he had only his little earnings with which to purchase it. The daughters gave him no money to spend. They argued that "father ain't fit to spend money." So his most urgent necessities were doled out to him.

When the property was divided, Malvina, the elder daughter, had for her share the homestead and a part of the money in the bank; Ellen, the younger, had the larger portion of the bank money and some wooded property. Malvina stipulated to furnish a home and care for the old man as long as he lived, and Ellen was to pay her sister a certain sum towards his support. Both daughters were married at the time; Malvina had one daughter of her own, Malvina had remained at her old home after her marriage,

but Ellen had removed to a town some twenty miles away. Her father had
visited there several times, but he never liked to remain long. He would
never have gone had not Malvina insisted upon it. She considered that her
sister ought to share her burden, and sometimes give her a relief. So Barney would go, although with reluctance; in fact, his little shoeshop was to
him his beloved home, his small solitary nest, where he could fold his old
wings in peace. Nobody knew how regretfully he thought of it during his
visits at Ellen's. While there he sat mostly in her kitchen, by the cooking-
stove, and miserably pored over the almanac or the religious paper. Occasionally he would steal out behind the barn and smoke a pipe, but there was
always a hard reckoning with Ellen afterwards, and it was a dearly purchased
pleasure. Ellen was a small, fair woman; she was delicate, much as her mother
had been, and her weakness and nervousness made her imperious will less
evident but more potent. Old Barney stood more in awe of her than
of Malvina. He was anxiously respectful towards her husband, who was a
stout, silent man, covering his own projects and his own defeats with taciturnity. He was a steady grubber on a farm, and very close with old Barney's
money, of which, however, his wife understood that she had full control.
She had had out of it a set of red plush parlor furniture and a new silk dress.
Once in a while old Barney, while on a visit, would stand on the parlor threshold and gaze admiringly in at the furniture; but did he venture to
step over, his daughter would check him. "Now don't go in there, father,"
she would cry out; "you'll track in somethin'."

"No, I ain't a-goin' in, Ellen," Barney would reply, and meekly
shuffle back.

Old Barney was intensely loyal towards both of his daughters; not even
to himself would he admit anything to their disadvantage. He always spoke
admiringly of them, and would acknowledge no preference for one above
the other. Still he undoubtedly preferred Malvina. She was a large, stout
woman, but some people thought that she looked like her father. When the
property was divided, Malvina had had every room in the house newly
painted and papered; then she stood before them like a vigilant watch-dog.
She had been neat before, but with her new paint and paper and a few new
carpets her neatness became almost a monomania. She was fairly fierce, and
her voice sounded like a bark sometimes when old Barney, with shoes heavy
with loam and clothes stained with tobacco juice, shuffled into her spotless
house. However, in a certain harsh way she did her duty by her simple old
father. She saw to it that his clothes were comfortably warm and mended,
and he had enough to eat, although his own individual tastes were never

consulted. Still, he was scrupulously bidden to meals, and his plate was well filled. She did not like to have him in the house, and showed that she did not, but she had no compunctions upon that point, for he preferred the shop. She never gave him spending-money, for she did not consider that he was capable of spending money judiciously. She bought all that he had herself. She was a good financier, and made a little go a long way.

Malvina's husband was dead, and her daughter was now eighteen years old. Her name was Annie. She was a pretty girl, and had a lover. She was to be married soon. They had not told old Barney about it, but he found it out two weeks before the wedding. He stood in his shop door one morning and called cautiously to Sarah Arnold. (The Arnolds lived in the next house, and Sarah was out in the yard picking some roses.) "Sary, come here a minute," he called. And Sarah came, with her roses in her hand. The old man beckoned her mysteriously into the shop. He drew well back from the door, after having peered sharply at the house windows. Then he began: "Ye heard on't, Sary," whispered he——"what's goin' on in there? Hey?" He gave his hand a backward jerk towards the house.

Sarah laughed. "I suppose so," said she.

"How long ye known it? Hey?"

"Well, I've heard 'twas coming off before long."

"The weddin's goin' to be in two weeks. Did ye know that? Hey?"

"I heard so."

"Well, it's the first I've heard on't. I know that young fellar'd been shinin' round there consider'ble, an' I spos'd 'twas comin' off some time or other, but I didn't have no idee 'twas goin' to be so soon. Look a-here, Sary" ——Sarah, placid and fair and pleasant, holding her roses, gazed attentively at him——"*I'm——a–goin' to——give her somethin'!*"

"What are you going to give her?"

"Ye'll see. I've got some money laid up, an' I know a way to raise a leetle more. Ye'll see when the time comes——ye'll see." The old man raised his pleasant cackle, then he hushed it suddenly, with a wary glance towards the house. "You mind you don't say nothin' about it, Sary," said he.

"No, I won't say a word about it," returned Sarah. Then she went home with her roses and her own thoughts. She herself was to be married soon, but there would be no such commotion over her wedding as over Annie's. The Arnolds were very humble folk, according to the social status of the village, and were not on very intimate terms with their neighbors. Old Mr. Arnold took care of people's gardens and sawed wood for a living, and Mrs. Arnold and Sarah sewed, and even went out for extra work when some of the more prosperous village people had company. However, Sarah was going to marry a young man who had saved quite a sum of money. He was building a new house on a cross street at the foot of a meadow that lay behind Barney Swan's shop. Sarah had told Barney all about it, and he often strolled down the meadow and watched the workmen on the new house with a wise and interested air. He was very fond of Sarah. Sarah had her own opinion about Annie and the old man's daughters, but she was calm about expressing it even to her mother. She was a womanly young girl. However, once in a while her indignation grew warm.

"I think it's a shame," she told her mother, when she carried her roses into the house, "that they haven't told Grandpa Swan about Annie's going to be married, and the poor old man's planning to give her a present." The tears stood in Sarah's blue eyes. She crowded the roses into a tumbler.

It was only the next day that old Barney called her into the shop to display the present. He had been so eager about it that he was not able to wait. However, the idea that the gift must not be presented to his granddaughter until her wedding-day was firmly fixed in his mind. He had obtained in some way this notion of etiquette, and he was resolved to abide by it, no matter how impatient he might be. "I've got it here all ready, but I ain't a-goin' to give it to her till the day she's married, ye know," he told Sarah while he was fumbling in the table-drawer(that was his poor little treasure-box). There he kept his surreptitious quids of tobacco and his pipe and his small hoards of pennies. His hands trembled as he drew out a little square parcel. He undid it with slow pains. "Look a-here!" In a little jeweller's box, on a bed of pink cotton, lay a gold-plated brooch with a red stone in the centre. The old man stood holding it, and looking at Sarah with a speechless appeal for admiration.

"Why, ain't it handsome!" said she; "it's just as pretty as it can be!"

Old Barney still did not speak; he stood holding the box, as silent as a statue whose sole purpose is to pose for admiration.

"Where did you get it?" asked Sarah.

The old man ushered in his words with an exultant chuckle. "Down to Bixby's; an' 'twas jest about the pertiest thing he had in his hull store. It cost consider'ble; I ain't a-goin' to tell ye how much, but I didn't pay no ninepence for't, I can tell ye. But I had a leetle somethin' laid up, an' there was some truck I traded off. I was bound I'd git somethin' wuth somethin' whilst I was about it."

As Barney spoke, Sarah noticed that his old silver watch-chain was gone, and a suspicion as to the "truck" seized her, but she did not speak of it.

She admired the brooch to Barney's full content, and he stowed it away in the drawer with pride and triumph. He was true to his resolution not to mention the present to his granddaughter, but he could not help throwing out sundry sly hints to the effect that one was forthcoming. However, no one paid any attention to them; they knew too well the state of Barney's exchequer to have any great expectations, and all the family were in the habit of disregarding the old man's chatter. He always talked a great deal, and asked many questions; and they seemed to look upon him much in the light of a venerable cricket, constantly chirping upon their hearth, which for some obscure religious reasons they were bound to harbor.

The question of old Barney's appearance at the marriage was quite a serious one. The wedding was to be a brilliant affair for the village, and the old man was not to be considered in the light of an ornament. Still the idea of not allowing him to be present could not decently be entertained, and Malvina began training him to make the best appearance possible. She instructed him as to his deportment and had even made a new black silk stock for him to wear at the wedding. He was so delighted that he wanted to take possession at once, and hide it away in his table-drawer, but she would not allow it. She had planned how he should be well shaven and thoroughly brushed, and his pockets searched for tobacco, on the wedding morning. "I should feel like goin' through the floor if your grandfather should come in lookin' the way he does sometimes," she told her daughter Annie.

Annie concerned herself very little about it. She was a young girl of a sweet, docile temperament. She was somewhat delicate physically, and was indolent, partly from that, partly from her nature. Now her mother was making her work so hard over her wedding clothes that she was half ill; her little forefinger was all covered with needle-pricks, and there were hollows under her eyes. Malvina had always been a veritable queen mother to Annie.

Ellen and her little boy visited Malvina for several weeks before the wedding. Ellen assisted about the sewing; she was a fine sewer.

Old Barney did not dare stay much in the house, but he wandered about the yard, and absurdly peeped in at the doors and windows. Back in his second childhood, he had all the delighted excitement of a child over a great occasion. It was perhaps a poor and pitiful happiness, but he was as happy in his own way as Annie was over her coming marriage, and, after all, happiness is only one's own heartful.

But three days before the wedding old Barney was attacked with a severe cold, and all his anticipations came to naught. The cold grew worse, and his daughters promptly decided he could not be present at the wedding. "There ain't no use talkin' 'bout it, father," said Malvina; "you can't go. You'd jest cough an' sneeze right through it, an' we can't have such work."

The old man pleaded, even with tears, but with no avail; on the wedding day he was almost forcibly exiled to his little shop in the yard. The excitement in the house reached a wild height, and he was not allowed to enter after breakfast; his dinner of bread and butter and tea was brought down to the shop. He sat in the door and watched the house and the hurrying people. He called Sarah Arnold over many times; he was in a panic over his present. "How am I goin' to give her that breastpin, if they don't let me go to the weddin'?" he queried, with sharp anxiety. "There sha'n't nobody else give her that pin nohow."

"I guess you'll have a chance," Sarah said, comfortingly. When it was time for the people to come to the wedding, Ellen, in her silk dress, with her hair finely crimped, came rustling out to the shop, and ordered old Barney away from the door.

"Do keep away from the door, father," said she, "for mercy sakes. Such a spectacle as you are, an' the folks beginnin' to come! I should think you'd know better." Ellen's forehead was all corrugated with anxious lines; she was nervous and fretful. She even pushed her father away from the door with a clash.

Then Barney stood at the window and watched. He held the little jewelry-box tightly clutched in his hand. The window-panes were all clouded and cobwebbed; it was hard for his dim old eyes to see through them, but he held back the stained curtain and peered as sharply as he could.

He saw the neighbors come to the wedding. Several covered wagons were hitched out in the yard. When the minister came into the yard he could scarcely keep himself from rushing to the door.

"There he is!" he said out loud to himself. "There he is! He's come to marry 'em!"

The hubbub of voices in the house reached old Barney's ears. A little after the minister arrived there was a hush. "He's marrin' of em!" ejaculated Barney. He danced up and down before the window.

After the hush the voices swelled out louder than before. Barney kept his eyes riveted upon the house. It was some two hours before people began to issue from the doors.

"The weddin's over!" shouted Barney. He looked quite wild; he gave himself a little shake, and opened the shop door and took up his stand there. Everybody could see him in his brown calico shirt-sleeves, and his slouching, untidy vest and trousers. His white locks straggled over his shoulders; his face was not very clean. Suddenly Ellen, standing and smirking in the house door, spied him. Presently she came across the yard, swaying her rattling skirts with a genteel air. She smiled all the way, and old Barney innocently smiled back at her when she reached him. But he jumped, her voice was so fierce.

"You go right in there this minute, father, an' keep that door *shut*," she said between her smiling lips.

She shut the door upon Barney, but she had no sooner reached the house than he opened it again and stood there. He still held the box.

The bridal pair were to set up housekeeping in a village ten miles away. They were to drive over that night. When at last the bridegroom and the bride appeared in the door, old Barney leaned forward, breathless. The bridegroom's glossy buggy and bay horse stood in the yard; the horse was restive, and a young man was holding him by the bridle.

Old Barney did not venture to step outside his shop door. Malvina and Ellen were both in the yard, but it was as if his soul were feeling for ways to approach the young couple. He leaned forward, his eyes were intent and prominent, the hand that held the jewelry-box shook with long, rigid motions.

The bride, at her husband's side, stepped across the green yard to the buggy. This was a simple country wedding, and Annie rode in her wedding dress to her new home. The wedding dress was white muslin, full of delicate frills and loops of ribbons that the wind caught. Annie, coming across the yard, was blown to one side like a white flower. Her slender neck and arms showed pink through the muslin, and she wore her wedding bonnet, which was all white, with bows of ribbon and plumes. Her cheeks were very red.

Old Barney opened his mouth wide. "Good Lord!" said he, with one gasp of admiration. He laughed in a kind of rapture; he forgot for a minute his wedding present. "Look at 'em!—jest look at 'em!" he repeated. Suddenly he called out, "Annie! jest look a-here! See what gran'pa's got for ye."

Annie stopped and looked. She hesitated, and seemed about to approach Barney, when the horse started; the young man had hard work to hold him. The bridegroom lifted the bride into the carriage as soon as the horse was quiet enough, sprang in after her, and they flew out of the yard, with everybody shouting merrily after them. Old Barney's piteous cry of "Annie! Annie! jest come here a minute!" was quite lost.

The old man went into the shop and closed the door of his own accord.

Then he replaced the little box in the table-drawer. Then he settled down on his old shoe-bench, and dropped his head on his hands. Soon he had a severe coughing-spell. Nobody came near him until it was quite dark; then Malvina came and asked him, in a hard, absent way, if he were not coming into the house to have any supper that night.

Old Barney arose and shuffled after her into the house; he ate the supper that she gave him; then he went to bed. He never took Annie's gold brooch out of the drawer again. He never spoke of it to Sarah Arnold nor any one else. He had the grieved dignity that pertains to the donor of a scorned gift. As the weeks went on, his cold grew no better; he coughed harder and harder. Once Malvina bought some cough medicine for him, but it did no good. The old man grew thinner and weaker, but she did not realize that; the cough arrested her attention; it tired her to hear it so constantly. She told him that there was no need of his coughing so much.

Sarah Arnold was married in August. She and her husband went to live in their new house across the meadow from old Barney's shop.

Sarah had been married a few weeks when one night old Barney came toddling down the meadow to her house. He was so weak that he tottered, but he almost ran. The short growth of golden-rod brushing his ankles seemed enough to throw him over. He waded through it as through a golden sea that would soon throw him from his footing and roll over him, but he never slackened his pace until he reached Sarah's door. She had seen him coming, and ran to meet him.

"Why, what is the matter?" she cried. Old Barney's face was pale and wild. He looked at her and gasped. She caught him by the arm and dragged him into the house, and set him in a chair. "What *is* the matter?" she asked again. She looked white and frightened herself.

Old Barney did not reply for a minute; he seemed to be collecting breath. Then he brust out in a great sobbing cry: "My shop! my shop! She's goin' to have my shop tore down! They're goin' to begin to-morrer. They're movin' my bench. Oh, oh!"

Sarah stood close to him and patted his head. "Who's goin' to have it torn down?"

"Mal——viny."

"When did she say so?"

"Jest——now——come out an' told me. Says the——old——thing looks dreadful bad out——in the yard, an' she wants it——tore down. She's goin' to have me——go to Ellen's an' stay——all winter. Puttin' my bench up——in the garret. I ain't——a-goin' to have the——bench to set on——no longer, I ain't."

Sarah's pleasant mouth was set hard. She made old Barney lie down on her sitting-room lounge, and got him a cup of tea. It was evident the old man was completely exhausted; he could not have walked home had he tried. Sarah sat down beside him and heard his complaint, and tried to comfort him. When her husband came home to tea she told him the story, and he went up across the meadow to the shop before he took off his coat.

"It's so," he growled, when he returned. "They're lugging the things out. It's a blasted shame. Poor old man!"

Sarah's husband had a brown boyish face and a set chin; he took off his coat and began washing his hands at the kitchen sink with such energy that the leather stains might have been the ingratitude of the world.

"Did you say anything about his being down here?" asked Sarah.

"No, I didn't. Let 'em hunt."

About nine o'clock that evening Malvina, holding her skirts up well, came striding over the meadow. She had missed her father, and traced him to Sarah's. Sarah and her husband had put him to bed in their pretty little spare chamber when Malvina came in. It was evident that the old man was very ill; he was wandering a little, and he had terrible paroxysms of coughing; his breathing was labored. Malvina stood looking at him; Sarah's husband kept opening his mouth to speak, and his wife kept nudging him to be silent. Finally he spoke——

"He's all upset because his shop's going to be torn down," said he; but his voice was not as bold as his intentions.

"Tain't that," replied Malvina. "He's dretful careless; he's been goin round in his stockin'-feet, an' he's got more cold. I dun know what's goin' to be done. I don't see how I can get him home to-night."

"He can stay here just as well as not," said Sarah, nudging her husband again.

"Well, I'll come over an' git him home in the mornin'," Malvina said.

But she could not get him home when she came over in the morning. Old Barney never went home again. He died the second day after he came to Sarah's. Both of his daughters came to see him, and did what they could, but he did not seem to notice them much. An hour before he died he called Sarah. She ran into the room. Just then there was nobody else in the house. Old Barney sat up in bed, and he was pointing out of the window over the meadow. His pointing forefinger shook, his face was ghastly, but there was a strange, childish delight in it.

"Look a-there, Sary——jest look a-there," said old Barney. "Over in the meader——look. There's Ellen a-comin', an' Viny, an' they look jest as they did when they was young; an' Ellen she's a-bringin' me some tea, an'

Viny she's a-bringin' me some custard puddin'. An' there's Willy a-dancin'
along. Jest see the leetle fellar a-comin' to see gran'pa all of his own accord.
An' there's Annie all in her white dress, jest as pretty as a pictur',
a-comin' arter her breastpin. Jest see 'em, Sary." The old man laughed. Out
of his ghastly, death-stricken features shone the expression of a happy child.
"Jest look at 'em, Sary," he repeated.

Sarah looked, and she saw only the meadow covered with a short waving crop of golden-rod, and over it the September sky.

STUDY QUESTIONS:

1. The action of the story runs from May into September. Why are these
months appropriate?

2. Why does the writer begin with the episode of Willy and the candy, why
does she emphasize Willy's dislike for physical contact with his grandfather, and
why is this immediately followed by the episode of the pudding?

3. Why is the irony of the sentence, "This was a simple country wedding,"
central to the total effect of the story?

4. How would this story appear if it were told from the point of view of
Willy? Of Annie? Of the village jeweler? Of Malvina?

5. The ending is perhaps sentimental—the "dying vision". How is it con-
sonant with Shakespeare?

THE STORY
OF BRAS-COUPÉ

GEORGE WASHINGTON CABLE

In his excellent anthology of selections from George Washington Cable (1844–1925) Arlin Turner tells the curious publishing history of "The Story of Bras-Coupé." As a short story then entitled "Bibi" it was rejected by *Scribner's Magazine* in 1873. Cable revised it and sent it in 1875 to the same magazine. It was again rejected. It was also rejected by every other magazine to which he submitted it, including the *Atlantic Monthly*, an editor of which explained that the public would not stand its "unmitigatedly distressing effect." Cable then made it a part of his masterly novel of Creole life in Louisiana, *The Grandissimes* (1880), of which it now forms chapters 28 and 29 (with a few additions). Today, removed from the novel and restored to its original status as a short story, it is recognized as a powerful and tragic tale of slavery and passion.

Since Cable had finally to fit his tale into the novel, he had to insert into it some material not germane to the story, which still remains. Perhaps some of this requires explanation. Joseph Frowenfeld, who makes one comment, is a Northerner who opened an apothecary shop in New Orleans and who, by virtue of his upright and sympathetic character, manages to remain on friendly terms with two fueding families, the Grandissime and the De

261

Grapion. There are, however, two Honoré Grandissime's: one is a white creole; the other is a freeman of color (f.m.c.), or in other words a mulatto. Palmyre was sold to the Grandissime family as a slave. She is passionately in love with the mulatto Honoré and that is why she does not wish to be married to Bras-Coupé, however she may admire his spirit. Agricola Fusilier belongs to a family that has intermarried with the Grandissime's. He is uncle to Honoré (the white creole) and in a duel occasioned by a charge of cheating at cards he has killed De Grapion Nancanou. The De Grapion plantation has been Cannes Brulées, but before his death De Grapion Nancanou arranged for it to pass into the possession of the Grandissimes in payment of debt. Don José Martinez, on whose plantation, La Renaissance, Bras-Coupé, first experiences slavery, stands apart from the feuding families.

Whether this information clarifies or confuses the story (Cable has a genius for alluding to matters outside his tale), the rush and power of the tragedy will carry the reader forward without too much bewilderment. It is perhaps essential to realize that Palmyre's love for Honoré is crossed by her devotion to her young white mistress; consequently the tension she feels when she is commanded to marry Bras-Coupé is a very great tension. It is also helpful to remember that Cable hated slavery and was angered by the power it gave the white man over the lives of the Negroes. It is likewise useful to realize that voodoo was a great and terrible force, or thought to be so, in the black belt and that even the whites were touched with fear by it. Hence the belief, essential to the story, that the curse Bras-Coupé puts on the plantation is really effective. But in general the story is a magnificent study of a savage temperament trapped by patterns of life it cannot understand.

"A very little more than eight years ago," began Honoré—but not only Honoré, but Raoul also; and not only they, but another, earlier on the same day,—Honoré, the f. m. c.[1] But we shall not exactly follow the words of any one of these.

Bras-Coupé, they said, had been, in Africa and under another name, a prince among his people. In a certain war of conquest, to which he had been driven by *ennui*, he was captured, stripped of his royalty, marched down upon the beach of the Atlantic, and, attired as a true son of Adam, with two goodly arms intact, became a commodity. Passing out of first hands in barter for a looking-glass, he was shipped in good order and condition on board

[1] (f. m. c.) A freeman of color; i.e., an emancipated slave.

the good schooner *Egalité*, whereof Blank was master, to be delivered without delay at the port of Nouvelle Orleans (the dangers of fire and navigation excepted), unto Blank Blank. In witness whereof, He that made men's skins — of different colors, but all blood of one, hath entered the same upon His book, and sealed it to the day of judgment.

Of the voyage little is recorded—here below; the less the better. Part of the living merchandise failed to keep; the weather was rough, the cargo large, the vessel small. However, the captain discovered there was room over the side, and there—all flesh is grass—from time to time during the voyage he jettisoned the unmerchantable.

Yet, when the reopened hatches let in the sweet smell of the land, Bras-Coupé had come to the upper—the favored—the buttered side of the world; the anchor slid with a rumble of relief down through the muddy fathoms of the Mississippi, and the prince could hear through the schooner's side the savage current of the river, leaping and licking about the bows, and whimpering low welcomes home. A splendid picture to the eyes of the royal captive, as his head came up out of the hatchway, was the little Franco-Spanish-American city that lay on the low, brimming bank. There were little forts that showed their whitewashed teeth; there was a green parade-ground, and yellow barracks, and cabildo[2], and hospital, and cavalry stables, and custom-house, and a most inviting jail, convenient to the cathedral—all of dazzling white and yellow, with a black stripe marking the track of the conflagration of 1794, and here and there among the low roofs a lofty one with round-topped dormer windows and a breezy belvedere looking out upon the plantations of coffee and indigo beyond the town.

When Bras-Coupé staggered ashore, he stood but a moment among a drove of "likely boys," before Agricola Fusilier, managing the business adventures of the Grandissime estate, as well as the residents thereon, and struck with admiration for the physical beauties of the chieftain (a man may even fancy a negro—as a negro), bought the lot, and loth to resell him with the rest to some unappreciative 'Cadian, induced Don José Martinez'[3] overseer to become his purchaser.

Down in the rich parish of St. Bernard (whose boundary line now touches that of the distended city) lay the plantation, known before Bras-Coupé passed away, as La Renaissance. Here it was that he entered at once

[2] Cabildo. The building that houses the town officials in a Spanish municipality. In New Orleans the Cabildo is one of the famous relics of Spanish architecture.

[3] Don José Martinez. A Spanish don who married into the de Grapion family. Note that there is a feud between the de Grapions and the de Grandissimes.

upon a chapter of agreeable surprises. He was humanely met, presented with
a clean garment, lifted into a cart drawn by oxen, taken to a whitewashed
cabin of logs, finer than his palace at home, and made to comprehend that
it was a free gift. He was also given some clean food, whereupon he fell sick.
At home it would have been the part of piety for the magnate next the throne
to launch him heavenward at once; but now, healing doses were administered, and to his amazement he recovered. It reminded him that he was no
longer king.

His name, he replied to an inquiry touching that subject, was ———
———, something in the Jaloff[4] tongue, which he by and by condescended
to render into Congo: Mioko-Koanga, in French Bras-Coupé, the Arm Cut
Off. Truly it would have been easy to admit, had this been his meaning, that
his tribe, in losing him, had lost its strong right arm close off at the
shoulder; not so easy for his high-paying purchaser to allow, if this other
was his intent; that the arm which might no longer shake the spear or swing
the wooden sword, was no better than a useless stump never to be lifted for
aught else. But whether easy to allow or not, that was his meaning. He made
himself a type of all Slavery, turning into flesh and blood the truth that all
Slavery is maiming.

He beheld more luxury in a week than all his subjects had seen in a
century. Here Congo girls were dressed in cottons and flannels worth,
where he came from, an elephant's tusk apiece. Everybody wore clothes—
children and lads alone excepted. Not a lion had invaded the settle-
ment since his immigration. The serpents were as nothing; an occasional
one coming up through the floor—that was all. True, there was more
emaciation than unassisted conjecture could explain—a profusion of en-
larged joints and diminished muscles, which, thank God, was even then
confined to a narrow section and disappeared with Spanish rule. He had no
experimental knowledge of it; nay, regular meals, on the contrary, gave him
anxious concern, yet had the effect—spite of his apprehension that he was
being fattened for a purpose—of restoring the herculean puissance which
formerly in Africa had made him the terror of the battle.

When one day he had come to be quite himself, he was invited out
into the sunshine, and escorted by the driver (a sort of foreman to the overseer), went forth dimly wondering. They reached a field where some men
and women were hoeing. He had seen men and women—subjects of his—
labor—a little—in Africa. The driver handed him a hoe; he examined it
with silent interest—until by signs he was requested to join the pastime.

[4] Jaloff. (Also spelled Djolof, Yoloffe, Wolof, etc.) An African "Kingdom" in Northwest
Senegal and Northern Gambia.

"What?"

He spoke, not with his lips, but with the recoil of his splendid frame and the ferocious expansion of his eyes. This invitation was a cataract of lightning leaping down an ink-black sky. In one instant of all-pervading clearness he read his sentence—WORK.

Bras-Coupé was six feet five. With a sweep as quick as instinct the back of the hoe smote the driver full in the head. Next, the prince lifted the nearest Congo crosswise, brought thirty-two teeth together in his wildly kicking leg and cast him away as a bad morsel; then, throwing another into the branches of a willow, and a woman over his head into a draining-ditch, he made one bound for freedom, and fell to his knees, rocking from side to side under the effect of a pistol-ball from the overseer. It had struck him in the forehead, and running around the skull in search of a penetrable spot, tradition—which sometimes jests—says came out despairingly, exactly where it had entered.

It so happened that, except the overseer, the whole company were black. Why should the trivial scandal be blabbed? A plaster or two made everything even in a short time, except in the driver's case—for the driver died. The woman whom Bras-Coupé had thrown over his head lived to sell calas[5] to Joseph Frowenfeld.[6]

Don José, young and austere, knew nothing about agriculture and cared as much about human nature. The overseer often thought this, but never said it; he would not trust even himself with the dangerous criticism. When he ventured to reveal the foregoing incidents to the señor he laid all the blame possible upon the man whom death had removed beyond the reach of correction, and brought his account to a climax by hazarding the assertion that Bras-Coupé was an animal that could not be whipped.

"Caramba[7]!" exclaimed the master, with gentle emphasis, "how so?"

"Perhaps señor had better ride down to the quarters," replied the overseer.

It was a great sacrifice of dignity, but the master made it.

"Bring him out."

They brought him out—chains on his feet, chains on his wrists, an iron yoke on his neck. The Spanish-Creole master had often seen the bull, with his long, keen horns and blazing eye, standing in the arena; but this was as though he had come face to face with a rhinoceros.

5 Calas. A kind of rice cake.

6 Joseph Frowenfeld. The "Yankee" immigrant who becomes a pharmacist in New Orleans and whose experiences are the basis of the novel The Grandissimes, from which this story comes.

7 Caramba. A mild Spanish exclamation, somewhat equivalent to: "Well, well!"

"This man is not a Congo," he said.

"He is a Jaloff," replied the encouraged overseer. "See his fine, straight nose; moreover, he is a *candio*—a prince. If I whip him he will die."

The dauntless captive and fearless master stood looking into each other's eyes until each recognized in the other his peer in physical courage, and each was struck with an admiration for the other which no after difference was sufficient entirely to destroy. Had Bras-Coupé's eye quailed but once— just for one little instant—he would have got the lash; but, as it was——

"Get an interpreter," said Don José; then, more privately, "and come to an understanding. I shall require it of you."

Where might one find an intrepreter—one not merely able to render a Jaloff's meaning into Creole French, or Spanish, but with such a turn for diplomatic correspondence as would bring about an "understanding" with this African buffalo? The overseer was left standing and thinking, and Clemence, who had not forgotten who threw her into the draining-ditch, cunningly passed by.

"Ah, Clemence——"

"*Mo pas capabe! Mo pas capabe!* (I cannot, I cannot!) *Ya, ya, ya! 'oir Miché Agricol' Fusilier! ouala yune bon monture, oui!*"—which was to signify that Agricola could interpret the very Papa Lébat[8].

"Agricola Fusilier! The last man on earth to make peace."

But there seemed to be no choice, and to Agricola the overseer went. It was but a little ride to the Grandissime place.

"I, Agricola Fusilier[9], stand as an interpreter to a negro? H-sir!"

"But I thought you might know of some person," said the weakening applicant, rubbing his ear with his hand.

"Ah!" replied Agricola, addressing the surrounding scenery, "if I did not—who would? You may take Palmyre."

The overseer softly smote his hands together at the happy thought.

"Yes," said Agricola, "take Palmyre; she has picked up as many negro dialects as I know European languages."

And she went to the don's plantation as interpretess, followed by Agricola's prayer to Fate that she might in some way be overtaken by disaster. The two hated each other with all the strength they had. He knew not only her pride, but her passion for the absent Honoré. He hated her, also, for her intelligence, for the high favor in which she stood with her mistress,

[8] Papa Lébat. A powerful demonic spirit called up in voodoo (voudou) ceremonies.

[9] Agricole Fusilier. Uncle to Honoré de Grandissime. The three branches of the de Grandissime family springing from the parent Grandissime stock are the Brahmin, the Mandarin, and the Fusilier.

and for her invincible spirit, which was more offensively patent to him than
to others, since he was himself the chief object of her silent detestation.

It was Palmyre's habit to do nothing without painstaking. "When
Mademoiselle comes to be Señora," thought she—she knew that her mistress and the don were affianced—"it will be well to have Señor's esteem.
I shall endeavor to succeed." It was from this motive, then, that with the
aid of her mistress she attired herself in a resplendence of scarlet and
beads and feathers that could not fail the double purpose of connecting her
with the children of Ethiopia and commanding the captive's instant
admiration.

Alas for those who succeed too well! No sooner did the African turn
his tiger glance upon her than the fire of his eyes died out; and when she
spoke to him in the dear accents of his native tongue, the matter of strife
vanished from his mind. He loved.

He sat down tamely in his irons and listened to Palmyre's argument
as a wrecked mariner would listen to ghostly churchbells. He would give a
short assent, feast his eyes, again assent, and feast his ears; but when
at length she made bold to approach the actual issue, and finally uttered
the loathed word, *Work*, he rose up, six feet five, a statue of indignation in
black marble.

And then Palmyre, too, rose up, glorying in him, and went to explain
to master and overseer. Bras-Coupé understood, she said, that he was
a slave—it was the fortune of war, and he was a warrior; but, according to
a generally recognized principle in African international law, he could not
reasonably be expected to work.

"As señor will remember I told him," remarked the overseer; "how
can a man expect to plow with a zebra?"

Here he recalled a fact in his early experience. An African of this stripe
had been found to answer admirably as a "driver" to make others work.
A second and third parley, extending through two or three days, were held
with the prince, looking to his appointment to the vacant office of driver; yet
what was the master's amazement to learn at length that his Highness declined
the proffered honor.

"Stop!" spoke the overseer again, detecting a look of alarm in
Palmyre's face as she turned away, "he doesn't do any such thing. If
Señor will let me take the man to Agricola——"

"No!" cried Palmyre, with an agonized look, "I will tell. He will take
the place and fill it if you will give me to him for his own—but oh,
messieurs, for the love of God—I do not want to be his wife!"

The overseer looked at the Señor, ready to approve whatever he should decide. Bras-Coupé's intrepid audacity took the Spaniard's heart by irresistible assault.

"I leave it entirely with Señor Fusilier," he said.

"But he is not my master; he has no right——"

"Silence!"

And she was silent; and so, sometimes, is fire in the wall.

Agricola's consent was given with malicious promptness, and as Bras-Coupé's fetters fell off it was decreed that, should he fill his office efficiently, there should be a wedding on the rear veranda of the Grandissime mansion simultaneously with the one already appointed to take place in the grand hall of the same house six months from that present day. In the meanwhile Palmyre should remain with Mademoiselle, who had promptly but quietly made up her mind that Palmyre should not be wed unless she wished to be. Bras-Coupé made no objection, was royally worthless for a time, but learned fast, mastered the "gumbo" dialect in a few weeks, and in six months was the most valuable man ever bought for gourde dollars. Nevertheless, there were but three persons within as many square miles who were not most vividly afraid of him.

The first was Palmyre. His bearing in her presence was ever one of solemn, exalted respect, which, whether from pure magnanimity in himself, or by reason of her magnetic eye, was something worth being there to see. "It was royal!" said the overseer.

The second was not that official. When Bras-Coupé said—as, at stated intervals, he did say—"*Mo courri c'ez Agricole Fusilier 'pou oir' n'-amourouse* (I go to Agricola Fusilier to see my betrothed,)" the overseer would sooner have intercepted a score of painted Chickasaws than that one lover. He would look after him and shake a prophetic head. "Trouble coming; better not deceive that fellow"; yet that was the very thing Palmyre dared do. Her admiration for Bras-Coupé was almost boundless. She rejoiced in his stature; she revelled in the contemplation of his untamable spirit; he seemed to her the gigantic embodiment of her own dark, fierce will, the expanded realization of her lifetime longing for terrible strength. But the single deficiency in all this impassioned regard was—what so many fairer loves have found impossible to explain to so many gentler lovers—an entire absence of preference; her heart she could not give him—she did not have it. Yet after her first prayer to the Spaniard and his overseer for deliverance, to the secret surprise and chagrin of her young mistress, she simulated content. It was artifice; she knew Agricola's power, and to seem to consent was her one chance with him. He might thus be beguiled into withdrawing his own consent. That failing, she had Mademoiselle's promise to come to the rescue, which she could use at the last moment; and that failing, there was a dirk in her bosom, for which a certain hard breast was not too hard. Another element of safety, of which she knew nothing, was a letter from the Cannes Brulée. The word had reached there that love had conquered—that, despite all hard words, and rancor, and positive injury, the Grandissime hand—the fairest of Grandissime hands—was about to be laid into that of one who without much stretch might be called a De Grapion; that there was, moreover, positive effort being made to induce a restitution of old gaming-table spoils. Honoré and Mademoiselle, his sister, one on each side of the Atlantic, were striving for this end. Don José sent this intelligence to his kinsman as glad tidings (a lover never imagines there are two sides to that which makes him happy), and, to add a touch of humor, told how Palmyre, also, was given to the chieftain. The letter that came back to the young Spaniard did not blame him too much: *he* was ignorant of all the facts; but a very formal one to Agricola begged to notify him that if Palmyre's union with Bras-Coupé should be completed, as sure as there was a God in heaven, the writer would have the life of the man who knowingly had thus endeavored to dishonor one who *shared the blood of the De Grapions*[10]. Thereupon Agricola, contrary to his general character, began to drop hints to Don José that the engagement of Bras-Coupé and Palmyre need not be considered irreversible; but the don was not desirous of disappointing his terrible pet. Palmyre, unluckily, played her game a little too deeply. She thought the moment had come for herself to insist on the match, and thus provoke Agricola to forbid it. To her incalculable dismay she saw him a second time reconsider and become silent.

The second person who did not fear Bras-Coupé was Mademoiselle. On one of the giant's early visits to see Palmyre he obeyed the summons which she brought him, to appear before the lady. A more artificial man might have objected on the score of dress, his attire being a single gaudy garment tightly enveloping the waist and thighs. As his eyes fell upon the beautiful white lady he prostrated himself upon the ground, his arms outstretched before him. He would not move till she was gone. Then he arose like a hermit who has seen a vision. *"Bras-Coupé 'n pas oulé oir zombis* (Bras-Coupé dares not look upon a spirit).'' From that hour he worshipped. He saw her often; every time, after

---

[10] . . . *shared the blood of the De Grapions.* Without going into the problem of Palmyre's ancestry, the point is that Palmyre had been given as a young girl to Aurore de Grapion, who married Nancanou. Palmyre was later emancipated.

one glance at her countenance, he would prostrate his gigantic length with his face in the dust.

The third person who did not fear him was—Agricola? Nay, it was the Spaniard—a man whose capability to fear anything in nature or beyond had never been discovered.

Long before the end of his probation Bras-Coupé would have slipped the entanglements of bondage, though as yet he felt them only as one feels a spider's web across the face, had not the master, according to a little affectation of the times, promoted him to be his game-keeper. Many a day did these two living magazines of wrath spend together in the dismal swamps and on the meagre intersecting ridges, making war upon deer and bear and wild-cat; or on the Mississippi after wild goose and pelican; when even a word mis-placed would have made either the slayer of the other. Yet the months ran smoothly round and the wedding night drew nigh. A goodly company had assembled. All things were ready. The bride was dressed, the bride-groom had come. On the great back piazza, which had been inclosed with sail-cloth and lighted with lanterns, was Palmyre, full of a new and deep design and playing her deceit to the last, robed in costly garments to whose beauty was added the charm of their having been worn once, and once only, by her beloved Mademoiselle.

But where was Bras-Coupé?

The question was asked of Palmyre by Agricola with a gaze that meant in English, "No tricks, girl!"

Among the servants who huddled at the windows and doors to see the inner magnificence a frightened whisper was already going round.

"We have made a sad discovery, Miché Fusilier," said the overseer. "Bras-Coupé is here; we have him in a room just yonder. But—the truth is, sir, Bras-Coupé is a voudou."

"Well, and suppose he is; what of it? Only hush; do not let his master know it. It is nothing; all the blacks are voudous, more or less."

"But he declines to dress himself—has painted himself all rings and stripes, antelope fashion."

"Tell him Agricola Fusilier says, 'dress immediately!' "

"Oh, Miché, we have said that five times already, and his answer—you will pardon me—his answer is—spitting on the ground—that you are a contemptible *dotchian* (white trash)."

There is nothing to do but privily to call the very bride—the lady her-self. She comes forth in all her glory, small, but oh, so beautiful! Slam! Bras-Coupé is upon his face, his finger-tips touching the tips of her snowy slippers. She gently bids him go and dress, and at once he goes.

Ah! now the question may be answered without whispering. There is Bras-Coupé, towering above all heads, in ridiculous red and blue regimentals, but with a look of savage dignity upon him that keeps every one from laughing. The murmur of admiration that passed along the thronged gallery leaped up into a shout in the bosom of Palmyre. Oh, Bras-Coupé—heroic soul! She would not falter. She would let the silly priest say his say—then her cunning should help her *not to be* his wife, yet to show his mighty arm how and when to strike.

"He is looking for Palmyre," said some, and at that moment he saw her. "Ho-o-o-o-o!"

Agricola's best roar was a penny trumpet to Bras-Coupé's note of joy. The whole masculine half of the in-door company flocked out to see what the matter was. Bras-Coupé was taking her hand in one of his and laying his other upon her head; and as some one made an unnecessary gesture for silence, he sang, beating slow and solemn time with his naked foot and with the hand that dropped hers to smite his breast:

> " *'En haut la montagne, zami,*
> *Mo pé coupé canne, zami,*
> *Pou' fé i' a' zen' zami*
> *Pou' mo baille Palmyre.*
> *Ah! Palmyre, Palmyre mo c'ere,*
> *Mo l'aimé' ou'—mo l'aimé ou'.'* "[11]

"Montagne?" asked one slave of another, *"qui ce çà, montagne? gnia pas quiç' ose comme çà dans la Louisiana?* (What's a mountain? We haven't such things in Louisiana.)"

"Mein ye gagnein plein montagnes dans l'Afrique,[12] listen!"

[11] "En haut . . ." etc. In modern French:

> Sur la montagne, ami.
> Je peux couper de la canne, ami.
> Il y en a faire, ami,
> Pour qu'on me donne Palmyre.
> Ah! Palmyre, Palmyre, ma chere,
> Je l'aime, oui: je l'aime, oui.

That is: On top of the mountain, my friend, I'll cut sugarcane, my friend. This I have to do, my friend, so that they may give me Palmyre. Ah! Palmyre, Palmyre my dear, I love her, yes; I love her, yes.

[12] "Mein ye gagnein . . ." etc. Mais, il y en tout plein de montagnes, en Afrique. That is, Africa is filled with mountains.

" 'Ah! Palmyre, Palmyre, mo' piti zozo,
Mo l'aimé'ou'—mo l'aimé, l'aimé'ou,' "13

"Bravissimo!—" but just then a counter-attraction drew the white
company back into the house. An old French priest with sandalled feet and
a dirty face had arrived. There was a moment of hand-shaking with
the good father, then a moment of palpitation and holding of the breath,
and then—you would have known it by the turning away of two or three
feminine heads in tears—the lily hand became the don's, to have and
to hold, by authority of the Church and the Spanish king. And all was merry,
save that outside there was coming up as villainous a night as ever
cast black looks in through snug windows.

It was just as the newly wed Spaniard, with Agricola and all the
guests, were concluding the by-play of marrying the darker couple, that the
hurricane struck the dwelling. The holy and jovial father had made faint
pretense of kissing this second bride; the ladies, colonels, dons, etc.,—though
the joke struck them as a trifle coarse—were beginning to laugh and clap
hands again and the gowned jester to bow to right and left, when Bras-Coupé,
tardily realizing the consummation of his hopes, stepped forward to embrace
his wife.

"Bras-Coupé!"

The voice was that of Palmyre's mistress. She had not been able to
comprehend her maid's behavior, but now Palmyre had darted upon her an
appealing look.

The warrior stopped as if a javelin had flashed over his head and
stuck in the wall.

"Bras-Coupé must wait till I give him his wife."

He sank, with hidden face, slowly to the floor.

"Bras-Coupé hears the voice of zombis14; the voice is sweet, but the
words are very strong; from the same sugar-cane comes sirop and tafia15;
Bras-Coupé says to zombis, 'Bras-Coupé will wait; but if the dotchians de-

13 "Ah! Palmyre . . ." etc. Ah, Palmyre, Palmyre, mon petit oiseau. Je l'aime, oui; je l'aime,
oui. That is, Palmyre, my little bird, I love her, yes: I love her.

14 Zombis. In voodoo faith, zombis are the reanimated bodies of the dead, who strike terror
in the living and gain control over them.

15 Tafia. A rum-like liquor obtained from the lower grades of molasses or from refuse
brown sugar.

ceive Bras-Coupé—' " he rose to his feet with his eyes closed and his great black fist lifted over his head—"Bras-Coupé will call Voudou-Magnan!"[16]

The crowd retreated and the storm fell like a burst of infernal applause. A whiff like fifty witches flouted up the canvas curtain of the gallery and a fierce black cloud, drawing the moon under its cloak, belched forth a stream of fire that seemed to flood the ground; a peal of thunder followed as if the sky had fallen in, the house quivered, the great oaks groaned, and every lesser thing bowed down before the awful blast. Every lip held its breath for a minute—or an hour, no one knew—there was a sudden lull of the wind, and the floods came down. Have you heard it thunder and rain in those Louisiana lowlands? Every clap seems to crack the world. It has rained a moment; you peer through the black pane—your house is an island, all the land is sea.

However, the supper was spread in the hall and in due time the guests were filled. Then a supper was spread in the big hall in the basement, below stairs, the sons and daughters of Ham[17] came down like the fowls of the air upon a rice-field, and Bras-Coupé, throwing his heels about with the joyous carelessness of a smutted Mercury, for the first time in his life tasted the blood of the grape. A second, a fifth, a tenth time he tasted it, drinking more deeply each time, and would have taken it ten times more had not his bride cunningly concealed it. It was like stealing a tiger's kittens.

The moment quickly came when he wanted his eleventh bumper. As he presented his request a silver shiver of consternation ran through the dark company; and when, in what the prince meant as a remonstrative tone, he repeated the petition—splitting the table with his fist by way of punctuation—there ensued a hustling up staircases and a cramming into dim corners that left him alone at the banquet.

Leaving the table, he strode upstairs and into the chirruping and dancing of the grand salon. There was a halt in the cotillion and a hush of amazement like the shutting off of steam. Bras-Coupé strode straight to his master, laid his paw upon his fellow-bridegroom's shoulder and in a thunder-tone demanded:

"More!"

The master swore a Spanish oath, lifted his hand and—fell, beneath the terrific fist of his slave, with a bang that jingled the candelabras. Dolorous stroke!—for the dealer of it. Given, apparently to him—poor, tipsy

---

[16] Voudou-Magnan. A powerful supernatural being according to voodoo belief.

[17] . . . sons and daughters of Ham. Negroes, supposed, according to folklore, to be the descendants of Ham, one of the three sons of Noah.

savage—in self-defence, punishable, in a white offender, by a small fine or a few days' imprisonment, it assured Bras-Coupé the death of a felon; such was the old *Code Noir*[18]. (We have a *Code Noir* now, but the new one is a mental reservation, not an enactment.)

The guests stood for an instant as if frozen, smitten stiff with the instant expectation of insurrection, conflagration and rapine (just as we do to-day whenever some poor swaggering Pompey rolls up his fist and gets a ball through his body), while, single-handed and naked-fisted in a room full of swords, the giant stood over his master, making strange signs and passes and rolling out in wrathful words of his mother tongue what it needed no interpreter to tell his swarming enemies was a voudou malediction.

"Nous sommes grigis!" screamed two or three ladies, "we are bewitched!"

"Look to your wives and daughters!" shouted a Brahmin-Mandarin.

"Shoot the black devils without mercy!" cried a Mandarin-Fusilier, unconsciously putting into a single outflash of words the whole Creole[19] treatment of race troubles.

With a single bound Bras-Coupé reached the drawing-room door; his gaudy regimentals made a red and blue streak down the hall; there was a rush of frilled and powdered gentlemen to the rear veranda, an avalanche of lightning with Bras-Coupé in the midst making for the swamp, and then all without was blackness of darkness and all within was a wild commingled chatter of Creole, French, and Spanish tongues,—in the midst of which the reluctant Agricola returned his dress-sword to its scabbard.

While the wet lanterns swung on crazily in the trees along the way by which the bridegroom was to have borne his bride; while Madame Grandissime prepared an impromptu bridal-chamber; while the Spanish bathed his eye and the blue gash on his cheek-bone; while Palmyre paced her room in a fever and wild tremor of conflicting emotions throughout the night and the guests splashed home after the storm as best they could, Bras-Coupé was practically declaring his independence on a slight rise of ground hardly sixty

[18] *Code Noir.* A set of legal regulations governing the lives and conduct of Negro slaves and others. The "new one" to which the parenthetical remark refers, is the mental reservation, not an enactment evident in racial discrimination, to which Cable was vigorously opposed. See page 190.

[19] Creole. Properly, any white person born of French or Spanish parentage in the West Indies, Louisiana, and other portions of the New World. The later reference to "Creole, French and Spanish tongues" differentiates "Creole" as a dialect of French spoken in Louisiana from the other two languages.

feet in circumference and lifted scarce above the water in the inmost depths
of the swamp.

And what surroundings! Endless colonnades of cypresses; long, motionless drapings of gray moss; broad sheets of noisome waters, pitchy black,
resting on bottomless ooze; cypress knees studding the surface; patches of
floating green, gleaming brilliantly here and there; yonder where the sun-
beams wedge themselves in, constellations of water-lilies, the many-hued iris,
and a multitude of flowers that no man had named; here, too, serpents great
and small, of wonderful colorings, and the dull and loathsome moccasin
sliding warily off the dead tree; in dimmer recesses the cow alligator, with
her nest hard by; turtles a century old; owls and bats, racoons, opossums,
rats, centipedes and creatures of like vileness; great vines of beautiful leaf
and scarlet fruit in deadly clusters; maddening mosquitoes, parasitic insects,
gorgeous dragon-flies and pretty water-lizards: the blue heron, the snowy
crane, the red-bird, the moss-bird, the night-hawk and the chuckwill's
widow; a solemn stillness and stifled air only now and then disturbed by
the call or whir of the summer duck, the dismal ventriloquous note of the
rain-crow, or the splash of a dead branch falling into the clear but
lifeless bayou.

The pack of Cuban hounds that howl from Don José's kennels cannot
snuff the trail of the stolen canoe that glides through the sombre blue va-
pors of the African's fastnesses. His arrows send no tell-tale reverberations
to the distant clearing. Many a wretch in his native wilderness has Bras-
Coupé himself, in palmier days, driven to just such an existence, to escape
the chains and horrors of the barracoons[20]; therefore not a whit broods he
over man's inhumanity, but, taking the affair as a matter of course, casts
about him for a future.

Bras-Coupé let the autumn pass, and wintered in his den.

Don José, in a majestic way, endeavored to be happy. He took his señora
to his hall, and under her rule it took on for a while a look and feeling which
turned it from a hunting-lodge into a home. Wherever the lady's steps turned
—or it is as correct to say wherever the proud tread of Palmyre turned—the
features of bachelor's hall disappeared; guns, dogs, oars, saddles, nets, went
their way into proper banishment, and the broad halls and lofty chambers—
the floors now muffled with mats of palmetto-leaf—no longer re-echoed
the tread of a lonely master, but breathed a redolence of flowers and a rippling
murmur of well-contented song.

[20] Barracoons. Enclosures or barracks in which black slaves were imprisoned. The word
was first used for slave-pens on the African coast.

But the song was not from the throat of Bras-Coupé's "*piti zozo.*" Silent and severe by day, she moaned away whole nights heaping reproaches upon herself for the impulse—now to her, because it had failed, inexplicable in its folly—which had permitted her hand to lie in Bras-Coupé's and the priest to bind them together.

For in the audacity of her pride, or, as Agricola would have said, in the immensity of her impudence, she had held herself consecrate to a hopeless love. But now she was a black man's wife; and even he unable to sit at her feet and learn the lesson she had hoped to teach him. She had heard of San Domingo, and for months the fierce heart within her silent bosom had been leaping and shouting and seeing visions of fire and blood, and when she brooded over the nearness of Agricola and the remoteness of Honoré these visions got from her a sort of mad consent. The lesson she would have taught the giant was Insurrection. But it was too late. Letting her dagger sleep in her bosom, and with an undefined belief in imaginary resources, she had consented to join hands with her giant hero before the priest; and when the wedding had come and gone, like a white sail, she was seized with a lasting, fierce despair. A wild aggressiveness that had formerly characterized her glance in moments of anger—moments which had grown more and more infrequent under the softening influence of her Mademoiselle's nature —now came back intensified and blazed in her eye perpetually. Whatever her secret love may have been in kind, its sinking beyond hope below the horizon had left her fifty times the mutineer she had been before—the mutineer who has nothing to lose.

"She loves her *candio*[21]," said the negroes.

"Simple creatures!" said the overseer, who prided himself on his discernment, "she loves nothing; she hates Agricola; it's a case of hate at first sight—the strongest kind."

Both were partly right; her feelings were wonderfully knit to the African; and she now dedicated herself to Agricola's ruin.

The señor, it has been said, endeavored to be happy; but now his heart conceived and brought forth its first-born fear, sired by superstition—the fear that he was bewitched. The negroes said that Bras-Coupé had cursed the land. Morning after morning the master looked out with apprehension toward his fields, until one night the worm came upon the indigo and between sunset and sunrise every green leaf had been eaten up, and there was nothing left for either insect or apprehension, to feed upon.

[21] *Candio.* A word about equivalent to sweetheart.

And then he said—and the echo came back from the Cannes Brulées—that the very bottom culpability of this thing rested on the Grandissimes, and specifically on their fugleman Agricola, through his putting the hellish African upon him. Moreover, fever and death, to a degree unknown before, fell upon his slaves. Those to whom life was spared—but to whom strength did not return—wandered about the place like scarecrows, looking for shelter, and made the very air dismal with the reiteration, "*No' ouanga* (we are bewitched), *Bras-Coupé fe moi des grigis* (the voudou's spells are on me)." The ripple of song was hushed and the flowers fell upon the floor.

"I have heard an English maxim," wrote Colonel De Grapion to his kinsman, "which I would recommend you to put into practice—'Fight the devil with fire.' "

No, he would not recognize devils as belligerents.

But if Rome commissioned exorcists, could not he employ one?

No, he would not! If his hounds could not catch Bras-Coupé, why, let him go. The overseer tried the hounds once more and came home with the best one across his saddle-bow, an arrow run half through its side.

Once the blacks attempted by certain familiar rum-pourings and nocturnal charm-singing to lift the curse; but the moment the master heard the wild monotone of their infernal worship, he stopped it with a word.

Early in February came the spring, and with it some resurrection of hope and courage. It may have been—it certainly was, in part—because young Honoré Grandissime[22] had returned. He was like the sun's warmth wherever he went; and the other Honoré was like his shadow. The fairer one quickly saw the meaning of these things, hastened to cheer the young don with hopes of a better future, and to effect, if he could, the restoration of Bras-Coupé to his master's favor. But this latter effort was an idle one. He had long sittings with his uncle Agricola to the same end, but they always ended fruitless and often angrily.

His dark half-brother had seen Palmyre and loved her. Honoré would gladly have solved one or two riddles by effecting their honorable union in marriage. The previous ceremony on the Grandissime back piazza need be no impediment; all slave-owners understood those things. Following Honoré's advice, the f. m. c., who had come into possession of his paternal portion, sent to Cannes Brulées a written offer, to buy Palmyre at any price that her master might name, stating his intention to free her and make her his wife.

[22] Honoré Grandissime. In the novel there are two Honoré Grandissimes. One is the legitimate white son of Numa de Grandissime; the other, his half-brother, is illegitimate, a free man of color. The halfbrother falls in love with Palmyre.

Colonel De Grapion could hardly hope to settle Palmyre's fate more satisfactorily, yet he could not forego an opportunity to indulge his pride
by following up the threat he had hung over Agricola to kill whosoever should give Palmyre to a black man. He referred the subject and the
wouldbe purchaser to him. It would open up to the old braggart a line of
retreat, thought the planter of the Cannes Brulées.

But the idea of retreat had left Citizen Fusilier.

"She is already married," said he to M. Honoré Grandissime, f. m. c.
"She is the lawful wife of Bras-Coupé; and what God has joined together
let no man put asunder. You know it, sirrah. You did this for impudence,
to make a show of your wealth. You intended it as an insinuation of equal-
ity. I overlook the impertinence for the sake of the man whose white blood
you carry; but h-mark you, if ever you bring your Parisian airs and self-
sufficient face on a level with mine again, h-I will slap it."

The quadroon, three nights after, was so indiscreet as to give him the
opportunity, and he did it—at that quadroon ball, to which Dr. Keene[23]
alluded in talking to Frowenfeld.

But Don José, we say, plucked up new spirit.

"Last year's disasters were but fortune's freaks," he said, "See others'
crops have failed all about us."

The overseer shook his head.

"*C'est ce maudit cocodri' là bas* (It is that accursed alligator, Bras-
Coupé, down yonder in the swamp)."

And by and by the master was again smitten with the same belief. He
and his neighbors put in their crops afresh. The spring waned, summer
passed, the fevers returned, the year wore round, but no harvest smiled.
"Alas!" cried the planters, "we are all poor men!" The worst among the
worst were the fields of Bras-Coupé's master—parched and shrivelled. "He
does not understand planting," said the neighbors; "neither does his overseer. Maybe, too, it is true as he says, that he is voudoued."

One day at high noon the master was taken sick with fever.

The third noon after—the sad wife sitting by the bedside—suddenly,
right in the centre of the room, with the open door behind him, stood the
magnificent, half-nude form of Bras-Coupé. He did not fall down as the mistress's eyes met his, though all his flesh quivered. The master was lying with
his eyes closed. The fever had done a fearful three days' work.

"*Mioko-koanga oulé so' femme* (Bras-Coupé wants his wife)."

The master started wildly and stared upon his slave.

[23] Dr. Keene. A character in the novel; he plays no part in "The Story of Bras-Coupe."

"*Bras-Coupé oulé so' femme!*" repeated the black.

"Seize him!" cried the sick man, trying to rise.

But, though several servants had ventured in with frightened faces, none dared molest the giant. The master turned his entreating eyes upon his wife, but she seemed stunned, and only covered her face with her hands and sat as if paralyzed by a foreknowledge of what was coming.

Bras-Coupé lifted his great, black palm and commenced:

"*Mo cé voudrai que la maison ci là et tout ça qui pas femme' ici s'raient encore maudits!* (May this house and all in it who are not women be accursed)."

The master fell back upon his pillow with a groan of helpless wrath.

The African pointed his finger through the open window.

"May its fields not know the plough nor nourish the cattle that overrun it."

The domestics, who had thus far stood their ground, suddenly rushed from the room like stampeded cattle, and at that moment appeared Palmyre.

"Speak to him," faintly cried the panting invalid.

She went firmly up to her husband and lifted her hand. With an easy motion, but quick as lightning, as a lion sets foot on a dog, he caught her by the arm.

"*Bras-Coupé oulé so' femme,*" he said, and just then Palmyre would have gone with him to the equator.

"You shall not have her!" gasped the master.

The African seemed to rise in height, and still holding his wife at arm's length, resumed his malediction:

"May weeds cover the ground until the air is full of their odor and the wild beasts of the forest come and lie down under their cover."

With a frantic effort the master lifted himself upon his elbow and extended his clenched fist in speechless defiance; but his brain reeled, his sight went out, and when again he saw, Palmyre and her mistress were bending over him, the overseer stood awkwardly by, and Bras-Coupé was gone.

The plantation became an invalid camp. The words of the voudou found fulfilment on every side. The plough went not out; the herds wandered through broken hedges from field to field and came up with staring bones and shrunken sides; a frenzied mob of weeds and thorns wrestled and throttled each other in a struggle for standing-room—rag-weed, smart-weed, sneeze-weed, bind-weed, iron-weed—until the burning skies of mid-summer checked their growth and crowned their unshorn tops with rank and dingy flowers.

"Why in the name of—St. Francis," asked the priest of the overseer, "didn't the señora use her power over the black scoundrel when he stood and cursed, that day?"

"Why, to tell you the truth, father," said the overseer, in a discreet whisper, "I can only suppose she thought Bras-Coupé had half a right to do it."

"Ah, ah, I see; like her brother Honoré—looks at both sides of a question—a miserable practice; but why couldn't Palmyre use *her* eyes? They would have stopped him."

"Palmyre? Why Palmyre has become the best *mon ture* (Plutonian[24] medium) in the parish. Agricola Fusilier himself is afraid of her. Sir, I think sometimes Bras-Coupé is dead and his spirit has gone into Palmyre. She would rather add to his curse than take from it."

"Ah!" said the jovial divine, with a fat smile, "castigation would help her case; the whip is a great sanctifier. I fancy it would even make a Christian of the inexpugnable Bras-Coupé."

But Bras-Coupé kept beyond the reach alike of the lash and of the Latin Bible.

By and by came a man with a rumor, whom the overseer brought to the master's sick-room, to tell that an enterprising Frenchman was attempting to produce a new staple in Louisiana, one that worms would not annihilate. It was that year of history when the despairing planters saw ruin hovering so close over them that they cried to heaven for succor. Providence raised up Etienne de Boré. "And if Etienne is successful," cried the newsbearer, "and gets the juice of the sugar-cane to crystallize, so shall all of us, after him, and shall yet save our lands and homes. Oh, Señor, it will make you strong again to see these fields all cane and the long rows of negroes and negresses cutting it, while they sing their song of those droll African numerals, counting the canes they cut," and the bearer of good tidings sang them for very joy:

> Anoqué, Anobia, Biatailla, Quereque, Nalleoua,
> Aumondé, Autapoté, Aupatoté, Auquéréqué, Bo

"And Honoré Grandissime is going to introduce it on his lands," said Don José.

"That is true," said Agricola Fusilier, coming in. Honoré, the inde-

---

[24] Plutonian. Satanic. Pluto was the Greek god of the underworld.

fatigable peace-maker, had brought his uncle and his brother-in-law for the moment not only to speaking but to friendly terms.

The señor smiled.

"I have some good tidings, too," he said; "my beloved lady has borne me a son."

"Another scion of the house of Grand—I mean Martinez!" exclaimed Agricola. "And now, Don José, let me say that *I* have an item of rare intelligence!"

The don lifted his feeble head and opened his inquiring eyes with a sudden, savage light in them.

"No," said Agricola, "he is not exactly taken yet, but they are on his track."

"Who?"

"The police. We may say he is virtually in our grasp."

It was on a Sabbath afternoon that a band of Choctaws having just played a game of racquette behind the city and a similar game being about to end between the white champions of two rival faubourgs, the beating of tom-toms, rattling of mules' jaw-bones and sounding of wooden horns drew the populace across the fields to a spot whose present name of Congo Square still preserves a reminder of its old barbaric pastimes. On a grassy plain under the ramparts, the performers of these hideous discords sat upon the ground facing each other, and in their midst the dancers danced. They gyrated in couples, a few at a time, throwing their bodies into the most startling attitudes and the wildest contortions, while the whole company of black lookers-on, incited by the tones of the weird music and the violent posturing of the dancers, swayed and writhed in passionate sympathy, beating their breasts, palms and thighs in time with the bones and drums, and at frequent intervals lifting, in that wild African unison no more to be described than forgotten, the unutterable songs of the Babouille and Counjaille dances, with their ejaculatory burdens of *"Aie! Aie! Voudou Magnan!"* and *"Aie Calinda! Dancé Calinda!"* The volume of sound rose and fell with the augmentation or diminution of the dancers' extravagances. Now a fresh man, young and supple, bounding into the ring, revived the flagging rattlers, drummers and trumpeters; now a wearied dancer, finding his strength going, gathered all his force at the cry of *"Dancé zisqu'a mort!"*[25] rallied to grand finale and with one magnificent antic, fell, foaming at the mouth.

The amusement had reached its height. Many participants had been

[25] *"Dance zisqu'a mort!"* Danser jusqu'au mort. That is, Dance until you die.

lugged out by the neck to avoid being danced on, and the enthusiasm had
risen to a frenzy, when there bounded into the ring the blackest of black
men, an athlete of superb figure, in breeches of "Indienne"—the stuff used
for slave women's best dresses—jingling with bells, his feet in moccasins,
his tight, crisp hair decked out with feathers, a necklace of alligator's teeth
rattling on his breast and a living serpent twined about his neck.

It chanced that but one couple was dancing. Whether they had been
sent there by advice of Agricola is not certain. Snatching a tambourine
from a bystander as he entered, the stranger thrust the male dancer aside,
faced the woman and began a series of saturnalian antics, compared with
which all that had gone before was tame and sluggish; and as he finally leaped, with tinkling heels, clean over his bewildered partner's head,
the multitude howled with rapture.

Ill-starred Bras-Coupé. He was in that extra-hazardous and irresponsible condition of mind and body known in the undignified present as
"drunk again."

By the strangest fortune, if not, as we have just hinted, by some design, the man whom he had once deposited in the willow bushes, and the
woman Clemence, were the very two dancers, and no other, whom he had
interrupted. The man first stupidly regarded, next admiringly gazed upon,
and then distinctly recognized, his whilom driver. Five minutes later the
Spanish police were putting their heads together to devise a quick and
permanent capture; and in the midst of the sixth minute, as the wonderful
fellow was rising in a yet more astounding leap than his last, a lasso fell
about his neck and brought him, crashing like a burnt tree, face upward upon the turf.

"The runaway slave," said the old French code, continued in force by
the Spaniards, "the runaway slave who shall continue to be so for one
month from the day of his being denounced to the officers of justice, shall
have his ears cut off and shall be branded with the flower de luce on the
shoulder; and on a second offence of the same nature, persisted in during
one month of his being denounced, he shall be hamstrung, and be marked
with the flower de luce on the other shoulder. On the third offence he shall
die." Bras-Coupé had run away only twice. "But," said Agricola, "these
'bossals' must be taught their place. Besides, there is Article 27 of the same
code: 'The slave who, having struck his master, shall have produced a
bruise, shall suffer capital punishment'—a very necessary law!" He concluded with a scowl upon Palmyre, who shot back a glance which he never
forgot.

The Spaniard showed himself very merciful—for a Spaniard; he spared the captive's life. He might have been more merciful still; but Honoré Grandissime said some indignant things in the African's favor, and as much to teach the Grandissimes a lesson as to punish the runaway, he would have repented his clemency, as he repented the momentary truce with Agricola, but for the tearful pleading of the señora and the hot, dry eyes of her maid. Because of these he overlooked the offence against his person and estate, and delivered Bras-Coupé to the law to suffer only the penalties of the crime he had committed against society by attempting to be a free man.

We repeat it for the credit of Palmyre, that she pleaded for Bras-Coupé. But what it cost her to make that intercession, knowing that his death would leave her free, and that if he lived she must be his wife, let us not attempt to say.

In the midst of the ancient town, in a part which is now crumbling away, stood the Calaboza,[26] with its humid vaults, grated cells, iron cages and its whips; and there, soon enough, they strapped Bras-Coupé face downward and laid on the lash. And yet not a sound came from the mutilated but unconquered African to annoy the ear of the sleeping city.

("And you suffered this thing to take place?" asked Joseph Frowenfeld of Honoré Grandissime.

"My-de'-seh!" exclaimed the Creole, "they lied to me—said they would not harm him!")

He was brought at sunrise to the plantation. The air was sweet with the smell of the weed-grown fields. The long-horned oxen that drew him and the naked boy that drove the team stopped before his cabin.

"You cannot put that creature in there," said the thoughtful overseer. "He would suffocate under a roof—he has been too long out-of-doors for that. Put him on my cottage porch." There, at last, Palmyre burst into tears and sank down, while before her on a soft bed of dry grass, rested the helpless form of the captive giant, a cloth thrown over his galled back, his ears shorn from his head, and the tendons behind his knees severed. His eyes were dry, but there was in them that unspeakable despair that fills the eye of the charger when, fallen in battle, he gazes with sidewise-bended neck upon the ruin wrought upon him. His eye turned sometimes slowly to his wife. He need not demand her now—she was always by him.

There was much talk over him—much idle talk; no power or circumstance has ever been found that will keep a Creole from talking. He merely lay still under it with a fixed frown; but once some incautious tongue drop-

[26] Calaboza. The jail (the American "calaboose").

ped the name of Agricola. The black man's eyes came so quickly round to
Palmyre that she thought he would speak; but no; his words were all in his
eyes. She answered their gleam with a fierce affirmative glance, whereupon
he slowly bent his head and spat upon the floor.

There was yet one more trial of his wild nature. The mandate came
from his master's sick-bed that he must lift the curse.

Bras-Coupé merely smiled. God keep thy enemy from such a smile!

The overseer, with a policy less Spanish than his master's, endeavored
to use persuasion. But the fallen prince would not so much as turn
one glance from his parted hamstrings. Palmyre was then besought to inter-
cede. She made one poor attempt, but her husband was nearer doing her an
unkindness than ever he had been before; he made a slow sign for silence
—with his fist; and every mouth was stopped.

At midnight following, there came, on the breeze that blew from the
mansion, a sound of running here and there, of wailing and sobbing—
another Bridegroom[27] was coming, and the Spaniard, with much such
a lamp in hand as most of us shall be found with, neither burning brightly
nor wholly gone out, went forth to meet Him.

"Bras-Coupé," said Palmyre, next evening, speaking low in his mangled
ear, "the master is dead; he is just buried. As he was dying, Bras-Coupé,
he asked that you would forgive him."

The maimed man looked steadfastly at his wife. He had not spoken
since the lash struck him, and he spoke not now; but in those large, clear
eyes, where his remaining strength seemed to have taken refuge as in
a citadel, the old fierceness flared up for a moment, and then, like an expir-
ing beacon, went out.

"Is your mistress well enough by this time to venture here?" whispered
the overseer to Palmyre. "Let her come. Tell her not to fear, but to bring
the babe—in her own arms, tell her—quickly!"

The lady came, her infant boy in her arms, knelt down beside the bed
of sweet grass and set the child within the hollow of the African's arm. Bras-
Coupé turned his gaze upon it; it smiled, its mother's smile, and put its hand
upon the runaway's face, and the first tears of Bras-Coupé's life, the dying testimony of his humanity, gushed from his eyes and rolled down his
cheek upon the infant's hand. He laid his own tenderly upon the babe's forehead, then removing it, waved it abroad, inaudibly moved his lips, dropped
his arm, and closed his eyes. The curse was lifted.

---

[27] Bridegroom. Christ.

"Le pauv' dgiab'!"[28] said the overseer, wiping his eyes and looking fieldward. "Palmyre, you must get the priest."

The priest came, in the identical gown in which he had appeared the night of the two weddings. To the good father's many tender questions Bras-Coupé turned a failing eye that gave no answers; until, at length:

"Do you know where you are going?" asked the holy man.

"Yes," answered his eyes, brightening.

"Where?"

He did not reply; he was lost in contemplation, and seemed looking far away.

So the question was repeated.

"Do you know where you are going?"

And again the answer of the eyes. He knew.

"Where?"

The overseer at the edge of the porch, the widow with her babe, and Palmyre and the priest bending over the dying bed, turned an eager ear to catch the answer.

"To—" the voice failed a moment; the departing hero essayed again; again it failed; he tried once more, lifted his hand, and with an ecstatic, upward smile, whispered, "To—Africa"—and was gone.

STUDY QUESTIONS:

1. Most of the Louisiana French dialect used in the story is translated, but some of it is not. Perhaps the reader can puzzle out the meaning. Even if it is not entirely intelligible, what does this add to the power of the tale?

2. By what devices does Cable make the reader aware of Bras-Coupé's continuing interpretation of events in terms of his primitive native culture?

3. Is the motivation of Palmyre both consistent and credible? In what ways?

4. What do you think of the handling of Don José Martinez? What does he add to the story?

5. Consider the ending - the baby on the breast of the fallen giant, the "ecstatic upward smile," the whispered phrase, "To Africa". Does this picture represent a true reconciliating of opposing passions, or is it merely a way to finish the story?

---

[28] *"Le pauv' dgiab'!"* Le pauvre diable. That is: Poor devil!

FLIGHT

JOHN STEINBECK

Few American authors in recent years have had more readers than John Steinbeck (1902–   ). Particularly popular have been his novels *Of Mice and Men* (1937), *The Grapes of Wrath* (1939), *Cannery Row* (1944), and *East of Eden,* (1952). A number of his stories have been made into successful motion pictures. "Flight" is taken from a collection of short stories titled *The Long Valley* (1938), and many young readers are familiar with "The Red Pony," one of the best animal stories of recent years.

Nearly all of Steinbeck's work deals with the geographical area he knows and likes best, the country of the High Sierras in California. He has spent most of his life there, and most of what he writes deals with the Salinas Valley and Monterey. Always in his stories, and particularly in stories like "Flight" and "The Red Pony" the natural detail is vividly and thoroughly presented. The reader realizes that the author knows the scene of which he writes and knows it with maximum accuracy.

Steinbeck has been interested also in the plight of the migratory workers in California. Because of the seasonal nature of their work and their forced movement from place to place, he sees them as an especially exploited people, and in two novels, *In Dubious Battle* (1936) and *The Grapes of*

Wrath he presented their plight with sympathy and power. The characters of the latter novel are people who had come into California from the eroded lands of the dust bowl, hoping for new opportunity in what they envisioned as a land of milk and honey, but finding only poverty, filth and cruelly low wages.

In "Flight" Steinbeck experiments with one of the most difficult of all writing problems: how to write a story with a single character. True, the reader meets the other members of Pepé's family in the first section of the tale, but the part of the story designed to provide the chief interest, as its title suggests, is Pepé's lone flight into the forest. The reader never knows specifically from whom the boy is fleeing (probably relatives or friends of the murdered man), but this is not really important. Neither does the reader see any great fear in the boy. What we get instead is the picture of a man reduced to an animal. Each of the incidents reduces his humanity so that he is as much at home in the forest as the mountain lions and the hawks. Each of the incidents takes one of the trappings of civilization away from him so that finally he is left as defenseless as a creature of the forest. It is then that the hunt can be completed, and his hunter moves in for the kill.

Through all of this, though we have only Pepé before our eyes, our interest is never diminished. Nature itself provides a large amount of the excitement, and this is made possible by Steinbeck's exactness of detail. The author has taken a difficult subject and succeeded.

About fifteen miles below Monterey, on the wild coast, the Torres family had their farm, a few sloping acres above a cliff that dropped to the brown reefs and to the hissing white waters of the ocean. Behind the farm the stone mountains stood up against the sky. The farm buildings huddled like little clinging aphids on the mountain skirts, crouched low to the ground as though the wind might blow them into the sea. The little shack, the rattling, rotting barn were grey-bitten with sea salt, beaten by the damp wind until they had taken on the color of the granite hills. Two horses, a red cow and a red calf, half a dozen pigs and a flock of lean, multi-colored chickens stocked the place. A little corn was raised on the sterile slope, and it grew short and thick under the wind, and all the cobs formed on the landward sides of the stalks.

Mama Torres, a lean, dry woman with ancient eyes, had ruled the farm for ten years, ever since her husband tripped over a stone in the field one day and fell full length on a rattlesnake. When one is bitten on the chest there is not much that can be done.

Mama Torres had three children, two undersized black ones of twelve and fourteen, Emilio and Rosy, whom Mama kept fishing on the rocks below the farm when the sea was kind and when the truant officer was in some distant part of Monterey County. And there was Pepé, the tall smiling son of nineteen, a gentle, affectionate boy, but very lazy. Pepé had a tall head, pointed at the top, and from its peak, coarse black hair grew down like a thatch all around. Over his smiling little eyes Mama cut a straight bang so he could see. Pepé had sharp Indian cheek bones and an eagle nose, but his mouth was as sweet and shapely as a girl's mouth, and his chin was fragile and chiseled. He was loose and gangling, all legs and feet and wrists, and he was very lazy. Mama thought him fine and brave, but she never told him so. She said, "Some lazy cow must have got into thy father's family, else how could I have a son like thee." And she said, "When I carried thee, a sneaking lazy coyote came out of the brush and looked at me one day. That must have made thee so."

Pepé smiled sheepishly and stabbed at the ground with his knife to keep the blade sharp and free from rust. It was his inheritance, that knife, his father's knife. The long heavy blade folded back into the black handle. There was a button on the handle. When Pepé pressed the button, the blade leaped out ready for use. The knife was with Pepé always, for it had been his father's knife.

One sunny morning when the sea below the cliff was glinting and blue and the white surf creamed on the reef, when even the stone mountains looked kindly, Mama Torres called out the door of the shack, "Pepé, I have a labor for thee."

There was no answer. Mama listened. From behind the barn she heard a burst of laughter. She lifted her full long skirt and walked in the direction of the noise.

Pepé was sitting on the ground with his back against a box. His white teeth glistened. On either side of him stood the two black ones, tense and expectant. Fifteen feet away a redwood post was set in the ground. Pepé's right hand lay limply in his lap, and in the palm the big black knife rested. The blade was closed back into the handle. Pepé looked smiling at the sky.

Suddenly Emilio cried, "Ya!"

Pepe's wrist flicked like the head of a snake. The blade seemed to fly open in mid-air, and with a thump the point dug into the redwood post, and the black handle quivered. The three burst into excited laughter. Rosy ran to the post and pulled out the knife and brought it back to Pepé. He closed the blade and settled the knife carefully in his listless palm again. He grinned self-consciously at the sky.

"Ya!"

The heavy knife lanced out and sunk into the post again. Mama moved forward like a ship and scattered the play.

"All day you do foolish things with the knife, like a toy baby," she stormed. "Get up on thy huge feet that eat up shoes. Get up!" She took him by one loose shoulder and hoisted at him. Pepé grinned sheepishly and came half-heartedly to his feet. "Look!" Mama cried. "Big lazy, you must catch the horse and put on him thy father's saddle. You must ride to Monterey. The medicine bottle is empty. There is no salt. Go thou now, Peanut! Catch the horse."

A revolution took place in the relaxed figure of Pepé. "To Monterey, me? Alone? *Sí*, Mama."

She scowled at him. "Do not think, big sheep, that you will buy candy. No, I will give you only enough for the medicine and the salt."

Pepé smiled. "Mama, you will put the hatband on the hat?"

She relented then. "Yes, Pepé. You may wear the hatband."

His voice grew insinuating, "And the green handkerchief, Mama?"

"Yes, if you go quickly and return with no trouble, the silk green handkerchief will go. If you make sure to take off the handkerchief when you eat so no spot may fall on it. . . ."

"*Sí*, Mama. I will be careful. I am a man."

"Thou? A man? Thou art a peanut."

He went into the rickety barn and brought out a rope, and he walked agilely enough up the hill to catch the horse.

When he was ready and mounted before the door, mounted on his father's saddle that was so old that the oaken frame showed through torn leather in many places, then Mama brought out the round black hat with the tooled leather band, and she reached up and knotted the green silk handkerchief about his neck. Pepé's blue denim coat was much darker than his jeans, for it had been washed much less often.

Mama handed up the big medicine bottle and the silver coins. "That for the medicine," she said, "and that for the salt. That for a candle to burn for the papa. That for *dulces*[1] for the little ones. Our friend Mrs. Rodriguez will give you dinner and maybe a bed for the night. When you go to the church say only ten Pater-nosters and only twenty-five Ave Marias. Oh! I know, big coyote. You would sit there flapping your mouth over Aves all day while you looked at the candles and the holy pictures. That is not good devotion to stare at the pretty things."

---

[1] *Dulces.* Sweets.

The black hat, covering the high pointed head and black thatched hair of Pepé, gave him dignity and age. He sat the rangy horse well. Mama thought how handsome he was, dark and lean and tall. "I would not send thee now alone, thou little one, except for the medicine," she said softly. "It is not good to have no medicine, for who knows when the toothache will come, or the sadness of the stomach. These things are."

"*Adios*, Mama," Pepé cried. "I will come back soon. You may send me often alone. I am a man."

"Thou art a foolish chicken."

He straightened his shoulders, flipped the reins against the horse's shoulder and rode away. He turned once and saw that they still watched him, Emilio and Rosy and Mama. Pepé grinned with pride and gladness and lifted the tough buckskin horse to a trot.

When he had dropped out of sight over a little dip in the road, Mama turned to the black ones, but she spoke to herself. "He is nearly a man now," she said. "It will be a nice thing to have a man in the house again." Her eyes sharpened on the children. "Go to the rocks now. The tide is going out. There will be abalones to be found." She put the iron hooks into their hands and saw them down the steep trail to the reefs. She brought the smooth stone *metate*[2] to the doorway and sat grinding her corn to flour and looking occasionally at the road over which Pepé had gone. The noon-day came and then the afternoon, when the little ones beat the abalones on a rock to make them tender and Mama patted the tortillas to make them thin. They ate their dinner as the red sun was plunging down toward the ocean. They sat on the doorsteps and watched the big white moon come over the mountain tops.

Mama said, "He is now at the house of our friend, Mrs. Rodriguez. She will give him nice things to eat and maybe a present."

Emilio said, "Some day I too will ride to Monterey for medicine. Did Pepé come to be a man today?"

Mama said wisely, "A boy gets to be a man when a man is needed. Remember this thing. I have known boys forty years old because there was no need for a man."

Soon afterwards they retired. Mama in her big oak bed on one side of the room, Emilio and Rosy in their boxes full of straw and sheepskins on the other side of the room.

The moon went over the sky and the surf roared on the rocks. The

[2] *Metate.* A hollowed stone in which the Indians ground corn into flour.

roosters crowed the first call. The surf subsided to a whispering surge against the reef. The moon dropped toward the sea. The roosters crowed again.

The moon was near down to the water when Pepé rode on a winded horse to his home flat. His dog bounced out and circled the horse yelping the pleasure. Pepé slid off the saddle to the ground. The weathered little shack was silver in the moonlight and the square shadow of it was black to the north and east. Against the east the piling mountains were misty with light; their tops melted into the sky.

Pepé walked wearily up the three steps and into the house. It was dark inside. There was a rustle in the corner.

Mama cried out from her bed. "Who comes? Pepé, is it thou?"

"*Sí*, Mama."

"Did you get the medicine?"

"*Sí*, Mama."

"Well, go to sleep, then. I thought you would be sleeping at the house of Mrs. Rodriguez." Pepé stood silently in the dark room. "Why do you stand there, Pepé? Did you drink wine?"

"*Sí*, Mama."

"Well, go to bed then and sleep out the wine."

His voice was tired and patient, but very firm. "Light the candle, Mama. I must go away into the mountains.

"What is this, Pepé? You are crazy." Mama struck a sulphur match and held the little blue burr until the flame spread up the stick. She set light to the candle on the floor beside her bed. "Now, Pepé, what is this you say?" She looked anxiously into his face.

He was changed. The fragile quality seemed to have gone from his chin. His mouth was less full than it had been, the lines of the lips were straighter, but in his eyes the greatest change had taken place. There was no laughter in them any more, nor any bashfulness. They were sharp and bright and purposeful.

He told her in a tired monotone, told her everything just as it had happened. A few people came into the kitchen of Mrs. Rodriguez. There was wine to drink. Pepé drank wine. The little quarrel—the man started toward Pepé and then the knife—it went almost by itself. It flew, it darted before Pepé knew it. As he talked, Mama's face grew stern, and it seemed to grow more lean. Pepé finished. "I am a man now, Mama. The man said names to me I could not allow."

Mama nodded. "Yes, thou art a man, my poor little Pepé. Thou art a

man. I have seen it coming on thee. I have watched you throwing the knife
into the post, and I have been afraid." For a moment her face had softened,
but now it grew stern again. "Come! We must get you ready. Go. Awaken
Emilio and Rosy. Go quickly."

Pepé stepped over to the corner where his brother and sister slept among
the sheepskins. He leaned down and shook them gently. "Come, Rosy!
Come, Emilio! The mama says you must arise."

The little black ones sat up and rubbed their eyes in the candlelight.
Mama was out of bed now, her long black skirt over her nightgown.
"Emilio," she cried. "Go up and catch the other horse for Pepé. Quickly,
now! Quickly." Emilio put his legs in his overalls and stumbled sleepily out
the door.

"You heard no one behind you on the road?" Mama demanded.

"No, Mama. I listened carefully. No one was on the road."

Mama darted like a bird about the room. From a nail on the wall she
took a canvas water bag and threw it on the floor. She stripped a blanket
from her bed and rolled it into a tight tube and tied the ends with string.
From a box beside the stove she lifted a flour sack half full of black stringy
jerky. "Your father's black coat, Pepé. Here, put it on."

Pepé stood in the middle of the floor watching her activity. She reached
behind the door and brought out the rifle, a long 38–56, worn shiny the
whole length of the barrel. Pepé took it from her and held it in the crook
of his elbow. Mama brought a little leather bag and counted the cartridges
into his hand. "Only ten left," she warned. "You must not waste them."

Emilio put his head in the door. " '*Qui'st 'l caballo*, Mama."[3]

"Put on the saddle from the other horse. Tie on the blanket. Here, tie
the jerky to the saddle horn."

Still Pepé stood silently watching his mother's frantic activity. His chin
looked hard, and his sweet mouth was drawn and thin. His little eyes followed Mama about the room almost suspiciously.

Rosy asked softly, "Where goes Pepé?"

Mama's eyes were fierce. "Pepé goes on a journey. Pepé is a man now.
He has a man's thing to do."

Pepé straightened his shoulders. His mouth changed until he looked
very much like Mama.

At last the preparation was finished. The loaded horse stood outside
the door. The water bag dripped a line of moisture down the bay shoulder.

[3] "*Qui'st 'l caballo*, Mama" Aqui esta el caballo. Mama (Here's the horse, mama).

The moonlight was being thinned by the dawn and the big white moon was near down to the sea. The family stood by the shack. Mama confronted Pepé. "Look, my son! Do not stop until it is dark again. Do not sleep even though you are tired. Take care of the horse in order that he may not stop of weariness. Remember to be careful with the bullets—there are only ten. Do not fill thy stomach with jerky[4] or it will make thee sick. Eat a little jerky and fill thy stomach with grass. When thou comest to the high mountains, if thou seest any of the dark watching men, go not near to them nor try to speak to them. And forget not thy prayers." She put her lean hands on Pepé's shoulders, stood on her toes and kissed him formally on both cheeks, and Pepé kissed her on both cheeks. Then he went to Emilio and Rosy and kissed both of their cheeks.

Pepé turned back to Mama. He seemed to look for a little softness, a little weakness in her. His eyes were searching, but Mama's face remained fierce. "Go now," she said. "Do not wait to be caught like a chicken."

Pepé pulled himself into the saddle. "I am a man," he said.

It was the first dawn when he rode up the hill toward the little canyon which let a trail into the mountains. Moonlight and daylight fought with each other, and the two warring qualities made it difficult to see. Before Pepé had gone a hundred yards, the outlines of his figure were misty; and long before he entered the canyon, he had become a grey, indefinite shadow.

Mama stood stiffly in front of her doorstep, and on either side of her stood Emilio and Rosy. They cast furtive glances at Mama now and then.

When the grey shape of Pepé melted into the hillside and disappeared, Mama relaxed. She began the high, whining keen of the death wail. "Our beautiful—our brave," she cried. "Our protector, our son is gone." Emilio and Rosy moaned beside her. "Our beautiful—our brave, he is gone." It was the formal wail. It rose to a high piercing whine and subsided to a moan. Mama raised it three times and then she turned and went into the house and shut the door.

Emilio and Rosy stood wondering in the dawn. They heard Mama whimpering in the house. They went out to sit on the cliff above the ocean. They touched shoulders. "When did Pepé come to be a man?" Emilio asked.

"Last night," said Rosy. "Last night in Monterey." The ocean clouds turned red with the sun that was behind the mountains.

"We will have no breakfast," said Emilio. "Mama will not want to cook." Rosy did not answer him. "Where is Pepé gone?" he asked.

---

[4] Jerky. Strips of dried meat.

Rosy looked around at him. She drew her knowledge from the quiet air. "He has gone on a journey. He will never come back."

"Is he dead? Do you think he is dead?"

Rosy looked back at the ocean again. A little steamer, drawing a line of smoke, sat on the edge of the horizon. "He is not dead," Rosy explained. "Not yet."

Pepé rested the big rifle across the saddle in front of him. He let the horse walk up the hill and he didn't look back. The stony slope took on a coat of short brush so that Pepé found the entrance to a trail and entered it.

When he came to the canyon opening, he swung once in his saddle and looked back, but the houses were swallowed in the misty light. Pepé jerked forward again. The high shoulder of the canyon closed in on him. His horse stretched out its neck and sighed and settled to the trail.

It was a well-worn path, dark soft leaf-mould earth strewn with broken pieces of sandstone. The trail rounded the shoulder of the canyon and dropped steeply into the bed of the stream. In the shallows the water ran smoothly, glinting in the first morning sun. Small round stones on the bottom were as brown as rust with sun moss. In the sand along the edges of the stream the tall, rich wild mint grew, while in the water itself the cress, old and tough, had gone to heavy seed.

The path went into the stream and emerged on the other side. The horse sloshed into the water and stopped. Pepé dropped his bridle and let the beast drink of the running water.

Soon the canyon sides became steep and the first giant sentinel redwoods guarded the trail, great round red trunks bearing foliage as green and lacy as ferns. Once Pepé was among the trees, the sun was lost. A perfumed and purple light lay in the pale green of the underbrush. Gooseberry bushes and blackberries and tall ferns lined the stream, and overhead the branches of the redwoods met and cut off the sky.

Pepé drank from the water bag, and he reached into the flour sack and brought out a black string of jerky. His white teeth gnawed at the string until the tough meat parted. He chewed slowly and drank occasionally from the water bag. His little eyes were slumberous and tired, but the muscles of his face were hard set. The earth of the trail was black now. It gave up a hollow sound under the walking hoofbeats.

The stream fell more sharply. Little waterfalls splashed on the stones. Five-fingered ferns hung over the water and dripped spray from their fingertips. Pepé rode half over in his saddle, dangling one leg loosely. He picked a bay leaf from a tree beside the way and put it into his mouth for a moment to flavor the dry jerky. He held the gun loosely across the pommel.

Suddenly he squared in his saddle, swung the horse from the trail and kicked it hurriedly up behind a big redwood tree. He pulled up the reins tight against the bit to keep the horse from whinnying. His face was intent and his nostrils quivered a little.

A hollow pounding came down the trail, and a horseman rode by, a fat man with red cheeks and a white stubble beard. His horse put down its head and blubbered at the trail when it came to the place where Pepé had turned off. "Hold up!" said the man and he pulled up his horse's head.

When the last sound of the hoofs died away, Pepé came back into the trail again. He did not relax in the saddle any more. He lifted the big rifle and swung the lever to throw a shell into the chamber, and then he let down the hammer to half cock.

The trail grew very steep. Now the redwood trees were smaller and their tops were dead, bitten dead where the wind reached them. The horse plodded on; the sun went slowly overhead and started down toward the afternoon.

Where the stream came out of a side canyon, the trail left it. Pepé dismounted and watered his horse and filled up his water bag. As soon as the trail had parted from the stream, the trees were gone and only the thick brittle sage and manzanita and chaparral edged the trail. And the soft black earth was gone, too, leaving only the light tan broken rock for the trail bed. Lizards scampered away into the brush as the horse rattled over the little stones.

Pepé turned in his saddle and looked back. He was in the open now: he could be seen from a distance. As he ascended the trail the country grew more rough and terrible and dry. The way wound about the bases of great square rocks. Little grey rabbits skittered in the brush. A bird made a monotonous high creaking. Eastward the bare rock mountaintops were pale and powder-dry under the dropping sun. The horse plodded up and up the trail toward a little V in the ridge which was the pass.

Pepé looked suspiciously back every minute or so, and his eyes sought the tops of the ridges ahead. Once, on a white barren spur, he saw a black figure for a moment, but he looked quickly away, for it was one of the dark watchers. No one knew who the watchers were, nor where they lived, but it was better to ignore them and never to show interest in them. They did not bother one who stayed on the trail and minded his own business.

The air was parched and full of light dust blown by the breeze from the eroding mountains. Pepé drank sparingly from his bag and corked it tightly and hung it on the horn again. The trail moved up the dry shale hillside, avoiding rocks, dropping under clefts, climbing in and out of old water scars. When he arrived at the little pass he stopped and looked back for a long time. No dark watchers were to be seen now. The trail behind was empty. Only the high tops of the redwoods indicated where the stream flowed.

Pepé rode on through the pass. His little eyes were nearly closed with weariness, but his face was stern, relentless and manly. The high mountain wind coasted sighing through the pass and whistled on the edges of the big blocks of broken granite. In the air, a red-tailed hawk sailed over close to the ridge and screamed angrily. Pepé went slowly through the broken jagged pass and looked down on the other side.

The trail dropped quickly, staggering among broken rock. At the bottom of the slope there was a dark crease, thick with brush, and on the other side of the crease a little flat, in which a grove of oak trees grew. A scar of green grass cut across the flat. And behind the flat another mountain rose, desolate with dead rocks and starving little black bushes. Pepé drank from the bag again for the air was so dry that it encrusted his nostrils and burned his lips. He put the horse down the trail. The hooves slipped and struggled on the steep way, starting little stones that rolled off into the brush. The sun was gone behind the westward mountain now, but still it glowed brilliantly on the oaks and on the grassy flat. The rocks and the hillsides still sent up waves of the heat they had gathered from the day's sun.

Pepé looked up to the top of the next dry withered ridge. He saw a dark form against the sky, a man's figure standing on top of a rock, and he glanced away quickly not to appear curious. When a moment later he looked up again, the figure was gone.

Downward the trail was quickly covered. Sometimes the horse floundered for footing, sometimes set his feet and slid a little way. They came at last to the bottom where the dark chaparral was higher than Pepé's head. He held up his rifle on one side and his arm on the other to shield his face from the sharp brittle fingers of the brush.

Up and out of the crease he rode, and up a little cliff. The grassy flat was before him, and the round comfortable oaks. For a moment he studied the trail down which he had come, but there was no movement and no sound from it. Finally he rode out over the flat, to the green streak, and at the upper end of the damp he found a little spring welling out of the earth and dropping into a dug basin before it seeped out over the flat.

Pepé filled his bag first, and then he let the thirsty horse drink out of the pool. He led the horse to the clump of oaks, and in the middle of the grove, fairly protected from sight on all sides, he took off the saddle and the bridle and laid them on the ground. The horse stretched his jaws side-ways and yawned. Pepé knotted the lead rope about the horse's neck and tied him to a sapling among the oaks, where he could graze in a fairly large circle.

When the horse was gnawing hungrily at the dry grass, Pepé went to the saddle and took a black string of jerky from the sack and strolled to an oak tree on the edge of the grove, from under which he could watch the trail. He sat down in the crisp dry oak leaves and automatically felt for his big black knife to cut the jerky, but he had no knife. He leaned back on his elbow and gnawed at the tough strong meat. His face was blank, but it was a man's face.

The bright evening light washed the eastern ridge, but the valley was darkening. Doves flew down from the hills to the spring, and the quail came running out of the brush and joined them, calling clearly to one another.

Out of the corner of his eye Pepé saw a shadow grow out of the bushy crease. He turned his head slowly. A big spotted wildcat was creeping toward the spring, belly to the ground, moving like thought.

Pepé cocked his rifle and edged the muzzle slowly around. Then he looked apprehensively up the trail and dropped the hammer again. From the ground beside him he picked an oak twig and threw it toward the spring. The quail flew up with a roar and the doves whistled away. The big cat stood up: for a long moment he looked at Pepé with cold yellow eyes, and then fearlessly walked back into the gulch.

The dusk gathered quickly in the deep valley. Pepé muttered his prayers, put his head down on his arm and went instantly to sleep.

The moon came up and filled the valley with cold blue light, and the wind swept rustling down from the peaks. The owls worked up and down the slopes looking for rabbits. Down in the brush of the gulch a coyote gab-bled. The oak trees whispered softly in the night breeze.

Pepé started up, listening. His horse had whinnied. The moon was just slipping behind the western ridge, leaving the valley in darkness behind it. Pepé sat tensely gripping his rifle. From far up the trail he heard an answering whinny and the crash of shod hooves on the broken rock. He jumped to his feet, ran to his horse and led it under the trees. He threw on the saddle and cinched it tight for the steep trail, caught the unwilling head and forced the bit into the mouth. He felt the saddle to make sure the water bag and the sack of jerky were there. Then he mounted and turned up the hill.

It was velvet dark. The horse found the entrance to the trail where it left the flat, and started up, stumbling and slipping on the rocks. Pepé's hand rose up to his head. His hat was gone. He had left it under the oak tree.

The horse had struggled far up the trail when the first change of dawn came into the air, a steel greyness as light mixed thoroughly with dark. Gradually the sharp snaggled edge of the ridge stood out above them, rotten granite tortured and eaten by the winds of time. Pepé had dropped his reins on the horn, leaving direction to the horse. The brush grabbed at his legs in the dark until one knee of his jeans was ripped.

Gradually the light flowed down over the ridge. The starved brush and rocks stood out in the half light, strange and lonely in high perspective. Then there came warmth into the light. Pepé drew up and looked back, but he could see nothing in the darker valley below. The sky turned blue over the coming sun. In the waste of the mountainside, the poor dry brush grew only three feet high. Here and there, big outcroppings of unrotted granite stood up like mouldering houses. Pepé relaxed a little. He drank from his water bag and bit off a piece of jerky. A single eagle flew over, high in the light.

Without warning Pepé's horse screamed and fell on its side. He was almost down before the rifle crash echoed up from the valley. From a hole behind the struggling shoulder, a stream of bright crimson blood pumped and stopped and pumped and stopped. The hooves threshed on the ground. Pepé lay half stunned beside the horse. He looked slowly down the hill. A piece of sage clipped off beside his head and another crash echoed up from side to side of the canyon. Pepé flung himself frantically behind a bush.

He crawled up the hill on his knees and one hand. His right hand held the rifle up off the ground and pushed it ahead of him. He moved with the instinctive care of an animal. Rapidly he wormed his way toward one of the big outcroppings of granite on the hill above him. Where the brush was high he doubled up and ran, but where the cover was slight he wriggled forward on his stomach, pushing the rifle ahead of him. In the last little distance there was no cover at all. Pepé poised and then he darted across the space and flashed around the corner of the rock.

He leaned panting against the stone. When his breath came easier he moved along behind the big rock until he came to a narrow split that offered a thin section of vision down the hill. Pepé lay on his stomach and pushed the rifle barrel through the slit and waited.

The sun reddened the western ridges now. Already the buzzards were settling down toward the place where the horse lay. A small brown bird scratched in the dead sage leaves directly in front of the rifle muzzle. The coasting eagle flew back toward the rising sun.

Pepé saw a little movement in the brush far below. His grip tightened on the gun. A little brown doe stepped daintily out on the trail and crossed it and disappeared into the brush again. For a long time Pepé waited. Far below he could see the little flat and the oak trees and the slash of green. Suddenly his eyes flashed back at the trail again. A quarter of a mile down there had been a quick movement in the chaparral. The rifle swung over. The front sight nestled in the V of the rear sight. Pepé studied for a moment and then raised the rear sight a notch. The little movement in the brush came again. The sight settled on it. Pepé squeezed the trigger. The explosion crashed down the mountain and up the other side, and came rattling back. The whole side of the slope grew still. No more movement. And then a white streak cut into the granite of the slit and a bullet whined away and a crash sounded up from below. Pepé felt a sharp pain in his right hand. A sliver of granite was sticking out from between his first and second knuckles and the point protruded from his palm. Carefully he pulled out the sliver of stone. The wound bled evenly and gently. No vein nor artery was cut.

Pepé looked into a little dusty cave in the rock and gathered a handful of spider web, and he pressed the mass into the cut, plastering the soft web into the blood. The flow stopped almost at once.

The rifle was on the ground. Pepé picked it up, levered a new shell into the chamber. And then he slid into the brush on his stomach. Far to the right he crawled, and then up the hill, moving slowly and carefully, crawling to cover and resting and then crawling again.

In the mountains the sun is high in its arc before it penetrates the gorges. The hot face looked over the hill and brought instant heat with it. The white light beat on the rocks and reflected from them and rose up quivering from the earth again, and the rocks and bushes seemed to quiver behind the air.

Pepé crawled in the general direction of the ridge peak, zigzagging for cover. The deep cut between his knuckles began to throb. He crawled close to a rattlesnake before he saw it, and when it raised its dry head and made a soft beginning whirr, he backed up and took another way. The quick grey lizards flashed in front of him, raising a tiny line of dust. He found another mass of spider web and pressed it against his throbbing hand.

Pepé was pushing the rifle with his left hand now. Little drops of sweat ran to the ends of his coarse black hair and rolled down his cheeks. His lips and tongue were growing thick and heavy. His lips writhed to draw saliva into his mouth. His little dark eyes were uneasy and suspicious. Once when a grey lizard paused in front of him on the parched ground and turned its head sideways he crushed it flat with a stone.

When the sun slid past noon he had not gone a mile. He crawled exhaustedly a last hundred yards to a patch of high sharp manzanita, crawled desperately, and when the patch was reached he wriggled in among the tough gnarly trunks and dropped his head on his left arm. There was little shade in the meager brush, but there was cover and safety. Pepé went to sleep as he lay and the sun beat on his back. A few little birds hopped close to him and peered and hopped away. Pepé squirmed in his sleep and he raised and dropped his wounded hand again and again.

The sun went down behind the peaks and the cool evening came, and then the dark. A coyote yelled from the hillside, Pepé started awake and looked about with misty eyes. His hand was swollen and heavy; a little thread of pain ran up the inside of his arm and settled in a pocket in his armpit. He peered about and then stood up, for the mountains were black and the moon had not yet risen. Pepé stood up in the dark. The coat of his father pressed on his arm. His tongue was swollen until it nearly filled his mouth. He wriggled out of the coat and dropped it in the brush, and then he struggled up the hill, falling over rocks and tearing his way through the brush. The rifle knocked against stones as he went. Little dry avalanches of gravel and shattered stone went whispering down the hill behind him.

·After a while the old moon came up and showed the jagged ridge top ahead of him. By moonlight Pepé traveled more easily. He bent forward so that his throbbing arm hung away from his body. The journey uphill was made in dashes and rests, a frantic rush up a few yards and then a rest. The wind coasted down the slope rattling the dry stems of the bushes.

The moon was at meridian when Pepé came at last to the sharp backbone of the ridge top. On the last hundred yards of the rise no soil had clung under the wearing winds. The way was on solid rock. He clambered to the top and looked down on the other side. There was a draw like the last below him, misty with moonlight, brushed with dry struggling sage and chaparral. On the other side the hill rose up sharply and at the top the jagged rotten teeth of the mountain showed against the sky. At the bottom of the cut the brush was thick and dark.

Pepé stumbled down the hill. His throat was almost closed with thirst.

At first he tried to run, but immediately he fell and rolled. After that he went more carefully. The moon was just disappearing behind the mountains when he came to the bottom. He crawled into the heavy brush feeling with his fingers for water. There was no water in the bed of the stream, only damp earth. Pepé laid his gun down and scooped up a handful of mud and put it in his mouth, and then he spluttered and scraped the earth from his tongue with his finger, for the mud drew at his mouth like a poultice. He dug a hole in the stream bed with his fingers, dug a little basin to catch water; but before it was very deep his head fell forward on the damp ground and he slept.

The dawn came and the heat of the day fell on the earth, and still Pepé slept. Late in the afternoon his head jerked up. He looked slowly around. His eyes were slits of wariness. Twenty feet away in the heavy brush a big tawny mountain lion stood looking at him. Its long thick tail waved gracefully, its ears were erect with interest, not laid back dangerously. The lion squatted down on its stomach and watched him.

Pepé looked at the hole he had dug in the earth. A half inch of muddy water had collected in the bottom. He tore the sleeve from his hurt arm, with his teeth ripped out a little square, soaked it in the water and put it in his mouth. Over and over he filled the cloth and sucked it.

Still the lion sat and watched him. The evening came down but there was no movement on the hills. No birds visited the dry bottom of the cut. Pepé looked occasionally at the lion. The eyes of the yellow beast drooped as though he were about to sleep. He yawned and his long thin red tongue curled out. Suddenly his head jerked around and his nostrils quivered. His big tail lashed. He stood up and slunk like a tawny shadow into the thick brush.

A moment later Pepé heard the sound, the faint far crash of horses' hooves on gravel. And he heard something else, a high whining yelp of a dog.

Pepé took his rifle in his left hand and he glided into the brush almost as quietly as the lion had. In the darkening evening he crouched up the hill toward the next ridge. Only when the dark came did he stand up. His energy was short. Once it was dark he fell over the rocks and slipped to his knees on the steep slope, but he moved on and on up the hill, climbing and scrabbling over the broken hillside.

When he was far up toward the top, he lay down and slept for a little while. The withered moon, shining on his face, awakened him. He stood up and moved up the hill. Fifty yards away he stopped and turned back, for he had forgotten his rifle. He walked heavily down and poked about in the brush, but he could not find his gun. At last he lay down to rest. The pocket of pain in his armpit had grown more sharp. His arm seemed to swell out and fall with every heartbeat. There was no position lying down where the heavy arm did not press against his armpit.

With the effort of a hurt beast, Pepé got up and moved again toward the top of the ridge. He held his swollen arm away from his body with his left hand. Up the steep hill he dragged himself, a few steps and a rest, and a few more steps. At last he was nearing the top. The moon showed the uneven sharp back of it against the sky.

Pepé's brain spun in a big spiral up and away from him. He slumped to the ground and lay still. The rock ridge top was only a hundred feet above him.

The moon moved over the sky. Pepé half turned on his back. His tongue tried to make words, but only a thick hissing came from between his lips.

When the dawn came, Pepé pulled himself up. His eyes were sane again. He drew his great puffed arm in front of him and looked at the angry wound. The black line ran from his wrist to his armpit. Automatically he reached in his pocket for the big black knife, but it was not there. His eyes searched the ground. He picked up a sharp blade of stone and scraped at the wound, sawed at the proud flesh and then squeezed the green juice out in big drops. Instantly he threw back his head and whined like a dog. His whole right side shuddered at the pain, but the pain cleared his head.

In the grey light he struggled up the last slope to the ridge and crawled over and lay down behind a line of rocks. Below him lay a deep canyon exactly like the last, waterless and desolate. There was no flat, no oak trees, not even heavy brush in the bottom of it. And on the other side a sharp ridge stood up, thinly brushed with starving sage, littered with broken granite. Strewn over the hill there were giant outcroppings, and on the top the granite teeth stood out against the sky.

The new day was light now. The flame of the sun came over the ridge and fell on Pepé where he lay on the ground. His coarse black hair was littered with twigs and bits of spider web. His eyes had retreated back into his head. Between his lips the tip of his black tongue showed.

He sat up and dragged his great arm into his lap and nursed it, rocking his body and moaning in his throat. He threw back his head and looked up into the pale sky. A big black bird circled nearly out of sight, and far to the left another was sailing near.

He lifted his head to listen, for a familiar sound had come to him from the valley he had climbed out of; it was the crying yelp of hounds, excited and feverish, on a trail.

Pepé bowed his head quickly. He tried to speak rapid words but only a thick hiss came from his lips. He drew a shaky cross on his breast with his left hand. It was a long struggle to get to his feet. He crawled slowly and mechanically to the top of a big rock on the ridge peak. Once there, he arose slowly, swaying to his feet, and stood erect. Far below he could see the dark brush where he had slept. He braced his feet and stood there, black against the morning sky.

There came a ripping sound at his feet. A piece of stone flew up and a bullet droned off into the next gorge. The hollow crash echoed up from below. Pepé looked down for a moment and then pulled himself straight again.

His body jarred back. His left hand fluttered helplessly toward his breast. The second crash sounded from below. Pepé swung forward and toppled from the rock. His body struck and rolled over and over, starting a little avalanche. And when at last he stopped against a bush, the avalanche slid slowly down and covered up his head.

STUDY QUESTIONS:

1. Pepé's mother makes a great deal of his having come to manhood, and yet he has actually committed a very serious crime. What does she mean? In what sense has he become a man?

2. How resourceful is Pepé? Do you think there is any way in which he might have saved his life? Did he make any mistakes in the forest? When and where?

3. Why do the creatures of the forest leave him alone?

4. What are some of the problems which an author has to face when he writes a story or long section of a story with only one character?

5. Read "To Build a Fire" by Jack London and "Big Two-Hearted River" by Ernest Hemingway and observe the manner in which these authors handle a story with a single character. Which of the two is more like "Flight"?

6. Could this story have been written with a happy ending? If so, what would have been the future of Pepé?

FOOTFALLS

WILBUR DANIEL STEELE

Wilbur Daniel Steele was born in Greensboro, North Carolina, in 1886. For many years he made Chapel Hill, seat of the University of North Carolina and a center for writers, his home, although he removed to Connecticut. He was originally an art student, who later discovered in himself a gift for writing. He has produced plays and novels, but his work as a short story writer has been paramount during the long years of his productivity. He has worked slowly. No other writer of short stories has been awarded so many prizes as Steele has won. "Footfalls" is characteristic of his method.

Steele devoted an immense amount of time, thought, and care to each of his stories—possibly the reason why their level has been constantly high. He is an expert craftsman with a compassion for mankind. Despite the apparent artlessness of its style and the deceptively sprawling quality of its structure, "Footfalls" is put together with extraordinary skill. The ending is unexpected, but rises above the mere trick-ending technique because it compels the reader to think about the nature of love and justice and to realize he should have known all along that Boaz Negro instantly realized who was murdered and who killed him. The dramatic turn the story takes hinges upon the acuity of a blind man's hearing, but it hinges also upon the blind man's notion of justice and his special ability to read character.

"Footfalls" is fascinating to analyze. To read it through the first time is to be entertained by what seems to be a straightforward tale of patience and poetic justice. To read it through a second time is to be aware of the small, cunning touches by which Steele prepares for the unexpected resolution of the plot—the inexplicable money sack, the clink of gold coin, the "quality of appeal, of despair, and of command" in Negro's voice, the card game, and the policeman's muttering of "Boaz is to bed tonight." To read it a third time is to note how, after the necessary exposition has been laid down, Steele manages to create a world of sound and hearing only, of incredible patience, and of primitive familial loyalty. No story in this collection more amply rewards an almost line by line analysis.

This is not an easy story; not a road for tender or for casual feet. Better the meadows. Let me warn you, it is as hard as that old man's soul and as sunless as his eyes. It has its inception in catastrophe, and its end in an act of almost incredible violence; between them it tells barely how a man, being blind, can become also deaf and dumb.

He lived in one of those old Puritan sea towns where the strain has come down austere and moribund, so that his act would not be quite unbelievable. Except that the town is no longer Puritan and Yankee. It has been betrayed; it has become an outpost of the Portuguese islands.

This man, this blind cobbler himself, was a Portuguese, from St. Michael, in the Western Islands, and his name was Boaz Negro.

He was happy. An unquenchable exuberance lived in him. When he arose in the morning he made vast, as it were uncontrollable, gestures with his stout arms. He came into his shop singing. His voice, strong and deep as the chest from which it emanated, rolled out through the doorway and along the street, and the fishermen, done with their morning work and lounging and smoking along the wharfs, said, "Boaz is to work already." Then they came up to sit in the shop.

In that town a cobbler's shop is a club. One sees the interior always dimly thronged. They sit on the benches watching the artisan at his work for hours, and they talk about everything in the world. A cobbler is known by the company he keeps.

Boaz Negro kept young company. He would have nothing to do with the old. On his own head the gray hairs set thickly.

He had a grown son. But the benches in his shop were for the lusty

and valiant young, men who could spend the night drinking and then at three
o'clock in the morning turn out in the rain and dark to pull at the weirs,
sing songs, buffet one another among the slippery fish in the boat's bottom,
and make loud jokes about the fundamental things, love and birth and death.
Hearkening to their boasts and strong prophecies, his breast heaved and his
heart beat faster. He was a large, full-blooded fellow, fashioned for exploits;
the flame in his darkness burned higher even to hear of them.

It is scarcely conceivable how Boaz Negro could have come through
this much of his life still possessed of that unquenchable and priceless
exuberance; how he would sing in the dawn; how, simply listening to the
recital of deeds in gale or brawl, he could easily forget himself a blind man,
tied to a shop and a last; easily make of himself a lusty young fellow breast-
ing the sunlit and adventurous tide of life.

He had had a wife, whom he had loved. Fate, which had scourged him
with the initial scourge of blindness, had seen fit to take his Angelina away.
He had had four sons. Three, one after another, had been removed, leaving
only Manuel, the youngest. Recovering slowly, with infinite agony, from each
of these recurrent blows, his unquenchable exuberance had lived. And there
was another thing quite as extraordinary. He had never done anything but
work, and that sort of thing may kill the flame where an abrupt catastrophe
fails. Work in the dark. Work, work, work! And accompanied by privation;
an almost miserly scale of personal economy. Yes, indeed, he had "skinned
his fingers," especially in the earlier years. When it tells most.

How he had worked! Not alone in the daytime, but also, sometimes,
when orders were heavy, far into the night. It was strange for one, passing
along that deserted street at midnight, to hear issuing from the black shop of
Boaz Negro the rhythmical tap-tap-tap of hammer on wooden peg.

Nor was that sound all: no man in town could get far past that shop in
his nocturnal wandering unobserved. No more than a dozen footfalls, and
from the darkness Boaz's voice rolled forth, fraternal, stentorian, "Good
night, Antone!" "Good night to you, Caleb Snow!"

To Boaz Negro it was still broad day.

Now, because of this, he was what might be called a substantial man.
He owned his place, his shop, opening on the sidewalk, and behind it the
dwelling house with trellised galleries upstairs and down.

And there was always something for his son, a "piece for the pocket,"
a dollar, five, even a ten-dollar bill if he had "got to have it." Manuel was
"a good boy." Boaz not only said this; he felt that he was assured of it in
his understanding, to the infinite peace of his heart.

It was curious that he should be ignorant only of the one nearest to him. Not because he was physically blind. Be certain he knew more of other men and of other men's son's than they or their neighbors did. More, that is to say, of their hearts, their understandings, their idiosyncrasies, and their ultimate weight in the balance pan of eternity.

His simple explanation of Manuel was that Manuel "wasn't too stout." To others he said this, and to himself. Manuel was not indeed too robust. How should he be vigorous when he never did anything to make him so? He never worked. Why should he work, when existence was provided for, and when there was always that "piece for the pocket"? Even a ten-dollar bill on a Saturday night! No. Manuel "wasn't too stout."

In the shop they let it go at that. The missteps and frailties of everyone else in the world were canvassed there with the most shameless publicity. But Boaz Negro was a blind man, and in a sense their host. Those reckless, strong young fellows respected and loved him. It was allowed to stand at that. Manuel was "a good boy." Which did not prevent them, by the way, from joining later in the general condemnation of that father's laxity—"the ruination of the boy!"

"He should have put him to work, that's what."

"He should have said to Manuel, 'Look here, if you want a dollar, go earn it first.' "

As a matter of fact, only one man ever gave Boaz the advice direct. That was Campbell Wood. And Wood never sat in that shop.

In every small town there is one young man who is spoken of as "rising." As often as not he is not a native, but "from away."

In this town Campbell Wood was that man. He had come from another part of the state to take a place in the bank. He lived in the upper story of Boaz Negro's house, the ground floor now doing for Boaz and the meager remnant of his family. The old woman who came in to tidy up for the cobbler looked after Wood's rooms as well.

Dealing with Wood, one had first of all the sense of his incorruptibility. A little ruthless perhaps, as if one could imagine him, in defense of his integrity, cutting off his friend, cutting off his own hand, cutting off the very stream flowing out from the wellsprings of human kindness. An exaggeration, perhaps.

He was by long odds the most eligible young man in town, good-looking in a spare, ruddy, sandy-haired Scottish fashion, important, incorruptible, "rising." But he took good care of his heart. Precisely that; like a sharp-eyed duenna to his own heart. One felt that here was the man if ever was the man, who held his destiny in his own hand. Failing, of course, some quite gratuitous and unforeseeable catastrophe.

Not that he was not human, or even incapable of laughter or passion. He was, in a way, immensely accessible. He never clapped one on the shoulder; on the other hand, he never failed to speak. Not even to Boaz.

Returning from the bank in the afternoon, he had always a word for the cobbler. Passing out again to supper at his boarding place, he had another, about the weather, the prospects of rain. And if Boaz was at work in the dark when he returned from an evening at the Board of Trade, there was a "Good night, Mr. Negro!"

On Boaz's part, his attitude toward his lodger was curious and paradoxical. He did not pretend to anything less than reverence for the young man's position; precisely on account of that position he was conscious toward Wood of a vague distrust. This was because he was an uneducated fellow.

To the uneducated the idea of large finance is as uncomfortable as the idea of the law. It must be said for Boaz that, responsive to Wood's unfailing civility, he fought against the sensation of dim and somehow shameful distrust.

Nevertheless his whole parental soul was in arms that evening when, returning from the bank and finding the shop empty of loungers, Wood paused a moment to propose the bit of advice already referred to.

"Haven't you ever thought of having Manuel learn the trade?"

A suspicion, a kind of premonition, lighted the fires of defense.

"Shoemaking," said Boaz, "is good enough for a blind man."

"Oh, I don't know. At least it's better than doing nothing at all."

Boaz's hammer was still. He sat silent, monumental. Outwardly. For once his unfailing response had failed him, "Manuel ain't too stout, you know." Perhaps it had become suddenly inadequate.

He hated Wood; he despised Wood; more than ever before, a hundredfold more, quite abruptly, he distrusted Wood.

How could a man say such things as Wood had said? And where Manuel himself might hear!

Where Manuel had heard! Boaz's other emotions—hatred and contempt and distrust—were overshadowed. Sitting in darkness, no sound had come to his ears, no footfall, no infinitesimal creaking of a floor plank. Yet by some sixth uncanny sense of the blind he was aware that Manuel was standing in the dusk of the entry joining the shop to the house.

Boaz made a Herculean effort. The voice came out of his throat, harsh, bitter, and loud enough to have carried ten times the distance to his son's ears.

"Manuel is a good boy!"

"Yes—h'm—yes—I suppose so."

Wood shifted his weight. He seemed uncomfortable.

"Well, I'll be running along, I—ugh! Heavens!"

Something was happening. Boaz heard exclamations, breathings, the rustle of sleeve cloth in large, frantic, and futile graspings—all without understanding. Immediately there was an impact on the floor, and with it the unmistakable clink of metal. Boaz even heard that the metal was minted, and that the coins were gold. He understood. A coin sack, gripped not quite carefully enough for a moment under the other's overcoat, had shifted, slipped, escaped, and fallen.

And Manuel had heard!

It was a deadful moment for Boaz, dreadful in its native sense, as full of dread. Why? It was a moment of horrid revelation, ruthless clarification. His son, his link with the departed Angelina, that "good boy"—Manuel, standing in the shadow of the entry, visible alone to the blind, had heard the clink of falling gold, and—and Boaz wished that he had not!

There, amazing, disconcerting, destroying, stood the sudden fact.

Sitting as impassive and monumental as ever, his strong, bleached hands at rest on his work, round drops of sweat came out on Boaz's forehead. He scarcely took the sense of what Wood was saying. Only fragments.

"Government money, understand—for the breakwater workings—huge —too many people know, here, everywhere—don't trust the safe—tin safe— 'Noah's Ark'—give you my word—heavens, no!"

It boiled down to this—the money, more money than was good for that antiquated "Noah's Ark" at the bank—and whose contemplated sojourn there overnight was public to too many minds—in short, Wood was not only incorruptible, he was canny. To what one of those minds, now, would it occur that he should take away that money bodily, under casual cover of his coat, to his own lodgings behind the cobbler shop of Boaz Negro? For this one, this important, night!

He was sorry the coin sack had slipped, because he did not like to have the responsibility of secret sharer cast upon anyone, even upon Boaz, even by accident. On the other hand, how tremendously fortunate that it had been Boaz and not another. So far as that went, Wood had no more anxiety now than before. One incorruptible knows another.

"I'd trust you, Mr. Negro" (that was one of the fragments which came and stuck in the cobbler's brain), "as far as I would myself. As long as it's only you. I'm just going up here and throw it under the bed. Oh yes, certainly."

Boaz ate no supper. For the first time in his life food was dry in his gullet. Even under those other successive crushing blows of Fate the full and generous habit of his functionings had carried on unabated; he had always eaten what was set before him. Tonight, over his untouched plate, he watched Manuel with his sightless eyes, keeping track of his every mouthful, word, intonation, breath. What profit he expected to extract from this cat-like surveillance it is impossible to say.

When they arose from the supper table Boaz made another Herculean effort. "Manuel, you're a good boy!"

The formula had a quality of appeal, of despair, and of command.

"Manuel, you should be short of money, maybe. Look, what's this? A tenner? Well, there's a piece for the pocket; go and enjoy yourself."

He would have been frightened had Manuel, upsetting tradition, declined the offering. With the morbid contrariness of the human imagination, the boy's avid grasping gave him no comfort.

He went out into the shop, where it was already dark, drew to him his last, his tools, mallets, cutters, pegs, leather. And having prepared to work, he remained idle. He found himself listening.

It has been observed that the large phenomena of sunlight and darkness were nothing to Boaz Negro. A busy night was broad day. Yet there was a difference; he knew it with the blind man's eyes, the ears.

Day was a vast confusion, or rather a wide fabric, of sounds; great and little sounds all woven together, voices, footfalls, wheels, far-off whistles and foghorns, flies buzzing in the sun. Night was another thing. Still there were voices and footfalls, but rare, emerging from the large, pure body of silence as definite, surprising, and yet familiar entities.

Tonight there was an easterly wind coming off the water and carrying the sound of waves. So far as other fugitive sounds were concerned it was the same as silence. The wind made little difference to the ears. It nullified, from one direction at least, the other two visual processes of the blind, the sense of touch and the sense of smell. It blew away from the shop, toward the living house.

As has been said, Boaz found himself listening, scrutinizing with an extraordinary attention this immense background of sound. He heard footfalls. The story of that night was written, for him, in footfalls.

He heard them moving about the house, the lower floor, prowling here, there, halting for long spaces, advancing, retreating softly on the planks. About this aimless, interminable perambulation there was something to twist the nerves, something led and at the same time driven, like a succession of frail and indecisive charges.

Boaz lifted himself from his chair. All his impulse called him to make a stir, join battle, cast in the breach the reinforcement of his presence, authority, good will. He sank back again; his hands fell down. The curious impotence of the spectator held him.

He heard footfalls, too, on the upper floor, a little fainter, borne to the inner rather than the outer ear, along the solid causeway of partitions and floor, the legs of his chair, the bony framework of his body. Very faint indeed. Sinking back easily into the background of the wind. They, too, came and went, this room, that, to the passage, the stairhead, and away. About them too there was the same quality of being led and at the same time of being driven.

Time went by. In his darkness it seemed to Boaz that hours must have passed. He heard voices. Together with the footfalls, that abrupt, brief, and (in view of Wood's position) astounding interchange of sentences made up his history of the night. Wood must have opened the door at the head of the stair; by the sound of his voice he would be standing there, peering below perhaps; perhaps listening.

"What's wrong down there?" he called. "Why don't you go to bed?"

After a moment came Manuel's voice, "Ain't sleepy."

"Neither am I. Look here, do you like to play cards?"

"What kind? Euchre? I like euchre all right. Or pitch."

"Well, what would you say to coming up and having a game of pitch then, Manuel? If you can't sleep?"

"That'd be all right."

The lower footfalls ascended to join the footfalls on the upper floor. There was the sound of a door closing.

Boaz sat still. In the gloom he might have been taken for a piece of furniture, of machinery, an extraordinary lay figure, perhaps, for the trying on of the boots he made. He seemed scarcely to breathe, only the sweat starting from his brow giving him an aspect of life.

He ought to have run, and leaped up that inner stair and pounded with his fists on that door. He seemed unable to move. At rare intervals feet passed on the sidewalk outside, just at his elbow, so to say, and yet somehow, tonight, immeasurably far away. Beyond the orbit of the moon. He heard Rugg, the policeman, noting the silence of the shop, muttering, "Boaz is to bed tonight," as he passed.

The wind increased. It poured against the shop with its deep, continuous sound of a river. Submerged in its body. Boaz caught the note of the town bell striking midnight.

Once more, after a long time, he heard footfalls. He heard them coming around the corner of the shop from the house, footfalls half swallowed by the wind, passing discreetly, without haste, retreating, merging step by step with the huge, incessant background of the wind.

Boaz's muscles tightened all over him. He had the impulse to start up, to fling open the door, shout into the night, "What are you doing? Stop there! Say! What are you doing and where are you going?"

And as before, the curious impotence of the spectator held him motionless. He had not stirred in his chair. And those footfalls, upon which hinged, as it were, that momentous decade of his life, were gone.

There was nothing to listen for now. Yet he continued to listen. Once or twice, half arousing himself, he drew toward him his unfinished work. And then relapsed into immobility.

As has been said, the wind, making little difference to the ears, made all the difference in the world with the sense of feeling and the sense of smell. From the one important direction of the house. That is how it could come about that Boaz Negro could sit, waiting and listening to nothing, in the shop and remain ignorant of disaster until the alarm had gone away and come back again, pounding, shouting, clanging.

"Fire!" he heard them bawling in the street. "Fire! Fire!"

Only slowly did he understand that the fire was in his own house.

There is nothing stiller in the world than the skeleton of a house in the dawn after a fire. It is as if everything living, positive, violent, had been completely drained in the one flaming act of violence, leaving nothing but negation till the end of time. It is worse than a tomb. A monstrous stillness! Even the footfalls of the searchers cannot disturb it, for they are separate and superficial. In its presence they are almost frivolous.

Half an hour after dawn the searchers found the body, if what was left from that consuming ordeal might be called a body. The discovery came as a shock. It seemed incredible that the occupant of that house, no cripple or invalid, but an able man in the prime of youth, should not have awakened and made good his escape. It was the upper floor which had caught; the stairs had stood to the last. It was beyond calculation. Even if he had been asleep!

And he had not been asleep. This second and infinitely more appalling discovery began to be known. Slowly. By a hint, a breath of rumor here; there an allusion, half taken back. The man whose incinerated body still lay curled in its bed of cinders had been dressed at the moment of disaster; even to the watch, the cuff buttons, the studs, the very scarf pin. Fully clothed to the last detail, precisely as those who had dealings at the bank might have seen Campbell Wood any weekday morning for the past eight months. A man does not sleep with his clothes on. The skull of the man had been broken, as if with a blunt instrument of iron. On the charred lacework of the floor lay the leg of an old andiron with which Boaz Negro and his Angelina had set up housekeeping in that new house.

It needed only Mr. Asa Whitelaw, coming up the street from the gaping "Noah's Ark" at the bank, to round out the scandalous circle of circumstance.

"Where is Manuel?"

Boaz Negro still sat in his shop, impassive, monumental, his thick, hairy arms resting on the arms of his chair. The tools and materials of his work remained scattered about him, as his irresolute gathering of the night before had left them. Into his eyes no change could come. He had lost his house, the visible monument of all those years of "skinning his fingers." It would seem that he had lost his son. And he had lost something incalculably precious—that hitherto unquenchable exuberance of the man.

"Where is Manuel?"

When he spoke his voice was unaccented and stale, like the voice of a man already dead.

"Yes, where is Manuel?"

He had answered them with their own question.

"When did you last see him?"

Neither he nor they seemed to take note of that profound irony.

"At supper."

"Tell us, Boaz, you knew about this money?"

The cobbler nodded his head.

"And did Manuel?"

He might have taken sanctuary in a legal doubt. How did he know what Manuel knew? Precisely! As before, he nodded his head.

"After supper, Boaz, you were in the shop? But you heard something?"

"Yes"

He went on to tell them what he had heard, the footfalls, below and above, the extraordinary conversation which had broken for a moment the silence of the inner hall. The account was bare, the phrases monosyllabic. He reported only what had been registered on the sensitive tympanums of his ears, to the last whisper of footfalls stealing past the dark wall of the shop. Of all the formless tangle of thoughts, suspicions, interpretations, and the special and personal knowledge given to the blind which moved in his brain, he said nothing.

He shut his lips there. He felt himself on the defensive. Just as he distrusted the higher ramifications of finance (his house had gone down unin-
sured), so before the rites and processes of that inscrutable creature, the
law, he felt himself menaced by the invisible and the unknown, helpless,
oppressed; in an abject sense, skeptical.

"Keep clear of the law!" they had told him in his youth. The monster
his imagination had summoned then still stood beside him in his age.

Having exhausted his monosyllabic and superficial evidence, they could
move him no farther. He became deaf and dumb. He sat before them, an
image cast in some immensely heavy stuff, inanimate. His lack of visible
emotion impressed them. Remembering his exuberance, it was only the
stranger to see him unmoving and unmoved. Only once did they catch sight
of something beyond. As they were preparing to leave he opened his mouth.
What he said was like a swan song to the years of his exuberant happiness.
Even now there was no color of expression in his words, which sounded
mechanical.

"Now I have lost everything. My house. My last son. Even my honor.
You would not think I would like to live. But I go to live. I go to work.
That *cachorra,* one day he shall come back again, in the dark night, to have
a look. I shall go to show you all. That *cachorra!*"

(And from that time on, it was noted, he never referred to the fugitive
by any other name than *cachorra,* which is a gender of dog. "That *cachorra!*"
As if he had forfeited the relationship not only of the family, but of the very
genus, the very race! "That *cachorra!*")

He pronounced this resolution without passion. When they assured
him that the culprit would come back again indeed, much sooner than he
expected, "with a rope around his neck," he shook his head slowly.

"No, you shall not catch that *cachorra* now. But one day . . ."

There was something about its very colorlessness which made it sound
oracular. It was at least prophetic. They searched, laid their traps, proceeded
with all their placards, descriptions, rewards, clues, trails. But on Manuel
Negro they never laid their hands.

Months passed and became years. Boaz Negro did not rebuild his house.
He might have done so, out of his earnings, for upon himself he spent scarcely
anything, reverting to his old habit of an almost miserly economy. Yet perhaps it would have been harder after all. For his earnings were less and less.
In that town a cobbler who sits in an empty shop is apt to want for trade.
Folk take their boots to mend where they take their bodies to rest and their
minds to be edified.

No longer did the walls of Boaz's shop resound to the boastful recol-
lections of young men. Boaz had changed. He had become not only different, but opposite. A metaphor will do best. The spirit of Boaz Negro had been
a meadowed hillside giving upon the open sea, the sun, the warm, wild winds
from beyond the blue horizon. And covered with flowers, always hungry and
thirsty for the sun and the fabulous wind and bright showers of rain. It had
become an entrenched camp, lying silent, sullen, verdureless, under a gray
sky. He stood solitary against the world. His approaches were closed. He
was blind, and he was also deaf and dumb.

Against that, what can young fellows do who wish for nothing but to
rest themselves and talk about their friends and enemies? They had come
and they had tried. They had raised their voices even higher than before.
Their boasts had grown louder, more presumptuous, more preposterous,
until, before the cold separation of that unmoving and as if contemptuous
presence in the cobbler's chair, they burst of their own air, like toy balloons.
And they went and left Boaz alone.

There was another thing which served, if not to keep them away, at
least not to entice them back. That was the aspect of the place. It was not
cheerful. It invited no one. In its way that fire-bitten ruin grew to be almost
as great a scandal as the act itself had been. It was plainly an eyesore. A
valuable property, on the town's main thoroughfare—and an eyesore! The
neighboring owners protested.

Their protestations might as well have gone against a stone wall. That
man was deaf and dumb. He had become, in a way, a kind of vegetable, for
the quality of a vegetable is that, while it is endowed with life, it remains
fixed in one spot. For years Boaz was scarcely seen to move foot out of that
shop which was left him, a small, square, blistered promontory on the
shores of ruin.

He must indeed have carried out some rudimentary sort of a domestic
program under the debris at the rear (he certainly did not sleep or eat in
the shop). One or two lower rooms were left fairly intact. The outward aspect
of the place was formless; it grew to be no more than a mound in time; the
charred timbers, one or two still standing, lean and naked against the sky,
lost their blackness and faded to a silvery gray. It would have seemed
strange, had they not grown accustomed to the thought, to imagine that blind
man, like a mole, or some slow slug, turning himself mysteriously in the
bowels of that gray mound—that time-silvered "eyesore."

When they saw him, however, he was in the shop. They opened the
door to take in their work (when other cobblers turned them off), and they

saw him seated in his chair in the half-darkness, his whole person, legs, torso, neck, head, as motionless as the vegetable of which we have spoken— only his hands and his bare arms endowed with visible life. The gloom had bleached the skin to the color of damp ivory, and against the background of his immobility they moved with a certain amazing monstrousness, interminably. No, they were never still. One wondered what they could be at. Surely he could not have had enough work now to keep those insatiable hands so monstrously in motion. Even far into the night. Tap-tap-tap! Blows continuous and powerful. On what? On nothing? On the bare iron last? And for what purpose? To what conceivable end?

Well, one could imagine those arms, growing paler, also growing thicker and more formidable with that unceasing labor; the muscles feeding themselves omnivorously on their own waste, the cords toughening, the bone tissues revitalizing themselves without end. One could imagine the whole aspiration of that mute and motionless man pouring itself out into those pallid arms, and the arms taking it up with a kind of blind greed. Storing it up. Against a day!

"That *cachorra!* One day . . ."

What were the thoughts of the man? What moved within that motionless cranium covered with long hair? Who can say? Behind everything, of course, stood that bitterness against the world—the blind world—blinder than he would ever be. And against "that *cachorra.*" But this was no longer a thought; it was the man.

Just as all muscular aspiration flowed into his arms, so all the energies of his senses turned to his ears. The man had become, you might say, two arms and two ears. Can you imagine a man listening, intently, through the waking hours of nine years?

Listening to footfalls. Marking with a special emphasis of concentration the beginning, rise, full passage, falling away, and dying of all the footfalls. By day, by night, winter and summer and winter again. Unraveling the skein of footfalls passing up and down the street!

For three years he wondered when they would come. For the next three years he wondered if they would ever come. It was during the last three that a doubt began to trouble him. It gnawed at his huge moral strength. Like a hidden seepage of water, it undermined (in anticipation) his terrible resolution. It was a sign perhaps of age, a slipping away of the reckless infallibility of youth.

Supposing, after all, that his ears should fail him? Supposing they were capable of being tricked, without his being able to know it? Supposing that that *cachorra* should come and go, and he, Boaz, living in some vast delusion, some unrealized distortion of memory, should let him pass unknown? Supposing precisely this thing had already happened!

Or the other way around. What if he should hear the footfalls coming, even into the very shop itself? What if he should be as sure of them as of his own soul? What, then, if he should strike? And what, then, if it were not that *cachorra* after all? How many tens and hundreds of millions of people were there in the world? Was it possible for them all to have footfalls distinct and different?

Then they would take him and hang him. And that *cachorra* might then come and go at his own will, undisturbed.

As he sat there sometimes the sweat rolled down his nose, cold as rain. Supposing!

Sometimes, quite suddenly, in broad day, in the booming silence of the night, he would start. Not outwardly. But beneath the pale integument of his skin all his muscles tightened and his nerves sang. His breathing stopped. It seemed almost as if his heart stopped.

Was that it? Were those the feet, there, emerging faintly from the distance? Yes, there was something about them. Yes! Memory was in travail. Yes, yes, yes! No! How could he be sure? Ice ran down into his empty eyes. The footfalls were already passing. They were gone, swallowed up already by time and space. Had that been that *cachorra?*

Nothing in his life had been so hard to meet as this insidious drain of distrust in his own powers; this sense of a traitor within the walls. His iron-gray hair had turned white. It was always this now, from the beginning of the day to the end of the night; how was he to know? How was he to be inevitably, unshakably sure?

Curiously, after all this purgatory of doubts, he did know them. For a moment at least, when he had heard them, he was unshakably sure.

It was on an evening of the winter holidays, the Portuguese festival of Menin' Jesus. Christ was born again in a hundred mangers on a hundred tiny altars; there was cake and wine; songs went shouting by to the accompaniment of mandolins and tramping feet. The wind blew cold under a clear sky. In all the houses there were lights; even in Boaz Negro's shop a lamp was lit just now, for a man had been in for a pair of boots which Boaz had patched. The man had gone out again. Boaz was thinking of blowing out the light. It meant nothing to him.

He leaned forward, judging the position of the lamp chimney by the heat on his face, and puffed out his cheeks to blow. Then his cheeks collapsed suddenly, and he sat back again.

It was not odd that he had failed to hear the footfalls until they were actually within the door. A crowd of merrymakers was passing just then; their songs and tramping almost shook the shop.

Boaz sat back. Beneath his passive exterior his nerves thrummed; his muscles had grown as hard as wood. Yes! Yes! But no! He had heard nothing; no more than a single step, a single foot pressure on the planks within the door. Dear God! He could not tell!

Going through the pain of an enormous effort, he opened his lips.

"What can I do for you?"

"Well, I—I don't know. To tell the truth——"

The voice was unfamiliar, but it might be assumed. Boaz held himself. His face remained blank, interrogating, slightly helpless.

"I am a little deaf," he said. "Come nearer."

The footfalls came halfway across the intervening floor, and there appeared to hesitate. The voice, too, had a note of uncertainty.

"I was just looking around. I have a pair of—well, you mend shoes?"

Boaz nodded his head. It was not in response to the words, for they meant nothing. What he had heard were the footfalls on the floor.

Now he was sure. As has been said, for a moment at least after he had heard them he was unshakably sure. The congestion of his muscles had passed. He was at peace.

The voice became audible once more. Before the massive preoccupation of the blind man it became still less certain of itself.

"Well, I haven't got the shoes with me. I was—just looking around."

It was amazing to Boaz, this miraculous sensation of peace.

"Wait!" Then, bending his head as if listening to the winter wind, "It's cold tonight. You've left the door open. But wait!" Leaning down, his hand fell on a rope's end hanging by the chair. The gesture was one continuous, undeviating movement of the hand. No hesitation. No groping. How many hundreds, how many thousands of times had his hand schooled itself in that gesture!

A single strong pull. With a little bang the front door had swung to and latched itself. Not only the front door. The other door, leading to the rear, had closed too and latched itself with a little bang. And leaning forward from his chair, Boaz blew out the light.

There was not a sound in the shop. Outside, feet continued to go by, ringing on the frozen road; voices were lifted; the wind hustled about the corners of the wooden shell with a continuous, shrill note of whistling. All of this outside, as on another planet. Within the blackness of the shop the complete silence persisted.

Boaz listened. Sitting on the edge of his chair, half couching, his head, with its long, unkempt white hair, bent slightly to one side, he concentrated upon this chambered silence the full powers of his senses. He hardly breathed. The other person in that room could not be breathing at all, it seemed.

No, there was not a breath, not the stirring of a sole on wood, not the infinitesimal rustle of any fabric. It was as if in this utter stoppage of sound, even the blood had ceased to flow in the veins and arteries of that man, who was like a rat caught in a trap.

It was appalling even to Boaz; even to the cat. Listening became more than a labor. He began to have to fight against a growing impulse to shout out loud, to leap, sprawl forward without aim in that unstirred darkness—do something. Sweat rolled down from behind his ears, into his shirt collar. He gripped the chair arms. To keep quiet he sank his teeth into his lower lip. He would not! He would not!

And of a sudden he heard before him, in the center of the room, an outburst of breath, an outrush from lungs in the extremity of pain, thick, laborious, fearful. A coughing up of dammed air.

Pushing himself from the arms of the chair, Boaz leaped.

His fingers, passing swiftly through the air, closed on something. It was a sheaf of hair, bristly and thick. It was a man's beard.

On the road outside, up and down the street for a hundred yards, merrymaking people turned to look at one another. With an abrupt cessation of laughter, of speech. Inquiringly. Even with an unconscious dilation of the pupils of their eyes.

"What was that?"

There had been a scream. There could be no doubt of that. A single, long-drawn note. Immensely high-pitched. Not as if it were human.

"God's sake! What was that? Where'd it come from?"

Those nearest said it came from the cobbler shop of Boaz Negro.

They went and tried the door. It was closed; even locked, as if for the night. There was no light behind the window shade. But Boaz would not have a light. They beat on the door. No answer.

But from where, then, had that prolonged, as if animal, note come?

They ran about, penetrating into the side lanes, interrogating, prying. Coming back at last, inevitably, to the neighborhood of Boaz Negro's shop.

The body lay on the floor at Boaz's feet, where it had tumbled down slowly after a moment from the spasmodic embrace of his arms; those ivory-colored arms which had beaten so long upon the bare iron surface of a last.

Blows continuous and powerful! It seemed incredible. They were so weak
now. They could not have lifted the hammer now.

But that beard! That bristly, thick, square beard of a stranger!

His hands remembered it. Standing with his shoulders fallen forward
and his weak arms hanging down. Boaz began to shiver. The whole thing
was incredible. What was on the floor there, upheld in the vast gulf of darkness, he could not see. Neither could he hear it; smell it. Nor (if he did not
move his foot) could he feel it. What he did not hear, smell, or touch did
not exist. It was not there. Incredible!

But that beard! All the accumulated doubtings of those years fell down
upon him. After all, the thing he had been so fearful of in his weak imagin-
ings had happened. He had killed a stranger. He, Boaz Negro, had
murdered an innocent man!

And all on account of that beard. His deep panic made him light-
headed. He began to confuse cause and effect. If it were not for that beard,
it would have been that *cachorra*.

On this basis he began to reason with a crazy directness. And to act.
He went and pried open the door into the entry. From a shelf he took down
his razor. A big, heavy-heeled blade, made long ago for a beard which
turned the jaw black again an hour after shaving. And the old, brown, polished strop. His hands began to hurry. And the mug, half full of soap. And
water. It would have to be cold water. But after all, he thought (lighthead-
edly), at this time of night . . .

Outside, they were at the shop again. The crowd's habit is to forget
a thing quickly, once it is out of sight and hearing. But there had
been something about that solitary cry which continued to bother them, even
in memory. Where had it been? Where had it come from? And those who
had stood nearest the cobbler shop were heard again. They were certain
now, dead certain. They could swear!

In the end they broke down the door.

If Boaz heard them he gave no sign. An absorption as complete as it
was monstrous wrapped him. Kneeling in the glare of the lantern they had
brought, as impervious as his own shadow sprawling behind him, he continued to shave the dead man on the floor.

No one touched him. Their minds and imaginations were arrested by
the gigantic proportions of the act. The unfathomable presumption of the
act. As throwing murder in their faces to the tune of a jig in a barbershop.
It is a fact that none of them so much as thought of touching him. No less
than all of them, together with all other men, shorn of their imaginations—

that is to say, the expressionless and imperturbable creature of the Law—
would be sufficient to touch that ghastly man.

On the other hand, they could not leave him alone. They could not go
away. They watched. They saw the damp, lather-soaked beard of that vic-
timized stranger falling away, stroke by stroke of the flashing, heavy razor.
The dead denuded by the blind!

It was seen that Boaz was about to speak. It was something important
he was to utter; something, one would say, fatal. The words would not come
all at once. They swelled his cheeks out. His razor was arrested. Lifting his
face, he encircled the watchers with a gaze at once of imploration and of
command. As if he could see them. As if he could read his answer in the
expressions of their faces.

"Tell me one thing now. Is it that *cachorra?*"

For the first time those men in the room made sounds. They shuffled
their feet. It was as if an uncontrollable impulse to ejaculation, laughter,
derision, forbidden by the presence of death, had gone down into their
boot soles.

"Manual?" one of them said. "You mean *Manual?*"

Boaz laid the razor down on the floor beside its work. He got up
from his knees slowly, as if his joints hurt. He sat down in his chair, rested
his hands on the arms, and once more encircled the company with his
sightless gaze.

"Not Manuel. Manuel was a good boy. But tell me now, is it
that *cachorra?*"

Here was something out of their calculations; something for them,
mentally, to chew on. Mystification is a good thing sometimes. It gives the
brain a fillip, stirs memory, puts the gears of imagination in mesh.
One man, an old, tobacco-chewing fellow, began to stare harder at the face
on the floor. Something moved in his intellect.

"No, but look here now, by God——"

He had even stopped chewing. But he was forestalled by another.

"Say now, if it don't look like that fellow Wood, himself. The bank
fellow—that was burned—remember? Himself."

"That *cachorra* was not burned. Not that Wood. You damned fool!"

Boaz spoke from his chair. They hardly knew his voice, emerging
from its long silence; it was so didactic and arid.

"That *cachorra* was not burned. It was my boy that was burned. It was
that *cachorra* called my boy upstairs. That *cachorra* killed my boy. That
cachorra put his clothes on my boy, and he set my house on fire. I knew

that all the time. Because when I heard those feet come out of my house and go away, I knew they were the feet of that *cachorra* from the bank. I did not know where he was going to. Something said to me, 'You better ask him where he is going to.' But then I said, 'You are foolish.' He had the money from the bank. I did not know. And then my house was on fire. No, it was not my boy that went away; it was that *cachorra* all the time. You damned fools! Did you think I was waiting for my own boy?

"Now I show you all," he said at the end. "And now I can get hanged."

No one ever touched Boaz Negro for that murder. For murder it was in the eye and letter of the Law. But the Law in a small town is sometimes a curious creature; it is sometimes blind only in one eye.

Their minds and imaginations in that town were arrested by the romantic proportions of the act. Simply, no one took it up. I believe the man, Wood, was understood to have died of heart failure.

When they asked Boaz why he had not told what he knew as to the identity of that fugitive in the night, he seemed to find it hard to say exactly. How could a man of no education define for them his own but half-defined misgivings about the Law, his sense of oppression, constraint, and awe, of being on the defensive, even, in an abject way, his skepticism? About his wanting, come what might, to "keep clear of the Law"?

He did say this, "You would have laughed at me."

And this, "If I told folks it was Wood went away, then I say he would not dare come back again."

That was the last. Very shortly he began to refuse to talk about the thing at all. The act was completed. Like the creature of fable, it had consumed itself. Out of that old man's consciousness it had departed. Amazingly. Like a dream dreamed out.

Slowly at first, in a makeshift, piece-at-a-time, poor man's way, Boaz commenced to rebuild his house. That "eyesore" vanished.

And slowly at first, like the miracle of a green shoot pressing out from the dead earth, that priceless and unquenchable exuberance of the man was seen returning. Unquenchable, after all.

STUDY QUESTIONS:

1. Is this a story about eternal justice or about paternal vengeance?

2. Why does Steele insist upon the "austere and moribund" character of the town's inheritance?

3. What hints, scattered through the earlier part of the narrative, prepare the reader for the unexpected revelation at the climax?

4. What connection do you see between the first two paragraphs and the "coda" beginning: "No one ever touched Boaz Negro for that murder"? Is the coda necessary?

5. Is the reiteration of the word *cachorra* a fair device?

6. Notice the paragraphing that the author uses. How is it effective in this story?

MY KINSMAN, MAJOR MOLINEUX

NATHANIEL HAWTHORNE

The short stories of Nathaniel Hawthorne (1804–1864) have always been popular. Readers get to know some of them—"The Great Stone Face," "The Gray Champion," "The Minister's Black Veil"—at a very early age. The two volumes from which most of Hawthorne's stories come, *Twice-Told Tales* (1837, 1842) and *Mosses from an Old Manse* (1846) are standard American classics, as are two of his novels, *The Scarlet Letter* (1850) and The House of the Seven Gables (1851). Indeed, several critics have remarked that it is with *The Scarlet Letter* that American literature comes of age.

Hawthorne was born in Salem, Massachusetts, and the city figures prominently in much of his work. His family had had a long connection with it; his great-great-grandfather had been a judge at one of the witchcraft trials. Both before and after his attendance at Bowdoin College, Hawthorne spent many hours of solitude and even seclusion in Salem, often taking long walks through parts of the town which, though it had once been one of the major ports of the New World, was now, in Hawthorne's day, already in decline. Hawthorne held a variety of governmental positions, including the consulship of Liverpool, to which he was appointed by President Franklin Pierce, who had been his classmate at Bowdoin. In 1842 Hawthorne married Sophia Peabody, member of another distinguished New England family, and through most of his life he was acquainted with Emerson, Thoreau, Longfellow, and, later, Melville.

The stories of Hawthorne now in vogue are dark tales of evil, mystery, witchcraft, death and the nature of sin, stories like "Rappacini's Daughter," "Young Goodman Brown," "The Serpent in the Bosom," and others. Hawthorne's interest in the demonic and the occult can be seen in nearly everything he wrote, but it is sometimes forgotten that his writing shows also a great deal of interest in the early history of America. "The Maypole of Merry Mount," "The Gray Champion," and, of course, *The Scarlet Letter* are cases in point. "My Kinsman, Major Molineux" manages to combine a knowledge of certain practices in the colonies with the dark narrative of a country boy coming into a community and becoming acquainted with a series of bewildering horrors, which he finally learns the meaning of in a scene of shocking cruelty.

The story is much more than that, however. Essentially it is a story of idea. As with much of the literature of early New England, the reader can take a "moral" or a lesson from it. Robin comes into the village with a supposed advantage; he is a relative of Major Molineux, the ruling authority. Whenever he announces this to the strangers whom he meets, he is met with silence, or laughter, or outright scorn. The advantage is only an illusion, and before the story is over the reader discovers why. What, then, is the idea of the work? Is Hawthorne saying that to attempt boastfully to use influence is often to be humiliated, and that when we want to become a member of a new group or community we had better do it on our own? The story invites the reader to consider a number of such intriguing questions.

After the kings of Great Britain had assumed the right of appointing the colonial governors, the measures of the latter seldom met with the ready and generous approbation which had been paid to those of their predecessors, under the original charters. The people looked with most jealous scrutiny to the exercise of power which did not emanate from themselves, and they usually rewarded their rulers with slender gratitude for the compliances by which, in softening their instructions from beyond the sea, they had incurred the reprehension of those who gave them. The annals of Massachusetts Bay will inform us, that of six governors in the space of about forty years from the surrender of the old charter, under James II.,

two were imprisoned by a popular insurrection; a third, as Hutchinson[1] in-
clines to believe, was driven from the province by the whizzing of a musket-
ball; a fourth, in the opinion of the same historian, was hastened to his grave
by continual bickerings with the House of Representatives; and the remaining
two, as well as their successors, till the Revolution, were favored with few
and brief intervals of peaceful sway. The inferior members of the court party,
in times of high political excitement, led scarcely a more desirable life. These
remarks may serve as a preface to the following adventures, which chanced
upon a summer night, not far from a hundred years ago. The reader, in
order to avoid a long and dry detail of colonial affairs, is requested to dis-
pense with an account of the train of circumstances that had caused much
temporary inflammation of the popular mind.

It was near nine o'clock of a moonlight evening, when a boat crossed
the ferry with a single passenger, who had obtained his conveyance at that
unusual hour by the promise of an extra fare. While he stood on the
landing-place, searching in either pocket for the means of fulfilling his
agreement, the ferryman lifted a lantern, by the aid of which, and the newly
risen moon, he took a very accurate survey of the stranger's figure. He was
a youth of barely eighteen years, evidently country-bred, and now, as
it should seem, upon his first visit to town. He was clad in a coarse gray
coat, well worn, but in excellent repair; his under garments were durably
constructed of leather, and fitted tight to a pair of serviceable and well-shaped
limbs; his stockings of blue yarn were the incontrovertible work of a
mother or a sister; and on his head was a three-cornered hat, which in its
better days had perhaps sheltered the graver brow of the lad's father.
Under his left arm was a heavy cudgel formed of an oak sapling, and retaining a part of the hardened root; and his equipment was completed by
a wallet, not so abundantly stocked as to incommode the vigorous shoulders on which it hung. Brown, curly hair, well-shaped features, and bright,
cheerful eyes were nature's gifts, and worth all that art could have done for
his adornment.

The youth, one of whose names was Robin, finally drew from his pocket
the half of a little province bill of five shillings, which, in the depreciation in
that sort of currency, did but satisfy the ferryman's demand, with the surplus of a sexangular piece of parchment, valued at three pence. He then
walked forward into the town, with as light a step as if his day's journey
had not already exceeded thirty miles, and with as eager an eye as if he were
entering London city, instead of the little metropolis of a New Eng-

---

[1] Hutchinson. Thomas Hutchinson (1711–1780) was a colonial administrator and historian.

land colony. Before Robin had proceeded far, however, it occurred to him that he knew not whither to direct his steps; so he paused, and looked up and down the narrow street, scrutinizing the small and mean wooden buildings that were scattered on either side.

"This low hovel cannot be my kinsman's dwelling," thought he, "nor yonder old house, where the moonlight enters at the broken casement; and truly I see none hereabouts that might be worthy of him. It would have been wise to inquire my way of the ferryman, and doubtless he would have gone with me, and earned a shilling from the Major for his pains. But the next man I meet will do as well."

He resumed his walk, and was glad to perceive that the street now became wider, and the houses more respectable in their appearance. He soon discerned a figure moving on moderately in advance, and hastened his steps to overtake it. As Robin drew nigh, he saw that the passenger was a man in years, with a full periwig of gray hair, a wide-skirted coat of dark cloth, and silk stockings rolled above his knees. He carried a long and polished cane, which he struck down perpendicularly before him at every step; and at regular intervals he uttered two successive hems, of a peculiarly solemn and sepulchral intonation. Having made these observations, Robin laid hold of the skirt of the old man's coat, just when the light from the open door and windows of a barber's shop fell upon both their figures.

"Good evening to you, honored sir," said he, making a low bow, and still retaining his hold of the skirt. "I pray you tell me whereabouts is the dwelling of my kinsman, Major Molineux."

The youth's question was uttered very loudly; and one of the barbers, whose razor was descending on a well-soaped chin, and another who was dressing a Ramillies wig,[2] left their occupations, and came to the door. The citizen, in the meantime, turned a long-favored countenance upon Robin, and answered him in a tone of excessive anger and annoyance. His two sepulchral hems, however, broke into the very centre of his rebuke, with most singular effect, like a thought of the cold grave obtruding among wrathful passions.

"Let go my garment, fellow! I tell you, I know not the man you speak of. What! I have authority, I have—hem, hem—authority; and if this be the respect you show for your betters, your feet shall be brought acquainted with the stocks by daylight, tomorrow morning!"

Robin released the old man's skirt, and hastened away, pursued by an

---

[2] Ramillies wig. A wig having a long plait hanging behind tied with a bow at the top of the plait and another bow at the bottom. It was named for Marlborough's victory at Ramillies in Belgium, in 1706.

ill-mannered roar of laughter from the barber's shop. He was at first considerably surprised by the result of his question, but, being a shrewd youth, soon thought himself able to account for the mystery.

"This is some country representative," was his conclusion, "who has never seen the inside of my kinsman's door, and lacks the breeding to answer a stranger civilly. The man is old, or verily—I might be tempted to turn back and smite him on the nose. Ah, Robin, Robin! even the barber's boys laugh at you for choosing such a guide! You will be wiser in time, friend Robin."

He now became entangled in a succession of crooked and narrow streets, which crossed each other, and meandered at no great distance from the water-side. The smell of tar was obvious to his nostrils, the masts of vessels pierced the moonlight above the tops of the buildings, and the numerous signs, which Robin paused to read, informed him that he was near the centre of business. But the streets were empty, the shops were closed, and lights were visible only in the second stories of a few dwelling-houses. At length, on the corner of a narrow lane, through which he was passing, he beheld the broad countenance of a British hero swinging before the door of an inn, whence proceeded the voices of many guests. The casement of one of the lower windows was thrown back, and a very thin curtain permitted Robin to distinguish a party at supper, round a well-furnished table. The fragrance of the good cheer steamed forth into the outer air, and the youth could not fail to recollect that the last remnant of his travelling stock of provision had yielded to his morning appetite, and that noon had found and left him dinnerless.

"Oh, that a parchment three-penny might give me a right to sit down at yonder table!" said Robin, with a sigh. "But the Major will make me welcome to the best of his victuals; so I will even step boldly in, and inquire my way to his dwelling."

He entered the tavern, and was guided by the murmur of voices and the fumes of tobacco to the public-room. It was a long and low apartment, with oaken walls, grown dark in the continual smoke, and a floor which was thickly sanded, but of no immaculate purity. A number of persons—the larger part of whom appeared to be mariners, or in some way connected with the sea—occupied the wooden benches, or leather-bottomed chairs, conversing on various matters, and occasionally lending their attention to some topic of general interest. Three or four little groups were draining as many bowls of punch, which the West India trade had long since made a familiar drink in the colony. Others, who had the appearance of men who lived by regular and laborious handicraft, preferred the insulated bliss of an unshared potation, and became more taciturn under its influence. Nearly all, in short, evinced a predilection for the Good Creature in some of its various shapes, for this is a vice to which, as Fast Day sermons of a hundred years ago will testify, we have a long hereditary claim. The only guests to whom Robin's sympathies inclined him were two or three sheepish countrymen, who were using the inn somewhat after the fashion of a Turkish caravansary; they had gotten themselves into the darkest corner of the room, and heedless of the Nicotian[3] atmosphere, were supping on the bread of their own ovens, and the bacon cured in their own chimney-smoke. But though Robin felt a sort of brotherhood with these strangers, his eyes were attracted from them to a person who stood near the door, holding whispered conversation with a group of ill-dressed associates. His features were separately striking almost to grotesqueness, and the whole face left a deep impression on the memory. The forehead bulged out into a double prominence, with a vale between; the nose came boldly forth in an irregular curve, and its bridge was of more than a finger's breadth; the eyebrows were deep and shaggy, and the eyes glowed beneath them like fire in a cave.

While Robin deliberated of whom to inquire respecting his kinsman's dwelling, he was accosted by the innkeeper, a little man in a stained white apron, who had come to pay his professional welcome to the stranger. Being in the second generation from a French Protestant, he seemed to have inherited the courtesy of his parent nation; but no variety of circumstances was ever known to change his voice from the one shrill note in which he now addressed Robin.

"From the country, I presume, sir?" said he, with a profound bow. "Beg leave to congratulate you on your arrival, and trust you intend a long stay with us. Fine town here, sir, beautiful buildings, and much that may interest a stranger. May I hope for the honor of your commands in respect to supper?"

"The man sees a family likeness! The rogue has guessed that I am related to the Major!" thought Robin, who had hitherto experienced little superfluous civility.

All eyes were now turned on the country lad, standing at the door, in his worn three-cornered hat, gray coat, leather breeches, and blue yarn stockings, leaning on an oaken cudgel, and bearing a wallet on his back.

Robin replied to the courteous innkeeper, with such an assumption of confidence as befitted the Major's relative. "My honest friend," he said, "I

[3] Nicotian. Tobacco-like. From Jean Nicot, (hence "nicotine"), who introduced tobacco into France.

shall make it a point to patronize your house on some occasion, when"—
here he could not help lowering his voice—"when I may have more than a
parchment three-pence in my pocket. My present business," continued he,
speaking with lofty confidence, "is merely to inquire my way to the dwelling of my kinsman, Major Molineux."

There was a sudden and general movement in the room, which Robin
interpreted as expressing the eagerness of each individual to become his
guide. But the innkeeper turned his eyes to a written paper on the wall, which
he read, or seemed to read, with occasional recurrences to the young man's
figure.

"What have we here?" said he, breaking his speech into little dry fragments. " 'Left the house of the subscriber, bounden servant, Hezekiah
Mudge,—had on, when he went away, gray coat, leather breeches, master's
third-best hat. One pound currency reward to whosoever shall lodge him in
any jail of the province.' Better trudge, boy; better trudge!"

Robin had begun to draw his hands towards the lighter end of the oak
cudgel, but a strange hostility in every countenance induced him to relin-
quish his purpose of breaking the courteous innkeeper's head. As he turned
to leave the room, he encountered a sneering glance from the bold-featured
personage whom he had before noticed; and no sooner was he beyond the
door, than he heard a general laugh, in which the innkeeper's voice might be
distinguished, like the dropping of small stones into a kettle.

"Now, is it not strange," thought Robin, with his usual shrewdness,—
"is it not strange that the confession of an empty pocket should outweigh
the name of my kinsman, Major Molineux? Oh, if I had one of those grinning
rascals in the woods, where I and my oak sapling grew up together, I would
teach him that my arm is heavy though my purse be light!"

On turning the corner of the narrow lane, Robin found himself in a
spacious street, with an unbroken line of lofty houses on each side, and a
steepled building at the upper end, whence the ringing of a bell announced
the hour of nine. The light of the moon, and the lamps from the numerous
shop-windows, discovered people promenading on the pavement, and
amongst them Robin had hoped to recognize his hitherto inscrutable relative. The result of his former inquiries made him unwilling to hazard another,
in a scene of such publicity, and he determined to walk slowly and silently
up the street, thrusting his face close to that of every elderly gentleman, in
search of the Major's lineaments. In his progress, Robin encountered many
gay and gallant figures. Embroidered garments of showy colors, enormous
periwigs, gold-laced hats, and silver-hilted swords glided past him and daz-

zled his optics. Travelled youths, imitators of the European fine gentlemen of the period, trod jauntily along, half dancing to the fashionable tunes which they hummed, and making poor Robin ashamed of his quiet and natural gait. At length, after many pauses to examine the gorgeous display of goods in the shop-windows, and after suffering some rebukes for the impertinence of his scrutiny into people's faces, the Major's kinsman found himself near the steepled building, still unsuccessful in his search. As yet, however, he had seen only one side of the thronged street; so Robin crossed, and continued the same sort of inquisition down the opposite pavement, with stronger hopes than the philosopher seeking an honest man, but with no better fortune. He had arrived about midway towards the lower end, from which his course began, when he overheard the approach of some one who struck down a cane on the flag-stones at every step, uttering at regular intervals, two sepulchral hems.

"Mercy on us!" quoth Robin, recognizing the sound.

Turning a corner, which chanced to be close at his right hand, he hastened to pursue his researches in some other part of the town. His patience now was wearing low, and he seemed to feel more fatigue from his rambles since he crossed the ferry, than from his journey of several days on the other side. Hunger also pleaded loudly within him, and Robin began to balance the propriety of demanding, violently, and with lifted cudgel, the necessary guidance from the first solitary passenger whom he should meet. While a resolution to this effect was gaining strength, he entered a street of mean appearance, on either side of which a row of ill-built houses was straggling towards the harbor. The moonlight fell upon no passenger along the whole extent, but in the third domicile which Robin passed there was a half-opened door, and his keen glance detected a woman's garment within.

"My luck may be better here," said he to himself.

Accordingly, he approached the door, and beheld it shut closer as he did so; yet an open space remained, sufficing for the fair occupant to observe the stranger, without a corresponding display on her part. All that Robin could discern was a strip of scarlet petticoat, and the occasional sparkle of an eye, as if the moonbeams were trembling on some bright thing.

"Pretty mistress," for I may call her so with a good conscience, thought the shrewd youth, since I know nothing to the contrary,—"my sweet pretty mistress, will you be kind enough to tell me whereabouts I must seek the dwelling of my kinsman, Major Molineux?"

Robin's voice was plaintive and winning, and the female, seeing nothing to be shunned in the handsome country youth, thrust open the door, and came forth into the moonlight. She was a dainty little figure, with a white neck, round arms, and a slender waist, at the extremity of which her scarlet petticoat jutted out over a hoop, as if she were standing in a balloon. Moreover, her face was oval and pretty, her hair dark beneath the little cap, and her bright eyes possessed a sly freedom, which triumphed over those of Robin.

"Major Molineux dwells here," said this fair woman.

Now, her voice was the sweetest Robin had heard that night, yet he could not help doubting whether that sweet voice spoke Gospel truth. He looked up and down the mean street, and then surveyed the house before which they stood. It was a small, dark edifice of two stories, the second of which projected over the lower floor, and the front apartment had the aspect of a shop for petty commodities.

"Now, truly, I am in luck," replied Robin, cunningly, "and so indeed is my kinsman, the Major, in having so pretty a housekeeper. But I prithee trouble him to step to the door; I will deliver him a message from his friends in the country, and then go back to my lodgings at the inn."

"Nay, the Major has been abed this hour or more," said the lady of the scarlet petticoat; "and it would be to little purpose to disturb him to-night, seeing his evening draught was of the strongest. But he is a kind-hearted man, and it would be as much as my life's worth to let a kinsman of his turn away from the door. You are the good old gentleman's very picture, and I could swear that was his rainy-weather hat. Also he has garments very much resembling those leather small-clothes. But come in, I pray, for I bid you hearty welcome in his name."

So saying, the fair and hospitable dame took our hero by the hand; and the touch was light, and the force was gentleness, and though Robin read in her eyes what he did not hear in her words, yet the slender-waisted woman in the scarlet petticoat proved stronger than the athletic country youth. She had drawn his half-willing footsteps nearly to the threshold, when the opening of a door in the neighborhood startled the Major's housekeeper, and, leaving the Major's kinsman, she vanished speedily into her own domicile. A heavy yawn preceded the appearance of a man, who, like the Moonshine of Pyramus and Thisbe,[4] carried a lantern, needlessly aiding his sister luminary in the heavens. As he walked sleepily up the street, he turned his broad, dull face on Robin, and displayed a long staff, spiked at the end.

[4] Moonshine of Pyramus and Thisbe. A reference to the play given by the workers in Shakespeare's *A Midsummer Night's Dream.*

"Home, vagabond, home!" said the watchman, in accents that seemed to fall asleep as soon as they were uttered. "Home, or we'll set you in the stocks by peep of day!"

"This is the second hint of the kind," thought Robin. "I wish they would end my difficulties, by setting me there to-night."

Nevertheless, the youth felt an instinctive antipathy towards the guardian of midnight order, which at first prevented him from asking his usual question. But just when the man was about to vanish behind the corner, Robin resolved not to lose the opportunity, and shouted lustily after him,—

"I say, friend! will you guide me to the house of my kinsman, Major Molineux?"

The watchman made no reply, but turned the corner and was gone; yet Robin seemed to hear the sound of drowsy laughter stealing along the solitary street. At that moment, also, a pleasant titter saluted him from the open window above his head; he looked up, and caught the sparkle of a saucy eye; a round arm beckoned to him, and next he heard light footsteps descending the staircase within. But Robin, being of the household of a New England clergyman, was a good youth, as well as a shrewd one; so he resisted temptation, and fled away.

He now roamed desperately, and at random, through the town, almost ready to believe that a spell was on him, like that by which a wizard of his country had once kept three pursuers wandering, a whole winter night, within twenty paces of the cottage which they sought. The streets lay before him, strange and desolate, and the lights were extinguished in almost every house. Twice, however, little parties of men, among whom Robin distinguished individuals in outlandish attire, came hurrying along; but, though on both occasions, they paused to address him, such intercourse did not at all enlighten his perplexity. They did but utter a few words in some language of which Robin knew nothing, and perceiving his inability to answer, bestowed a curse upon him in plain English and hastened away. Finally, the lad determined to knock at the door of every mansion that might appear worthy to be occupied by his kinsman, trusting that perseverance would overcome the fatality that had hitherto thwarted him. Firm in this resolve, he was passing beneath the walls of a church, which formed the corner of two streets, when, as he turned into the shade of its steeple, he encountered a bulky stranger, muffled in a cloak. The man was proceeding with the speed of earnest business, but Robin planted himself full before him, holding the oak cudgel with both hands across his body as a bar to further passage.

"Halt, honest man, and answer me a question," said he, very resolutely. "Tell me, this instant, whereabouts is the dwelling of my kinsman, Major Molineux!"

"Keep your tongue between your teeth, fool, and let me pass!" said a deep, gruff voice, which Robin partly remembered. "Let me pass, or I'll strike you to the earth!"

"No, no, neighbor!" cried Robin, flourishing his cudgel, and then thrusting its larger end close to the man's muffled face. "No, no, I'm not the fool you take me for, nor do you pass till I have an answer to my question. Whereabouts is the dwelling of my kinsman, Major Molineux?"

The stranger, instead of attempting to force his passage, stepped back into the moonlight, unmuffled his face, and stared full into that of Robin.

"Watch here an hour, and Major Molineux will pass by," said he.

Robin gazed with dismay and astonishment on the unprecedented physiognomy of the speaker. The forehead with its double prominence, the broad hooked nose, the shaggy eyebrows, and fiery eyes were those which he had noticed at the inn, but the man's complexion had undergone a singular, or, more properly, a twofold change. One side of the face blazed an intense red, while the other was black as midnight, the division line being in the broad bridge of the nose; and a mouth which seemed to extend from ear to ear was black or red, in contrast to the color of the cheek. The effect was as if two individual devils, a fiend of fire and a fiend of darkness, had united themselves to form this infernal visage. The stranger grinned in Robin's face, muffled his party-colored features, and was out of sight in a moment.

"Strange things we travellers see!" ejaculated Robin.

He seated himself, however, upon the steps of the church-door, resolving to wait the appointed time for his kinsman. A few moments were consumed in philosophical speculations upon the species of man who had just left him; but having settled this point shrewdly, rationally, and satisfactorily, he was compelled to look elsewhere for his amusement. And first he threw his eyes along the street. It was of more respectable appearance than most of those into which he had wandered; and the moon, creating, like the imaginative power, a beautiful strangeness in familiar objects, gave something of romance to a scene that might not have possessed it in the light of day. The irregular and often quaint architecture of the houses, some of whose roofs were broken into numerous little peaks, while others ascended, steep and narrow, into a single point, and others again were square; the pure snow-white of some of their complexions, the aged darkness of others, and the thousand sparklings, reflected from bright substances in the walls of many; these matters engaged Robin's attention for a while, and then began to grow wearisome. Next he endeavored to define the forms of distant objects, starting away, with almost ghostly indistinctness, just as his eye appeared to grasp them; and finally he took a minute survey of an edifice which stood on the opposite side of the street, directly in front of the church-door, where he was stationed. It was a large, square mansion, distinguished from its neighbors by a balcony, which rested on tall pillars, and by an elaborate Gothic window, communicating therewith.

"Perhaps this is the very house I have been seeking," thought Robin.

Then he strove to speed away the time, by listening to a murmur which swept continually along the street, yet was scarcely audible, except to an unaccustomed ear like his; it was a low, dull, dreamy sound, compounded of many noises, each of which was at too great a distance to be separately heard. Robin marvelled at this snore of a sleeping town, and marvelled more whenever its continuity was broken by now and then a distant shout, apparently loud where it originated. But altogether it was a sleep-inspiring sound, and, to shake off its drowsy influence, Robin arose, and climbed a window-frame, that he might view the interior of the church. There the moonbeams came trembling in, and fell down upon the deserted pews, and extended along the quiet aisles. A fainter yet more awful radiance was hovering around the pulpit, and one solitary ray had dared to rest upon the open page of the great Bible. Had nature, in that deep hour, become a worshipper in the house which man had builded? Or was that heavenly light the visible sanctity of the place,—visible because no earthly and impure feet were within the walls? The scene made Robin's heart shiver with a sensation of loneliness stronger than he had ever felt in the remotest depths of his native woods; so he turned away and sat down again before the door. There were graves around the church, and now an uneasy thought obtruded into Robin's breast. What if the object of his search, which had been so often and so strangely thwarted, were all the time mouldering in his shroud? What if his kinsman should glide through yonder gate, and nod and smile to him in dimly passing by?

"Oh that any breathing thing were here with me!" said Robin.

Recalling his thoughts from this uncomfortable track, he sent them over forest, hill, and stream, and attempted to imagine how that evening of ambiguity and weariness had been spent by his father's household. He pictured them assembled at the door, beneath the tree, the great old tree, which had been spared for its huge twisted trunk and venerable shade, when a thousand leafy brethren fell. There, at the going down of the summer sun, it was his father's custom to perform domestic worship, that the neighbors might come and join with him like brothers of the family, and that the wayfaring man might pause to drink at that fountain, and keep his heart pure by freshening the memory of home. Robin distinguished the seat of every individual of the little audience; he saw the good man in the midst, holding the Scriptures in the golden light that fell from the western clouds; he beheld him close the book and all rise up to pray. He heard the old thanksgivings for daily mercies, the old supplications for their continuance, to which he had so often listened in weariness, but which were now among his dear remembrances. He perceived the slight inequality of his father's voice when he came to speak of the absent one; he noted how his mother turned her face to the broad and knotted trunk; how his elder brother scorned, because the beard was rough upon his upper lip, to permit his features to be moved; how the younger sister drew down a low hanging branch before her eyes; and how the little one of all, whose sports had hitherto broken the decorum of the scene, understood the prayer for her playmate, and burst into clamorous grief. Then he saw them go in at the door; and when Robin would have entered also, the latch tinkled into its place, and he was excluded from his home.

"Am I here, or there?" cried Robin, starting; for all at once, when his thoughts had become visible and audible in a dream, the long, wide, solitary street shone out before him.

He aroused himself, and endeavored to fix his attention steadily upon the large edifice which he had surveyed before. But still his mind kept vibrating between fancy and reality; by turns, the pillars of the balcony lengthened into the tall, bare stems of pines, dwindled down to human figures, settled again into their true shape and size, and then commenced a new succession of changes. For a single moment, when he deemed himself awake, he could have sworn that a visage—one which he seemed to remember, yet could not absolutely name as his kinsman's—was looking towards him from the Gothic window. A deeper sleep wrestled with and nearly overcame him, but fled at the sound of footsteps along the opposite pavement. Robin rubbed his eyes, discerned a man passing at the foot of the balcony, and addressed him in a loud, peevish, and lamentable cry.

"Hallo, friend! must I wait here all night for my kinsman, Major Molineux?"

The sleeping echoes awoke, and answered the voice; and the passenger, barely able to discern a figure sitting in the oblique shade of the steeple, traversed the street to obtain a nearer view. He was himself a gentleman in his prime, of open, intelligent, cheerful, and altogether prepossessing countenance. Perceiving a country youth, apparently homeless and without friends, he accosted him in a tone of real kindness, which had become strange to Robin's ears.

"Well, my good lad, why are you sitting here?" inquired he. "Can I be of service to you in any way?"

"I am afraid not, sir," replied Robin, despondingly; "yet I shall take it kindly, if you'll answer me a single question. I've been searching, half the night, for one Major Molineux. Now, sir, is there really such a person in these parts, or am I dreaming?"

"Major Molineux! The name is not altogether strange to me," said the gentleman, smiling. "Have you any objection to telling me the nature of your business with him?"

Then Robin briefly related that his father was a clergyman, settled on a small salary, at a long distance back in the country, and that he and Major Molineux were brothers' children. The Major, having inherited riches, and acquired civil and military rank, had visited his cousin, in great pomp, a year or two before; had manifested much interest in Robin and an elder brother, and, being childless himself, had thrown out hints respecting the future establishment of one of them in life. The elder brother was destined to succeed to the farm which his father cultivated in the interval of sacred duties; it was therefore determined that Robin should profit by his kinsman's generous intentions, especially as he seemed to be rather the favorite, and was thought to possess other necessary endowments.

"For I have the name of being a shrewd youth," observed Robin, in this part of his story.

"I doubt not you deserve it," replied his new friend, good-naturedly; "but pray proceed."

"Well, sir, being nearly eighteen years old, and well grown, as you see," continued Robin, drawing himself up to his full height, "I thought it high time to begin in the world. So my mother and sister put me in handsome trim, and my father gave me half the remnant of his last year's salary, and five days ago I started for this place, to pay the Major a visit. But, would you believe it, sir! I crossed the ferry a little after dark, and have yet found nobody that would show me the way to his dwelling; only, an hour or two since, I was told to wait here, and Major Molineux would pass by."

"Can you describe the man who told you this?" inquired the gentleman.

"Oh, he was a very ill-favored fellow, sir," replied Robin, "with two great bumps on his forehead, a hook nose, fiery eyes; and, what struck me as the strangest, his face was of two different colors. Do you happen to know such a man, sir?"

"Not intimately," answered the stranger, "but I chanced to meet him a little time previous to your stopping me. I believe you may trust his word, and that the Major will very shortly pass through this street. In the meantime, as I have a singular curiosity to witness your meeting, I will sit down here upon the steps and bear you company."

He seated himself accordingly, and soon engaged his companion in animated discourse. It was but of brief continuance, however, for a noise of shouting, which had long been remotely audible, drew so much nearer that Robin inquired its cause.

"What may be the meaning of this uproar?" asked he. "Truly, if your town be always as noisy, I shall find little sleep while I am an inhabitant."

"Why, indeed, friend Robin, there do appear to be three or four riotous fellows abroad to-night," replied the gentleman. "You must not expect all the stillness of your native woods here in our streets. But the watch will shortly be at the heels of these lads and"—

"Ay, and set them in the stocks by peep of day," interrupted Robin, recollecting his own encounter with the drowsy lantern-bearer. "But, dear sir, if I may trust my ears, an army of watchmen would never make head against such a multitude of rioters. There were at least a thousand voices went up to make that one shout."

"May not a man have several voices, Robin, as well as two complexions?" said his friend.

"Perhaps a man may; but Heaven forbid that a woman should!" responded the shrewd youth, thinking of the seductive tones of the Major's housekeeper.

The sounds of a trumpet in some neighboring street now became so evident and continual, that Robin's curiosity was strongly excited. In addition to the shouts, he heard frequent bursts from many instruments of discord, and a wild and confused laughter filled up the intervals. Robin rose from the steps, and looked wistfully towards a point whither people seemed to be hastening.

"Surely some prodigious merry-making is going on," exclaimed he. "I have laughed very little since I left home, sir, and should be sorry to lose an opportunity. Shall we step round the corner by that darkish house, and take our share of the fun?"

"Sit down again, sit down, good Robin," replied the gentleman, laying his hand on the skirt of the gray coat. "You forget that we must wait here for your kinsman; and there is reason to believe that he will pass by, in the course of a very few moments."

The near approach of the uproar had now disturbed the neighborhood; windows flew open on all sides; and many heads, in the attire of the pillow, and confused by sleep suddenly broken, were protruded to the gaze of whoever had leisure to observe them. Eager voices hailed each other from house to house, all demanding the explanation, which not a soul could give. Half-dressed men hurried towards the unknown commotion, stumbling as they went over the stone steps that thrust themselves into the narrow footwalk. The shouts, the laughter, and the tuneless bray, the antipodes of music, came onwards with increasing din, till scattered individuals, and then denser bodies, began to appear round a corner at the distance of a hundred yards.

"Will you recognize your kinsman, if he passes in this crowd?" inquired the gentleman.

"Indeed, I can't warrant it, sir; but I'll take my stand here, and keep a bright lookout," answered Robin, descending to the outer edge of the pavement.

A mighty stream of people now emptied into the street, and came rolling slowly towards the church. A single horseman wheeled the corner in the midst of them, and close behind him came a band of fearful wind-instruments, sending forth a fresher discord now that no intervening buildings kept it from the ear. Then a redder light disturbed the moonbeams, and a dense multitude of torches shone along the street, concealing, by their glare, whatever object they illuminated. The single horseman, clad in a military dress, and bearing a drawn sword, rode onward as the leader, and, by his fierce and variegated countenance, appeared like war personified; the red of one cheek was an emblem of fire and sword; the blackness of the other betokened the mourning that attends them. In his train were wild figures in the Indian dress, and many fantastic shapes without a model, giving the whole march a visionary air, as if a dream had broken forth from some feverish brain, and were sweeping visibly through the midnight streets. A mass of people, inactive, except as applauding spectators, hemmed the procession in; and several women ran along the sidewalk, piercing the confusion of heavier sounds with their shrill voices of mirth or terror.

"The double-faced fellow has his eye upon me," muttered Robin, with an indefinite but an uncomfortable idea that he was himself to bear a part in the pageantry.

The leader turned himself in the saddle, and fixed his glance full upon the country youth, as the steed went slowly by. When Robin had freed his eyes from those fiery ones, the musicians were passing before him, and the torches were close at hand; but the unsteady brightness of the latter formed a veil which he could not penetrate. The rattling of wheels over the stones sometimes found its way to his ear, and confused traces of a human form appeared at intervals, and then melted into the vivid light. A moment more, and the leader thundered a command to halt: the trumpets vomited a horrid breath, and then held their peace; the shouts and laughter of the people died away, and there remained only a universal hum, allied to silence. Right before Robin's eyes was an uncovered cart. There the torches blazed the brightest, there the moon shone out like day, and there, in tar-and-feathery dignity, sat his kinsman, Major Molineux!

He was an elderly man, of large and majestic person, and strong, square features, betokening a steady soul; but steady as it was, his enemies had found means to shake it. His face was pale as death, and far more ghastly; the broad forehead was contracted in his agony, so that his eyebrows formed one grizzled line; his eyes were red and wild, and the foam hung white upon his quivering lip. His whole frame was agitated by a quick and continual tremor, which his pride strove to quell, even in those circumstances of overwhelming humiliation. But perhaps the bitterest pang of all was when his eyes met those of Robin; for he evidently knew him on the instant, as the youth stood witnessing the foul disgrace of a head grown gray in honor. They stared at each other in silence, and Robin's knees shook, and his hair bristled, with a mixture of pity and terror. Soon, however, a bewildering excitement began to seize upon his mind; the preceding adventures of the night, the unexpected appearance of the crowd, the torches, the confused din and the hush that followed, the spectre of his kinsman reviled by that great multitude,—all this, and, more than all, a perception of tremendous ridicule in the whole scene, affected him with a sort of mental inebriety. At that moment a voice of sluggish merriment saluted Robin's ears; he turned instinctively, and just behind the corner of the church stood the lantern-bearer, rubbing his eyes, and drowsily enjoying the lad's amazement. Then he heard a peal of laughter like the ringing of silvery bells; a woman twitched his arm, a saucy eye met his, and he saw the lady of the scarlet petticoat. A sharp, dry cachinnation appealed to his memory, and standing on tiptoe in the crowd, with his white apron over his head, he beheld the courteous little innkeeper. And lastly, there sailed over the heads of the multitude a great, broad laugh, broken in the midst by two sepulchral hems; thus, "Haw, haw, haw,—hem, hem,—haw, haw, haw, haw!"

The sound proceeded from the balcony of the opposite edifice, and thither Robin turned his eyes. In front of the Gothic window stood the old citizen, wrapped in a wide gown, his gray periwig exchanged for a nightcap, which was thrust back from his forehead, and his silk stockings hanging about his legs. He supported himself on his polished cane in a fit of convulsive merriment, which manifested itself on his solemn old features like a funny inscription on a tombstone. Then Robin seemed to hear the voices of the barbers, of the guests of the inn, and of all who had made sport of him that night. The contagion was spreading among the multitude, when all at once, it seized upon Robin, and he sent forth a shout of laughter that echoed through the street,—every man shook his sides, every man emptied his lungs, but Robin's shout was the loudest there. The cloud-spirits peeped from their silvery islands, as the congregated mirth went roaring up the sky! The Man in the Moon heard the far bellow. "Oho," quoth he, "the old earth is frolicsome to-night!"

When there was a momentary calm in that tempestuous sea of sound, the leader gave the sign, the procession resumed its march. On they went, like fiends that throng in mockery around some dead potentate, mighty no more, but majestic still in his agony. On they went, in counterfeited pomp, in senseless uproar, in frenzied merriment, trampling all on an old man's heart. On swept the tumult, and left a silent street behind.

"Well, Robin, are you dreaming?" inquired the gentleman, laying his hand on the youth's shoulder.

Robin started, and withdrew his arm from the stone post to which he had instinctively clung, as the living stream rolled by him. His cheek was somewhat pale, and his eye not quite as lively as in the earlier part of the evening.

"Will you be kind enough to show me the way to the ferry?" said he, after a moment's pause.

"You have, then, adopted a new subject of inquiry?" observed his companion, with a smile.

"Why, yes, sir," replied Robin, rather dryly. "Thanks to you, and to my other friends, I have at last met my kinsman, and he will scarce desire to see my face again. I begin to grow weary of a town life, sir. Will you show me the way to the ferry?"

"No, my good friend Robin,—not to-night, at least," said the gentleman. "Some few days hence, if you wish it, I will speed you on your journey. Or, if you prefer to remain with us, perhaps, as you are a shrewd youth, you may rise in the world without the help of your kinsman, Major Molineux."

STUDY QUESTIONS:

1. Writing about this story Robert Cantwell says that the subject is "the grotesque unconnection between the human being and the social unit" and that "the strongest, boldest, most novel thing about it is that it is done with humor." Comment on Mr. Cantwell's statement.

2. Hawthorne was a writer who liked constantly to use symbols in his stories, and there are a number of symbols in this one. Can you find several? What do you think Robin's cudgel might stand for?

3. Notice how laughter grows in this story, until at the very end the whole community is laughing. Why does Robin laugh when he sees his kinsman in disgrace?

4. Why does the stranger insist that Robin remain in the town for a few days?

5. The desecration of an individual by an entire community is a fairly common theme in literature. Can you think of other works in which a person is disgraced and brutalized in the manner of Major Molineux?

I'M A FOOL

SHERWOOD ANDERSON

Sherwood Anderson (1876–1941), who, tiring of a business life, came to writing when he was forty, achieved his first success with a book called *Winesburg, Ohio* (1919), a collection of inter-related stories and sketches about the citizens of a small town. The point of the book is the gap between what is conventionally expected of them as respectable and normal persons, and their actual, inner lives. Anderson was a member of the literary generation that changed the whole trend of American writing, particularly of fiction, by insisting that the essential life of a human lies deep within him and is not measurable in terms of logic and formal motive and behavior.

The sub-title of one of the collections of Anderson's work is informative: "A book of impressions from American life in tales and poems." Impressions—that is, the giving back to the reader, if I am a writer, of my subjective or private responses to experience or of those responses of a character into whose being I have deeply entered—were for Anderson the true stuff of art. If writing is to accomplish this, any line between prose and poetry will tend to disappear, and the formal elements of structure become less important than truth in phrasing what the author (or the character) feels.

343

"I'm A Fool" retains a formal structure. The narrative leads up to a
climax in which the boy sees the folly of pretense and dishonesty. Because
he has told a stupid lie in order to impress his new friends, he knows that
they can be friends of his no longer. But though the form of the story is
conventional, the narrative concerns what the boy feels more than what he
does. To make us realize this vividly Anderson pretends the boy is writing
his narrative. Thus he keeps within the range of a boy's talk (just as Mark
Twain does in *Huckleberry Finn*); he deliberately commits grammatical and
syntactical errors that are natural to such a boy, and he lets his boy refer
to Negroes (a race the lad admires for their loyalty) as niggers because that
word is in the boy's tradition and means no harm. It is wonderful how richly
Anderson creates a teen-ager's view of the world. Some of the boy's slang
seems dated to us now, but his feelings in this acutely embarrassing situation are genuine and wholly understandable.

It was a hard jolt for me, one of the most bitterest I ever had to face.
And it all came about through my own foolishness, too. Even yet sometimes,
when I think of it, I want to cry or swear or kick myself. Perhaps, even now,
after all this time, there will be a kind of satisfaction in making myself look
cheap by telling of it.

It began at three o'clock one October afternoon as I sat in the grandstand at the fall trotting and pacing meet at Sandusky, Ohio.

To tell the truth, I felt a little foolish that I should be sitting in the
grandstand at all. During the summer before I had left my home town with
Harry Whitehead and, with a nigger named Burt, had taken a job as swipe
with one of the two horses Harry was campaigning through the fall race meets
that year. Mother cried, and my sister Mildred, who wanted to get a job as
a school-teacher in our town that fall, stormed and scolded about the house
all during the week before I left. They both thought it something disgraceful
that one of our family should take a place as a swipe with race-horses. I've
an idea Mildred thought my taking the place would stand in the way of her
getting the job she'd been working so long for.

But after all, I had to work, and there was no other work to be got. A
big lumbering fellow of nineteen couldn't just hang around the house, and
I had got too big to mow people's lawns and sell newspapers. Little chaps
who could get next to people's sympathies by their sizes were always getting
jobs away from me. There was one fellow who kept saying to everyone who
wanted a lawn mowed or a cistern cleaned, that he was saving money to
work his way through college, and I used to lay awake nights thinking up

ways to injure him without being found out. I kept thinking of wagons running over him and bricks falling on his head as he walked along the street. But never mind him.

I got the place with Harry and I liked Burt fine. We got along splendid together. He was a big nigger with a lazy, sprawling body and soft, kind eyes, and when it came to a fight, he could hit like Jack Johnson. He had Bucephalus, a big black pacing stallion that could do 2.09 or 2.10 if he had to, and I had a little gelding named Doctor Fritz that never lost a race all fall when Harry wanted him to win.

We set out from home late in July in a boxcar with the two horses, and after that, until late November, we kept moving along to the race meets and the fairs. It was a peachy time for me, I'll say that. Sometimes now I think that boys who are raised regular in houses, and never have a fine nigger like Burt for best friend, and go to high schools and college, and never steal anything, or get drunk a little, or learn to swear from fellows who know how, or come walking up in front of a grandstand in their shirt-sleeves and with dirty horsey pants on when the races are going on and the grandstand is full of people all dressed up—— What's the use of talking about it? Such fellows don't know nothing at all. They've never had no opportunity.

But I did. Burt taught me how to rub down a horse and put the bandages on after a race and steam a horse out and a lot of valuable things for any man to know. He could wrap a bandage on a horse's leg so smooth that if it had been the same color you would think it was his skin, and I guess he'd have been a big driver, too, and got to the top like Murphy and Walter Cox and the others if he hadn't been black.

Gee whizz, it was fun. You got to a county-seat town, maybe say on a Saturday or Sunday, and the fair began the next Tuesday and lasted until Friday afternoon. Doctor Fritz would be, say in the 2.25 trot on Tuesday afternoon, and on Thursday afternoon Bucephalus would knock 'em cold in the 'free-for-all' pace. It left you a lot of time to hang around and listen to horse talk, and see Burt knock some yap cold that got too gay, and you'd find out about horses and men and pick up a lot of stuff you could use all the rest of your life, if you had some sense and salted down what you heard and felt and saw.

And then at the end of the week when the race meet was over, and Harry had run home to tend up to his livery-stable business, you and Burt hitched the two horses to carts and drove slow and steady across country, to the place for the next meeting, so as to not overheat the horses, etc., etc., you know.

Gee whizz, Gosh amighty, the nice hickory-nut and beech-nut and oaks and other kinds of trees along the roads, all brown and red, and the good smells, and Burt singing a song that was called Deep River, and the country girls at the windows of houses and everything. You can stick your colleges up your nose for all me. I guess I know where I got my education.

Why, one of those little burgs of towns you come to on the way, say now on a Saturday afternoon, and Burt says, 'Let's lay up here.' And you did.

And you took the horses to a livery stable and fed them, and you got your good clothes out of a box and put them on.

And the town was full of farmers gaping, because they could see you were race-horse people, and the kids maybe never see a nigger before and was afraid and run away when the two of us walked down their main street.

And that was before prohibition and all that foolishness, and so you went into a saloon, the two of you, and all the yaps come and stood around, and there was always someone pretended he was horsey and knew things and spoke up and began asking questions, and all you did was to lie and lie all you could about what horses you had, and I said I owned them, and then some fellow said, 'Will you have a drink of whiskey?' and Burt knocked his eye out the way he could say, offhand like, 'Oh, well, all right I'm agreeable to a little nip. I'll split a quart with you.' Gee whizz.

But that isn't what I want to tell my story about. We got home late in November and I promised mother I'd quit the race-horses for good. There's a lot of things you've got to promise a mother because she don't know any better.

And so, there not being any work in our town any more than when I left there to go to the races, I went off to Sandusky and got a pretty good place taking care of horses for a man who owned a teaming and delivery and storage and coal and real estate business there. It was a pretty good place with good eats, and a day off each week, and sleeping on a cot in a big barn, and mostly just shoveling in hay and oats to a lot of big good-enough skates of horses, that couldn't have trotted a race with a toad. I wasn't dissatisfied and I could send money home.

And then, as I started to tell you, the fall races come to Sandusky and I got the day off and I went. I left the job at noon and had on my good clothes and my new brown derby hat, I'd just bought the Saturday before, and a stand-up collar.

First of all I went downtown and walked about with the dudes. I've always thought to myself, 'Put up a good front,' and so I did it. I had forty dollars in my pocket and so I went into the West House, a big hotel, and walked up to the cigar stand. 'Give me three twenty-five-cent cigars,' I said. There was a lot of horsemen and strangers and dressed-up people from other towns standing around in the lobby and in the bar, and I mingled amongst them. In the bar there was a fellow with a cane and a Windsor tie on, that it made me sick to look at him. I like a man to be a man and dress up, but not to go put on that kind of airs. So I pushed him aside, kind of rough, and had me a drink of whiskey. And then he looked at me, as though he thought maybe he'd get gay, but he changed his mind and didn't say anything. And then I had another drink of whiskey, just to show him something, and went out and had a hack out to the races, all to myself, and when I got there I bought myself the best seat I could get up in the grandstand, but didn't go in for any of these boxes. That's putting on too many airs.

And so there I was, sitting up in the grandstand as gay as you please and looking down on the swipes coming out with their horses, and with their dirty horsey pants on and the horse blankets swung over their shoulders, same as I had been doing all the year before. I liked one thing about the same as the other, sitting up there and feeling grand and being down there and looking up at the yaps and feeling grander and more important, too. One thing's about as good as another, if you take it just right. I've often said that.

Well, right in front of me, in the grandstand that day, there was a fellow with a couple of girls and they was about my age. The young fellow was a nice guy all right. He was the kind maybe that goes to college and then comes to be a lawyer or maybe a newspaper editor or something like that, but he wasn't stuck on himself. There are some of that kind are all right and he was one of the ones.

He had his sister with him and another girl and the sister looked around over his shoulder, accidental at first, not intending to start anything—she wasn't that kind—and her eyes and mine happened to meet.

You know how it is. Gee, she was a peach! She had on a soft dress, kind of a blue stuff and it looked carelessly made, but was well sewed and made and everything. I knew that much. I blushed when she looked right at me and so did she. She was the nicest girl I've ever seen in my life. She wasn't stuck on herself and she could talk proper grammar without being like a school-teacher or something like that. What I mean is, she was O.K. I think maybe her father was well-to-do, but not rich to make her chesty because she was his daughter, as some are. Maybe he owned a drugstore or a dry-goods store in their home town, or something like that. She never told me and I never asked.

My own people are all O.K. too, when you come to that. My grandfather was Welsh and over in the old country, in Wales he was——— But never mind that.

The first heat of the first race come off and the young fellow setting there with the two girls left them and went down to make a bet. I knew what he was up to, but he didn't talk big and noisy and let everyone around know he was a sport, as some do. He wasn't that kind. Well, he come back and I heard him tell the two girls what horse he'd bet on, and when the heat was trotted they all half got to their feet and acted in the excited, sweaty way people do when they've got money down on a race, and the horse they bet on is up there pretty close at the end, and they think maybe he'll come on with a rush, but he never does because he hasn't got the old juice in him, come right down to it.

And then, pretty soon, the horses came out for the 2.18 pace and there was a horse in it I knew. He was a horse Bob French had in his string, but Bob didn't own him. He was a horse owned by a Mr. Mathers down at Marietta, Ohio.

This Mr. Mathers had a lot of money and owned some coal mines or something, and he had a swell place out in the country, and he was stuck on race-horses, but was a Presbyterian or something, and I think more than likely his wife was one, too, maybe a stiffer one than himself. So he never raced his horses hisself, and the story round the Ohio race-tracks was that when one of his horses got ready to go to the races, he turned him over to Bob French and pretended to his wife he was sold.

So Bob had the horses and he did pretty much as he pleased and you can't blame Bob, at least, I never did. Sometimes he was out to win and sometimes he wasn't. I never cared much about that when I was swiping a horse. What I did want to know was that my horse had the speed and could go out in front, if you wanted him to.

And, as I'm telling you, there was Bob in this race with one of Mr. Mathers' horses, was named 'About Ben Ahem' or something like that, and was fast as a streak. He was a gelding and had a mark of 2.21, but could step in .08 or .09.

Because when Burt and I were out, as I've told you, the year before, there was a nigger Burt knew, worked for Mr. Mathers and we went out there one day when we didn't have no race on at the Marietta Fair and our boss Harry was gone home.

And so everyone was gone to the fair but just this one nigger and he took us all through Mr. Mathers' swell house and he and Burt tapped a bottle of wine Mr. Mathers had hid in his bedroom, back in a closet, without his wife knowing, and he showed us this Ahem horse. Burt was always stuck on being a driver, but didn't have much chance to get to the top, being a nigger, and he and the other nigger gulped that whole bottle of wine and Burt got a little lit up.

So the nigger let Burt take this About Ben Ahem and step him a mile in a track Mr. Mathers had all to himself, right there on the farm. And Mr. Mathers had one child, a daughter, kinda sick and not very good-looking, and she came home and we had to hustle and get About Ben Ahem stuck back in the barn.

I'm only telling you to get everything straight. At Sandusky, that afternoon I was at the fair, this young fellow with the two girls was fussed, being with the girls and losing his bet. You know how a fellow is that way. One of them was his girl and the other his sister. I had figured that out.

'Gee whizz,' I says to myself, 'I'm going to give him the dope.' He was mighty nice when I touched him on the shoulder. He and the girls were nice to me right from the start and clear to the end. I'm not blaming them.

And so he leaned back and I give him the dope on About Ben Ahem. 'Don't bet a cent on this first heat because he'll go like an oxen hitched to a plow, but when the first heat is over go right down and lay on your pile.' That's what I told him.

Well, I never saw a fellow treat any one sweller. There was a fat man sitting beside the little girl, that had looked at me twice by this time, and I at her, and both blushing, and what did he do but have the nerve to turn and ask the fat man to get up and change places with me so I could set with his crowd.

Gee whizz, craps almighty. There I was. What a chump I was to go and get gay up there in the West House bar, and just because that dude was standing there with a cane and that kind of a necktie on, to go and get all balled up and drink that whiskey, just to show off.

Of course she would know, me setting right beside her and letting her smell of my breath. I could have kicked myself right down out of that grandstand and all around that race track and made a faster record than most of the skates of horses they had there that year.

Because that girl wasn't any mutt of a girl. What wouldn't I have give right then for a stick of chewing gum to chew, or a lozenger, or some liquorice, or most anything. I was glad I had those twenty-five-cent cigars in my pocket and right away I give that fellow one and lit one myself. Then that fat man got up and we changed places and there I was, plunked right down beside her.

They introduced themselves and the fellow's best girl, he had with him, was named Miss Elinor Woodbury, and her father was a manufacturer of barrels from a place called Tiffin, Ohio. And the fellow himself was named Wilbur Wessen and his sister was Miss Lucy Wessen.

I suppose it was their having such swell names got me off my trolley. A fellow, just because he has been a swipe with a race-horse, and works taking care of horses for a man in the teaming, delivery, and storage business, isn't any better or worse than anyone else. I've often thought that, and said it too.

But you know how a fellow is. There's something in that kind of nice clothes, and the kind of nice eyes she had, and the way she had looked at me, awhile before, over her brother's shoulder, and me looking back at her, and both of us blushing.

I couldn't show her up for a boob, could I?

I made a fool of myself, that's what I did. I said my name was Walter Mathers from Marietta, Ohio, and then I told all three of them the smashingest lie you ever heard. What I said was that my father owned the horse About Ben Ahem and that he had let him out to this Bob French for racing purposes, because our family was proud and had never gone into racing that way, in our own name, I mean. Then I had got started and they were all leaning over and listening, and Miss Lucy Wessen's eyes were shining, and I went the whole hog.

I told about our place down at Marietta, and about the big stables and the grand brick house we had on a hill, up above the Ohio River, but I knew enough not to do it in no bragging way. What I did was to start things and then let them drag the rest out of me. I acted just as reluctant to tell as I could. Our family hasn' got any barrel factory, and, since I've known us, we've always been pretty poor, but not asking anything of any one at that, and my grandfather, over in Wales—but never mind that.

We set there talking like we had known each other for years and years, and I went and told them that my father had been expecting maybe this Bob French wasn't on the square, and had sent me up to Sandusky on the sly to find out what I could.

And I bluffed it through I had found out all about the 2.18 pace, in which About Ben Ahem was to start.

I said he would lose the first heat by pacing like a lame cow and then he would come back and skin 'em alive after that. And to back up what I said I took thirty dollars out of my pocket and handed it to Mr. Wilbur Wessen and asked him, would he mind, after the first heat, to go down and place it on About Ben Ahem for whatever odds he could get. What I said was that I didn't want Bob French to see me and none of the swipes.

Sure enough the first heat come off and About Ben Ahem went off his stride, up the back stretch, and looked like a wooden horse or a sick one, and come in to be last. Then this Wilbur Wessen went down to the betting place under the grandstand and there I was with the two girls, and when that Miss Woodbury was looking the other way once, Lucy Wessen kinda, with her shoulder you know, kinda touched me. Not just tucking down, I don't mean. You know how a woman can do. They get close, but not getting gay either. You know what they do. Gee whiz.

And then they give me a jolt. What they had done, when I didn't know, was to get together, and they had decided Wilbur Wessen would bet fifty dollars, and the two girls had gone and put in ten dollars each, of their own money, too. I was sick then, but I was sicker later.

About the gelding, About Ben Ahem, and their winning their money, I wasn't worried a lot about that. It come out O.K. Ahem stepped the next three heats like a bushel of spoiled eggs going to market before they could be found out, and Wilbur Wessen had got nine to two for the money. There was something else eating at me.

Because Wilbur come back, after he had bet the money, and after that he spent most of his time talking to that Miss Woodbury, and Lucy Wessen and I was left alone together like on a desert island. Gee, if I'd only been on the square or if there had been any way of getting myself on the square. There ain't any Walter Mathers, like I said to her and them, and there hasn't ever been one, but if there was, I bet I'd go to Marietta, Ohio, and shoot him tomorrow.

There I was, big boob that I am. Pretty soon the race was over, and Wilbur had gone down and collected our money, and we had a hack downtown, and he stood us a swell supper at the West House, and a bottle of champagne beside.

And I was with that girl and she wasn't saying much, and I wasn't saying much either. One thing I know. She wasn't stuck on me because of the lie about my father being rich and all that. There's a way you know. . . . Craps amighty. There's a kind of girl, you see just once in your life, and if you don't get busy and make hay, then you're gone for good and all, and might as well go jump off a bridge. They give you a look from inside of them somewhere, and it ain't no vamping, and what it means is—you want that girl to be your wife, and you want nice things around her like flowers and swell clothes, and you want her to have the kids you're going to have, and you want good music played and no ragtime. Gee whizz.

There's a place over near Sandusky, across a kind of bay, and it's called Cedar Point. And after we had supper we went over to it in a launch, all by ourselves. Wilbur and Miss Lucy and that Miss Woodbury had to catch a ten-o'clock train back to Tiffin, Ohio, because, when you're out with girls like that, you can't get careless and miss any trains and stay out all night, like you can with some kinds of dames.

And Wilbur blowed himself to the launch and it cost him fifteen cold plunks, but I wouldn't never have knew if I hadn't listened. He wasn't no tin-horn kind of a sport.

Over at the Cedar Point place, we didn't stay around where there was a gang of common kind of cattle at all.

There was big dance halls and dining places for yaps, and there was a beach you could walk along and get where it was dark, and we went there.

She didn't talk hardly at all and neither did I, and I was thinking how glad I was my mother was all right, and always made us kids learn to eat with a fork at table, and not swill soup, and not be noisy and rough like a gang you see around a race track that way.

Then Wilbur and his girl went away up the beach and Lucy and I sat down in a dark place, where there was some roots of old trees the water had washed up, and after that the time, till we had to go back in the launch and they had to catch their trains, wasn't nothing at all. It went like winking your eye.

Here's how it was. The place we were setting in was dark, like I said, and there was the roots from that old stump sticking up like arms, and there was a watery smell, and the night was like—as if you could put your hand out and feel it—so warm and soft and dark and sweet like an orange.

I most cried and I most swore and I most jumped up and danced, I was so mad and happy and sad.

When Wilbur come back from being alone with his girl, and she saw him coming, Lucy she says, 'we got to go to the train now,' and she was most crying too, but she never knew anything I knew, and she couldn't be so all busted up. And then, before Wilbur and Miss Woodbury got up to where we was, she put her face up and kissed me quick and put her head up against me and she was all quivering and——Gee whizz.

Sometimes I hope I have cancer and die. I guess you know what I mean. We went in the launch across the bay to the train like that, and it was dark, too. She whispered and said it was like she and I could get out of the boat and walk on the water, and it sounded foolish, but I knew what she meant.

And then quick we were right at the depot, and there was a big bang of yaps, the kind that goes to the fairs, and crowded and milling around like cattle, and how could I tell her? 'It won't be long because you'll write and I'll write to you.' That's all she said.

I got a chance like a hay barn afire. A swell chance I got.

And maybe she would write me, down at Marietta that way, and the letter would come back, and stamped on the front of it by the U.S.A. 'There ain't any such guy,' or something like that, whatever they stamp on a letter that way.

And me trying to pass myself off for a bigbug and a swell—to her, as decent a little body as God ever made. Craps amighty—a swell chance I got!

And then the train come in, and she got on it, and Wilbur Wessen he come and shook hands with me, and that Miss Woodbury was nice too and bowed to me, and I at her, and the train went and I busted out and cried like a kid.

Gee, I could have run after that train and made Dan Patch look like a freight train after a wreck, but, socks amighty, what was the use? Did you ever see such a fool?

I'll bet you what—if I had an arm broke right now or a train had run over my foot—I wouldn't go to no doctor at all. I'd go set down and let her hurt and hurt—that's what I'd do.

I'll bet you what—if I hadn't drunk that booze I'd a never been such a boob as to go tell such a lie—that couldn't never be made straight to a lady like her.

I wish I had that fellow right here that had on a Windsor tie and carried a cane. I'd smash him for fair. Gosh darn his eyes. He's a big fool—that's what he is.

And if I'm not another you just go find me one and I'll quit working and be a bum and give him my job. I don't care nothing for working, and earning money, and saving it for no such boob as myself.

STUDY QUESTIONS:

1. Here is a quotation from one of *The Adventurer* papers by Dr. Samuel Johnson. How does it apply to "I'm A Fool"?

> At length the journey was at and end; and time and chance, that strip off all disguises, have discovered that the intimate of lords and dukes is a nobleman's butler, who has furnished a shop with the money he has saved; the man who deals so largely in the funds is a clerk of a broker in 'Change Alley; the lady who so carefully concealed her quality keeps a cook-shop behind the Exchange; and the young man who is so happy

in the friendship of judges engrosses and transcribes for bread in a garret of the Temple . . .

I could not forbear to reflect on the folly of practising a fraud
which, as the event showed, had been practised too often to succeed, and
by the success of which no advantage could have been obtained; of
assuming a character which was to end with the day, and of claiming upon
false pretences honours which must perish with the breath that paid them.

2. This is, to be sure, a story about the consequences of a lie, but isn't it
something more as well? How is it also the story of a boy becoming a man?

3. "I'm A Fool" is rich in Americana—that is, in the objects, fads, and
interests characteristic of American life at a particular period. List evidences of
Americana in the story and then write a paragraph on what you think the life of
that time (1910–1915) was like.

4. This, again, is a first-person narrator story. Do you think the boy's
account of everything is *absolutely* to be believed? How much is he boasting? For
example, do you think he had had enough whisky so that his new friends would
have smelled it on his breath?

5. Horse racing is one of the oldest of American sporting interests. How
much does the color of the race track add to the story?

6. You may be interested in comparing this story with "I Want To Know
Why," another story by Sherwood Anderson about horse racing; or even with "The
Rocking-Horse Winner," by D. H. Lawrence, which is in this book. If so, write
a brief analysis in which you contrast the *tone* of the stories.

MADAM LA GIMP

DAMON RUNYON

Damon Runyon (1884–1946), one of the most beloved figures in modern journalism, particularly among his fellow newspapermen, had a lively career as a reporter. His first jobs were in the West, and he worked successively on the Denver *News*, the Denver *Post*, the Denver *Republican*, and the San Francisco *Post*. Eventually he came to New York to cover sports events for the New York *American*. Baseball and boxing were his particular interests. His editors were quick to see that he was much more than the routine reporter and soon his work was being syndicated by King Features and eventually by International News Service. Later he had his own column, "The Brighter Day," and many of the pieces by which he is best remembered made their first appearance here.

As a newspaperman he was brought into contact with a lot of colorful people, some of them only a few steps ahead of the law. New York reporters keep very late hours, and they tend to gather at a few all-night restaurants where they might be able to pick up a story. At these places they naturally run into big-city types of all varieties, night-club entertainers, fight promoters, gamblers, and the riff-raff of the streets. Damon Runyon created a fictional world of these people in a group of short stories which appeared in popular magazines like *Collier's* (no longer published) and *The Saturday Evening Post*. He gave the characters names that sound wildly implausible, though readers of Runyon who know his scene insist that they are accurate enough. At any rate, the world of his stories, as "Madam La Gimp" demonstrates, is a zany one, where morality is very casual and everyone is out to "make a fast buck."

It is also a curiously sentimental world. The theme of the tough guy with a heart of gold is a persistent one in American literature. One finds it in Mark Twain, Bret Harte, O. Henry. It is the stock-in-trade of the melodramatist; consequently it is most popular with the writer of sentimental ballads, television serials, and Grade B (or, for that matter, often Grade A) motion picture scenarios. Damon Runyon's characters, however unscrupulous they may be, pretty generally have hearts of gold, and it is this constant insistence on the sentimental which keeps Runyon from the first rank of writers of fiction.

Some readers of Runyon have insisted that his stories are very severe indictments of modern society and that they should be read somewhat as we read the stories of Maxim Gorki or Emile Zola—stories of degradation, of men and women whom the city has forced into predatory viciousness. Certainly there is unpleasantness enough in Runyon, but the main emphasis is the humor, and it is because "Madam La Gimp" is a funny story and represents one kind of humorous short story which has been exceedingly popular in our time that it is included here. It has its very "corny" moments, but, for that matter, so has Charles Dickens.

One night I am passing the corner of Fiftieth Street and Broadway, and what do I see but Dave the Dude standing in a doorway talking to a busted-down old Spanish doll by the name of Madame La Gimp. Or rather Madame La Gimp is talking to Dave the Dude, and what is more he is listening to her, because I can hear him say yes, yes, as he always does when he is really listening to anybody, which is very seldom.

Now this is a most surprising sight to me, because Madame La Gimp is not such an old doll as anybody will wish to listen to especially Dave the Dude. In fact, she is nothing but an old haybag, and generally somewhat ginned up. For fifteen years, or maybe sixteen, I see Madame La Gimp up and down Broadway, or sliding along through the Forties, sometimes selling newspapers, and sometimes selling flowers, and in all these years I seldom see her but what she seems to have about half a heat on from drinking gin.

Of course nobody ever takes the newspapers she sells, even after they buy them off of her, because they are generally yesterday's papers, and sometimes last week's, and nobody ever wants her flowers, even after they pay her for them, because they are flowers such as she gets off an undertaker over in Tenth Avenue, and they are very tired flowers, indeed.

Personally, I consider Madame La Gimp nothing but an old pest, but kind-hearted guys like Dave the Dude always stake her to a few pieces of silver when she comes shuffling along putting on the moan about her tough luck. She walks with a gimp in one leg, which is why she is called Madame La Gimp, and years ago I hear somebody say Madame La Gimp is once a Spanish dancer, and a big shot on Broadway, but that she meets up with an accident which puts her out of the dancing dodge, and that a busted romance makes her become a gin-head.

I remember somebody telling me once that Madame La Gimp is quite a beauty in her day, and has her own servants, and all this and that, but I always hear the same thing about every bum on Broadway, male and female, including some I know are bums, in spades, right from taw, so I do not pay any attention to these stories.

Still, I am willing to allow that maybe Madame La Gimp is once a fair looker, at that, and the chances are has a fair shape, because once or twice I see her when she is not ginned up, and has her hair combed, and she is not so bad-looking, although even then if you put her in a claiming race I do not think there is any danger of anybody claiming her out of it.

Mostly she is wearing raggedy clothes, and busted shoes, and her gray hair is generally hanging down her face, and when I say she is maybe fifty years old I am giving her plenty the best of it. Although she is Spanish, Madame La Gimp talks good English, and in fact she can cuss in English as good as anybody I ever hear, barring Dave the Dude.

Well, anyway, when Dave the Dude sees me as he is listening to Madame La Gimp, he motions me to wait, so I wait until she finally gets through gabbing to him and goes gimping away. Then Dave the Dude comes over to me looking much worried.

"This is quite a situation," Dave says. "The old doll is in a tough spot. It seems that she once has a baby which she calls by the name of Eulalie, being it is a girl baby, and she ships this baby off to her sister in a little town in Spain to raise up, because Madame La Gimp figures a baby is not apt to get much raising-up off of her as long as she is on Broadway. Well, this baby is on her way here. In fact," Dave says, "she will land next Saturday and here it is Wednesday already."

"Where is the baby's papa?" I ask Dave the Dude.

"Well," Dave says, "I do not ask Madame La Gimp this, because I do not consider it a fair question. A guy who goes around this town asking where babies' papas are, or even who they are, is apt to get the name of being nosey. Anyway, this has nothing whatever to do with the proposition, which is that Madame La Gimp's baby, Eulalie, is arriving here.

"Now," Dave says, "it seems that Madame La Gimp's baby, being now eighteen years old, is engaged to marry the son of a very proud old Spanish nobleman who lives in this little town in Spain, and it also seems that the very proud old Spanish nobleman, and his ever-loving wife, and the son, and Madame La Gimp's sister, are all with the baby. They are making a tour of the whole world, and will stop over here a couple of days just to see Madame La Gimp."

"It is commencing to sound to me like a movie such as a guy is apt to see at a midnight show," I say.

"Wait a minute," Dave says, getting impatient. "You are too gabby to suit me. Now it seems that the proud old Spanish nobleman does not wish his son to marry any lob, and one reason he is coming here is to look over Madame La Gimp, and see that she is okay. He thinks that Madame La Gimp's baby's own papa is dead, and that Madame La Gimp is now married to one of the richest and most aristocratic guys in America."

"How does the proud old Spanish nobleman get such an idea as this?" I ask. "It is a sure thing he never sees Madame La Gimp, or even a photograph of her as she is at present."

"I will tell you how," Dave the Dude says. "It seems Madame La Gimp gives her baby the idea that such is the case in her letters to her. It seems Madame La Gimp does a little scrubbing business around a swell apartment hotel in Park Avenue that is called the Marberry, and she cops stationery there and writes her baby in Spain on this stationery saying this is where she lives, and how rich and aristocratic her husband is. And what is more, Madame La Gimp has letters from her baby sent to her in care of the hotel and gets them out of the employees' mail."

"Why," I say, "Madame La Gimp is nothing but an old fraud to deceive people in this manner, especially a proud old Spanish nobleman. And," I say, "this proud old Spanish nobleman must be something of a chump to believe a mother will keep away from her baby all these years, especially if the mother has plenty of dough, although of course I do not know just how smart a proud old Spanish nobleman can be."

"Well," Dave says, "Madame La Gimp tells me the thing that makes the biggest hit of all with the proud old Spanish nobleman is that she keeps her baby in Spain all these years because she wishes her raised up a true Spanish baby in every respect until she is old enough to know what time it is. But I judge the proud old Spanish nobleman is none too bright, at that," Dave says, "because Madame La Gimp tells me he always lives in this little town which does not even have running water in the bathrooms.

"But what I am getting at is this," Dave says. "We must have Madame La Gimp in a swell apartment in the Marberry with a rich and aristocratic guy for a husband by the time her baby gets here, because if the proud old Spanish nobleman finds out Madame La Gimp is nothing but a bum, it is a hundred to one he will cancel his son's engagement to Madame La Gimp's baby and break a lot of people's hearts, including his son's.

"Madame La Gimp tells me her baby is daffy about the young guy, and he is daffy about her, and there are enough broken hearts in this town as it is. I know how I will get the apartment, so you go and bring me Judge Henry G. Blake for a rich and aristocratic husband, or anyway for a husband."

Well, I know Dave the Dude to do many a daffy thing but never a thing as daffy as this. But I know there is no use arguing with him when he gets an idea, because if you argue with Dave the Dude too much he is apt to reach over and lay his Sunday punch on your snoot, and no argument is worth a punch on the snoot, especially from Dave the Dude.

So I go out looking for Judge Henry G. Blake to be Madame La Gimp's husband, although I am not so sure Judge Henry G. Blake will care to be anybody's husband, and especially Madame La Gimp's after he gets a load of her, for Judge Henry G. Blake is kind of a classy old guy.

To look at Judge Henry G. Blake, with his gray hair, and his nose glasses, and his stomach, you will think he is very important people, indeed. Of course Judge Henry G. Blake is not a judge, and never is a judge, but they call him Judge because he looks like a judge, and talks slow, and puts in many long words, which very few people understand.

They tell me Judge Blake once has plenty of dough, and is quite a guy in Wall Street, and a high shot along Broadway, but he misses a few guesses at the market, and winds up without much dough, as guys generally do who miss guesses at the market. What Judge Henry G. Blake does for a living at this time nobody knows, because he does nothing much whatever, and yet he seems to be a producer in a small way at all times.

Now and then he makes a trip across the ocean with such as Little Manuel, and other guys who ride the tubs, and sits in with them on games of bridge, and one thing and another, when they need him. Very often when he is riding the tubs, Little Manuel runs into some guy he cannot cheat, so he has to call in Judge Henry G. Blake to outplay the guy on the level, although of course Little Manuel will much rather get a guy's dough by cheating him than by outplaying him on the level. Why this is, I do not know, but this is the way Little Manuel is.

Anyway, you cannot say Judge Henry G. Blake is a bum, especially as he wears good clothes, with a wing collar, and a derby hat, and most people consider him a very nice old man. Personally I never catch the judge out of line on any proposition whatever, and he always says hello to me, very pleasant.

It takes me several hours to find Judge Henry G. Blake, but finally I locate him in Derle's billiard room playing a game of pool with a guy from Providence, Rhode Island. It seems the judge is playing the guy from Providence for five cents a ball, and the judge is about thirteen balls behind when I step into the joint, because naturally at five cents a ball the judge wishes the guy from Providence to win, so as to encourage him to play for maybe twenty-five cents a ball, the judge being very cute this way.

Well, when I step in I see the judge miss a shot anybody can make blindfolded, but as soon as I give him the office I wish to speak to him, the judge hauls off and belts in every ball on the table, bingity-bing, the last shot being a bank that will make Al de Oro stop and think, because when it comes to pool, the old judge is just naturally a curly wolf.

Afterwards he tells me he is very sorry I make him hurry up this way, because of course after the last shot he is never going to get the guy from Providence to play him pool even for fun, and the judge tells me the guy sizes up as a right good thing, at that.

Now Judge Henry G. Blake is not so excited when I tell him what Dave the Dude wishes to see him about, but naturally he is willing to do anything for Dave, because he knows that guys who are not willing to do things for Dave the Dude often have bad luck. The judge tells me that he is afraid he will not make much of a husband because he tries it before several times on his own hook and is always a bust, but as long as this time it is not to be anything serious, he will tackle it. Anyway, Judge Henry G. Blake says, being aristocratic will come natural to him.

Well, when Dave the Dude starts out on any proposition, he is a wonder for fast working. The first thing he does is to turn Madame La Gimp over to Miss Billy Perry, who is now Dave's ever-loving wife which he takes out of tap-dancing in Miss Missouri Martin's Sixteen Hundred Club, and Miss Billy Perry calls in Miss Missouri Martin to help.

This is water on Miss Missouri Martin's wheel, because if there is anything she loves it is to stick her nose in other people's business, no matter what it is, but she is quite a help at that, although at first they have a tough time keeping her from telling Waldo Winchester, the scribe, about the whole cat-hop, so he will put a story in the *Morning Item* about it, with Miss Missouri Martin's name in it. Miss Missouri Martin does not believe in ever overlooking any publicity bets on the layout.

Anyway, it seems that between them Miss Billy Perry and Miss Missouri Martin get Madame La Gimp dolled up in a lot of new clothes, and run her through one of these beauty joints until she comes out very much changed, indeed. Afterwards I hear Miss Billy Perry and Miss Missouri Martin have quite a few words, because Miss Missouri Martin wishes to paint Madame La Gimp's hair the same color as her own, which is a high yellow, and buy her the same kind of dresses which Miss Missouri Martin wears herself, and Miss Missouri Martin gets much insulted when Miss Billy Perry says no, they are trying to dress Madame La Gimp to look like a lady.

They tell me Miss Missouri Martin thinks some of putting the slug on Miss Billy Perry for this crack, but happens to remember just in time that Miss Billy Perry is now Dave the Dude's ever-loving wife, and that nobody in this town, can put the slug on Dave's ever-loving wife, except maybe Dave himself.

Now the next thing anybody knows, Madame La Gimp is in a swell eight- or nine-room apartment in the Marberry, and the way this comes about is as follows: It seems that one of Dave the Dude's most important champagne customers is a guy by the name of Rodney B. Emerson, who owns the apartment, but who is at his summer home in Newport, with his family, or anyway with his ever-loving wife.

This Rodney B. Emerson is quite a guy along Broadway, and a great hand for spending dough and looking for laughs, and he is very popular with the mob. Furthermore, he is obligated to Dave the Dude, because Dave sells him good champagne when most guys are trying to hand him the old phonus bolonus, and naturally Rodney B. Emerson appreciates this kind treatment.

He is a short, fat guy, with a round, red face, and a big laugh, and the kind of a guy Dave the Dude can call up at his home in Newport and explain the situation and ask for the loan of the apartment, which Dave does.

Well, it seems Rodney B. Emerson gets a big bang out of the idea, and he says to Dave the Dude like this:

"You not only can have the apartment, Dave, but I will come over and help you out. It will save a lot of explaining around the Marberry if I am there."

So he hops right over from Newport, and joins in with Dave the Dude, and I wish to say Rodney B. Emerson will always be kindly remembered by one and all for his cooperation, and nobody will ever again try to hand him the phonus bolonus when he is buying champagne, even if he is not buying it off of Dave the Dude.

Well, it is coming on Saturday and the boat from Spain is due, so Dave the Dude hires a big town car, and puts his own driver, Wop Sam, on it, as he does not wish any strange driver tipping off anybody that it is a hired car. Miss Missouri Martin is anxious to go to the boat with Madame La Gimp, and take her jazz band, the Hi Hi Boys, from her Sixteen Hundred Club with her to make it a real welcome, but nobody thinks much of this idea. Only Madame La Gimp and her husband, Judge Henry G. Blake, and Miss Billy Perry go, though the judge holds out for some time for Little Manuel, because Judge Blake says he wishes somebody around to tip him off in case there are any bad cracks made about him as a husband in Spanish, and Little Manuel is very Spanish.

The morning they go to meet the boat is the first time Judge Henry G. Blake gets a load of his ever-loving wife, Madame La Gimp, and by this time Miss Billy Perry and Miss Missouri Martin give Madame La Gimp such a going-over that she is by no means the worst looker in the world. In fact, she looks first-rate, especially as she is off gin and says she is off it for good.

Judge Henry G. Blake is really quite surprised by her looks as he figures all along she will turn out to be a crow. In fact, Judge Blake hurls a couple of shots into himself to nerve himself for the ordeal, as he explains it, before he appears to go to the boat. Between these shots, and the nice clothes, and the good cleaning-up Miss Billy Perry and Miss Missouri Martin give Madame La Gimp, she is really a pleasant sight to the judge.

They tell me the meeting at the dock between Madame La Gimp and her baby is very affecting indeed, and when the proud old Spanish nobleman and his wife, and their son, and Madame La Gimp's sister, all go into action, too, there are enough tears around there to float all the battleships we once sink for Spain. Even Miss Billy Perry and Judge Henry G. Blake do some first-class crying, although the chances are the judge is worked up to the crying more by the shots he takes for his courage than by the meeting.

Still, I hear the old judge does himself proud, what with kissing Madame La Gimp's baby plenty, and duking the proud old Spanish nobleman, and his wife, and son, and giving Madame La Gimp's sister a good strong hug that squeezes her tongue out.

It turns out that the proud old Spanish nobleman has white sideburns, and is entitled Conde de Something, so his ever-loving wife is the Condesa, and the son is a very nice-looking quiet young guy any way you take him, who blushes every time anybody looks at him. As for Madame La Gimp's baby, she is as pretty as they come, and many guys are sorry they do not get Judge Henry G. Blake's job as stepfather, because he is able to take a kiss at Madame La Gimp's baby on what seems to be very small excuse. I never see a nicer-looking young couple, and anybody can see they are very fond of each other, indeed.

Madame La Gimp's sister is not such a doll as I will wish to have sawed off on me, and is up in the paints as regards to age, but she is also very quiet. None of the bunch talk any English, so Miss Billy Perry and Judge Henry G. Blake are pretty much outsiders on the way uptown. Anyway, the judge takes the wind as soon as they reach the Marberry, because the judge is now getting a little tired of being a husband. He says he has to take a trip out to Pittsburgh to buy four or five coal mines, but will be back the next day.

Well, it seems to me that everything is going perfect so far, and that it is good judgment to let it lay as it is, but nothing will do Dave the Dude but to have a reception the following night. I advise Dave the Dude against this idea, because I am afraid something will happen to spoil the whole cat-hop, but he will not listen to me, especially as Rodney B. Emerson is now in town and is a strong booster for the party, as he wishes to drink some of the good champagne he has planted in his apartment.

Furthermore, Miss Billy Perry and Miss Missouri Martin are very indignant at me when they hear about my advice, as it seems they both buy new dresses out of Dave the Dude's bank roll when they are dressing up Madame La Gimp, and they wish to spring these dresses somewhere where they can be seen. So the party is on.

I get to the Marberry around nine o'clock and who opens the door of Madame La Gimp's apartment for me but Moosh, the door man from Miss Missouri Martin's Sixteen Hundred Club. Furthermore, he is in his Sixteen Hundred Club uniform, except he has a clean shave. I wish Moosh a hello, and he never raps to me but only bows, and takes my hat.

The next guy I see is Rodney B. Emerson in evening clothes, and the minute he sees me he yells out, "Mister O. O. McIntyre." Well, of course

I am not Mister O. O. McIntyre, and never put myself away as Mister O. O. McIntyre, and furthermore there is no resemblance whatever between Mister O. O. McIntyre and me, because I am a fairly good-looking guy, and I start to give Rodney B. Emerson an argument, when he whispers to me like this:

"Listen," he whispers, "we must have big names at this affair, so as to impress these people. The chances are they read the newspapers back there in Spain, and we must let them meet the folks they read about, so they will see Madame La Gimp is a real big shot to get such names to a party."

Then he takes me by the arm and leads me to a group of people in a corner of the room, which is about the size of the Grand Central waiting room.

"Mister O. O. McIntyre, the big writer!" Rodney B. Emerson says, and the next thing I know I am shaking hands with Mr. and Mrs. Conde, and their son, and with Madame La Gimp and her baby, and Madame La Gimp's sister, and finally with Judge Henry G. Blake, who has on a swallowtail coat, and does not give me much of a tumble. I figure the chances are Judge Henry G. Blake is getting a swelled head already, not to tumble up a guy who helps him get his job, but even at that I wish to say the old judge looks immense in his swallowtail coat, bowing and giving one and all the old castor oil smile.

Madame La Gimp is in a low-neck black dress and is wearing a lot of Miss Missouri Martin's diamonds, such as rings and bracelets, which Miss Missouri Martin insists on hanging on her, although I hear afterwards that Miss Missouri Martin has Johnny Brannigan, the plain clothes copper, watching these diamonds. I wonder at the time why Johnny is there but figure it is because he is a friend of Dave the Dude's. Miss Missouri Martin is no sucker, even if she is kind-hearted.

Anybody looking at Madame La Gimp will bet you all the coffee in Java that she never lives in a cellar over in Tenth Avenue, and drinks plenty of gin in her day. She has her gray hair piled up high on her head, with a big Spanish comb in it, and she reminds me of a picture I see somewhere, but I do not remember just where. And her baby, Eulalie, in a white dress is about as pretty a little doll as you will wish to see, and nobody can blame Judge Henry G. Blake for copping a kiss off of her now and then.

Well, pretty soon I hear Rodney B. Emerson bawling, "Mister Willie K. Vanderbilt," and in comes nobody but Big Nig, and Rodney B. Emerson leads him over to the group and introduces him.

Little Manuel is standing alongside Judge Henry G. Blake, and he explains in Spanish to Mr. and Mrs. Conde and the others that "Willie K. Vanderbilt" is a very large millionaire, and Mr. and Mrs. Conde seem much interested, anyway, though naturally Madame La Gimp and Judge Henry G. Blake are jerry to Big Nig, while Madame La Gimp's baby and the young guy are interested in nobody but each other.

Then I hear, "Mister Al Jolson," and in comes nobody but Tony Bertazzola, from the Chicken Club, who looks about as much like Al as I do like O. O. McIntyre, which is not at all. Next comes the "Very Reverend John Roach Straton," who seems to be Skeets Bolivar to me, then "the Honorable Mayor James J. Walker," and who is it but Good Time Charley Bernstein.

"Mister Otto H. Kahn" turns out ot be Rochester Red, and "Mister Heywood Broun" is Nick the Greek, who asks me privately who Heywood Broun is, and gets very sore at Rodney B. Emerson when I describe Heywood Broun to him.

Finally there is quite a commotion at the door and Rodney B. Emerson announces "Mister Herbert Bayard Swope" in an extra loud voice which makes everybody look around, but it is nobody but the Pale Face Kid. He gets me to one side, too, and wishes to know who Herbert Bayard Swope is, and when I explain to him, the Pale Face Kid gets so swelled up he will not speak to Death House Donegan, who is only "Mister William Muldoon."

Well, it seems to me they are getting too strong when they announce "Vice-President of the United States, the Honorable Charles Curtis," and in pops Guinea Mike, and I say as much to Dave the Dude, who is running around every which way looking after things, but he only says, "Well, if you do not know it is Guinea Mike, will you know it is not Vice-President Curtis?"

But it seems to me all this is most disrespectful to our leading citizens, especially when Rodney B. Emerson calls, "The Honorable Police Commissioner, Mister Grover A. Whalen," and in pops Wild William Wilkins, who is a very hot man at this time, being wanted in several spots for different raps. Dave the Dude takes personal charge of Wild William and removes a rod from his pants pocket, because none of the guests are supposed to come rodded up, this being strictly a social matter.

I watch Mr. and Mrs. Conde, and I do not see that these names are making any impression on them, and I afterwards find out that they never get any newspapers in their town in Spain except a little local bladder which only prints the home news. In fact, Mr. and Mrs. Conde seem somewhat bored, although Mr. Conde cheers up no little and looks interested when a

lot of dolls drift in. They are mainly dolls from Miss Missouri Martin's Sixteen Hundred Club, and the Hot Box, but Rodney B. Emerson introduces
them as "Sophie Tucker," and "Theda Bara," and "Jeanne Eagels," and
"Helen Morgan" and "Aunt Jemima," and one thing and another.

Well, pretty soon in comes Miss Missouri Martin's jazz band, the Hi
Hi Boys, and the party commences getting up steam, especially when Dave
the Dude gets Rodney B. Emerson to breaking out the old grape. By and by
there is dancing going on, and a good time is being had by one and all, including Mr. and Mrs. Conde. In fact, after Mr. Conde gets a couple of jolts
of the old grape, he turns out to be a pretty nice old skate, even if nobody
can understand what he is talking about.

As for Judge Henry G. Blake, he is full of speed, indeed. By this time
anybody can see that the judge is commencing to believe that all this is on
the level and that he is really entertaining celebrities in his own home. You
put a quart of good grape inside the old judge and he will believe anything.
He soon dances himself plumb out of wind, and then I notice he is hanging
around Madame La Gimp a lot.

Along about midnight, Dave the Dude has to go out into the kitchen
and settle a battle there over a crap game, but otherwise everything is very
peaceful. It seems that "Herbert Bayard Swope," "Vice-President Curtis"
and "Grover Whalen" get a little game going, when "the Reverend John
Roach Straton" steps up and cleans them in four passes, but it seems they
soon discover that "the Reverend John Roach Straton" is using tops
on them, which are very dishonest dice, and so they put the slug on "the
Reverend John Roach Straton" and Dave the Dude has to split them out.

By and by I figure on taking the wind, and I look for Mr. and Mrs.
Conde to tell them good night, but Mr. Conde and Miss Missouri Martin
are still dancing, and Miss Missouri Martin is pouring conversation into
Mr. Conde's ear by the bucketful, and while Mr. Conde does not savvy a
word she says, this makes no difference to Miss Missouri Martin. Let Miss
Missouri Martin do all the talking, and she does not care a whoop if anybody understands her.

Mrs. Conde is over in a corner with "Herbert Bayard Swope," or the
Pale Face Kid, who is trying to find out from her by using hog Latin and
signs on her if there is any chance for a good twenty-one dealer in Spain,
and of course Mrs. Conde is not able to make heads or tails of what
he means, so I hunt up Madame La Gimp.

She is sitting in a darkish corner off by herself and I really do not see

Judge Henry G. Blake leaning over her until I am almost on top of them, so I cannot help hearing what the judge is saying.

"I am wondering for two days," he says, "if by any chance you remember me. Do you know who I am?"

"I remember you," Madame La Gimp says. "I remember you—oh, so very well, Henry. How can I forget you? But I have no idea you recognize me after all these years."

"Twenty of them now," Judge Henry G. Blake says. "You are beautiful then. You are still beautiful."

Well, I can see the old grape is working first-class on Judge Henry G. Blake to make such remarks as this, although at that, in the half light, with the smile on her face, Madame La Gimp is not so bad. Still, give me them carrying a little less weight for age.

"Well, it is all your fault," Judge Henry G. Blake says. "You go and marry that chile con carne guy, and look what happens!"

I can see there is no sense in me horning in on Madame La Gimp and Judge Henry G. Blake while they are cutting up old touches in this manner, so I think I will just say good-by to the young people and let it go at that, but while I am looking for Madame La Gimp's baby, and her guy, I run into Dave the Dude.

"You will not find them here," Dave says. "By this time they are being married over at Saint Malachy's with my ever-loving wife and Big Nig standing up with them. We get the license for them yesterday afternoon. Can you imagine a couple of young saps wishing to wait until they go plumb around the world before getting married?"

Well, of course this elopement creates much excitement for a few minutes, but by Monday Mr. and Mrs. Conde and the young folks and Madame La Gimp's sister take a train for California to keep on going around the world, leaving us nothing to talk about but old Judge Henry G. Blake and Madame La Gimp getting themselves married too, and going to Detroit where Judge Henry G. Blake claims he has a brother in the plumbing business who will give him a job, although personally I think Judge Henry G. Blake figures to do a little booting on his own hook in and out of Canada. It is not like Judge Henry G. Blake to tie himself up to the plumbing business.

So there is nothing more to the story, except that Dave the Dude is around a few days later with a big sheet of paper in his duke and very, very indignant.

"If every single article listed here is not kicked back to the owners of the different joints in the Marberry that they are taken from by next Tuesday night, I will bust a lot of noses around this town," Dave says. "I am greatly mortified by such happenings at my social affairs, and everything must be returned at once. Especially," Dave says, "the baby grand piano that is removed from Apartment 9-D."

STUDY QUESTIONS:

1. Runyon's characters speak a peculiar kind of language. It has elements of big-city slang, yet it is not without its pretensions of gentility. Side-by-side we see vulgarity and grammatical over-elaborateness. How does this language serve both Runyon's humor and the theme of his story?

2. Stories like this "date" quickly. Why?

3. What evidences are there of Runyon's long career as a newspaperman in the way he writes?

4. This story has been used by motion pictures, television, and radio. Why is it especially suitable for dramatic presentation?

THE ROCKING-
HORSE WINNER

D. H. LAWRENCE

D(avid) H(erbert) Lawrence (1885–1930) was a man of many literary talents. He wrote novels, poems, literary criticism, travel books, controversial essays, an enormous number of letters, and, of course, short stories. He was born in poverty in the Nottinghamshire mining district of England, the child of badly mismated parents. They quarreled violently and constantly, to the terror of young David, who favored his mother, an ambitious and somewhat cultured former schoolteacher, against his father, whom the boy considered crude and brutal. Lawrence put much of this unhappy condition into his first novel, *Sons and Lovers* (1913), showing how his hero, whom he calls Paul Morel, had to overcome the effects of his home life and of his mother's strong influence. It is an excellent novel about a sensitive boy's coming to manhood in extremely difficult surroundings.

Lawrence's short stories cover a variety of themes. In one sense "The Rocking-Horse Winner" is sheer fantasy. The thought of a young boy winning fantastic sums of money on horseracing seems preposterous enough, but the manner in which he determines the winners of particular races seems even more absurd. There are other incredible elements in the story, too—for example, the voices in the house always demanding more money. Surely this would seem the most unrealistic of stories.

The language of the story, however, makes us realize at once that the factual details of the story are not going to be very important. The story opens, "There was a woman who was beautiful, who started with all the advantages, yet she had no luck." The tone is that of a fairy-tale, or an old legend, or, even more accurately, of one of the parables of the Bible. Lawrence never relaxes this parable-like quality in the story. The sentences are short and direct, sometimes almost to the point of monotony. The characters are presented with the briefest detail, almost like stick figures. The greatest reality for us is the intensity of the boy Paul, so determined to provide his mother with more and more money.

This story can be read on several levels of meaning, one or two of them very disturbing indeed. Each time the reader comes to it he ought to be prepared to see a little more than he saw previously. Like every parable of the Bible it provides moral advice, but the wise reader will not be in too great a hurry to say what that advice is. What the story most certainly is not is just another warning against gambling. The gambling is probably the least important element in "The Rocking-Horse Winner."

There was a woman who was beautiful, who started with all the advantages, yet she had no luck. She married for love, and the love turned to dust. She had bonny children, yet she felt they had been thrust upon her, and she could not love them. They looked at her coldly, as if they were finding fault with her. And hurriedly she felt she must cover up some fault in herself. Yet what it was that she must cover up she never knew. Nevertheless, when her children were present, she always felt the centre of her heart go hard. This troubled her, and in her manner she was all the more gentle and anxious for her children, as if she loved them very much. Only she herself knew that at the centre of her heart was a hard little place that could not feel love, no, not for anybody. Everybody else said of her: "She is such a good mother. She adores her children." Only she herself and her children themselves, knew it was not so. They read it in each other's eyes.

There were a boy and two little girls. They lived in a pleasant house, with a garden, and they had discreet servants, and felt themselves superior to anyone in the neighbourhood.

Although they lived in style, they felt always an anxiety in the house. There was never enough money. The mother had a small income, and the

[1] At the time Lawrence wrote this story, a pound would have been worth about five dollars.

[handwritten: remote character]

father had a small income, but not nearly enough for the social position which they had to keep up. The father went into town to some office. But though he had good prospects, these prospects never materialized. There was always the grinding sense of the shortage of money, though the style was always kept up.

At last the mother said: "I will see if I can't make something." But she did not know where to begin. She racked her brains, and tried this thing and the other, but could not find anything successful. The failure made deep lines come into her face. Her children were growing up, they would have to go to school. There must be more money, there must be more money. The father, who was always very handsome and expensive in his tastes, seemed as if he never would be able to do anything worth doing. And the mother, who had a great belief in herself, did not succeed any better, and her tastes were just as expensive. *[handwritten: Gobbled up by appearances]*

And so the house came to be haunted by the unspoken phrase: There must be more money! There must be more money! The children could hear it all the time, though nobody said it aloud. They heard it at Christmas, when the expensive and splendid toys filled the nursery. Behind the shining modern rocking-horse, behind the smart doll's-house, a voice would start whispering: "There must be more money! There must be more money!" And the children would stop playing, to listen for a moment. They would look into each other's eyes, to see if they had all heard. And each one saw in the eyes of the other two that they too had heard. "There must be more money! There must be more money!" *[handwritten: live in a world of externals; not by internals]*

It came whispering from the springs of the still-swaying rocking-horse, and even the horse, bending his wooden, champing head, heard it. The big doll, sitting so pink and smirking in her new pram, could hear it quite plainly, and seemed to be smirking all the more self-consciously because of it. The foolish puppy, too, that took the place of the teddy-bear, he was looking so extraordinarily foolish for no other reason but that he heard the secret whisper all over the house: "There must be more money!"

Yet nobody ever said it aloud. The whisper was everywhere, and therefore no one spoke it. Just as no one ever says: "We are breathing!" in spite of the fact that breath is coming and going all the time.

"Mother," said the boy Paul one day, "why don't we keep a car of our own? Why do we always use uncle's or else a taxi?" *[handwritten: Why are we different; poor]*

"Because we're the poor members of the family," said the mother.

"But why are we, mother?"

"Well—I suppose," she said slowly and bitterly, "it's because your father has no luck." *[handwritten: Father is a failure; putting responsibility on Father]*

D. H. LAWRENCE

The boy was silent for some time.

"Is luck money, mother?" he asked, rather timidly.

"No, Paul. Not quite. It's what causes you to have money."

"Oh!" said Paul vaguely. "I thought when Uncle Oscar said filthy lucker, it meant money."

"Filthy lucre does mean money," said the mother. "But it's lucre, not luck."

"Oh!" said the boy. "Then what is luck, mother?"

"It's what causes you to have money. If you're lucky you have money. That's why it's better to be born lucky than rich. If you're rich, you may lose your money. But if you're lucky, you will always get more money."

"Oh! Will you? And is father not lucky?"

"Very unlucky, I should say," she said bitterly.

The boy watched her with unsure eyes.

"Why?" he asked.

"I don't know. Nobody ever knows why one person is lucky and another unlucky."

"Don't they? Nobody at all? Does nobody know?"

"Perhaps God. But He never tells."

"He ought to, then. And aren't you lucky either, mother?"

"I can't be, if I married an unlucky husband."

"But by yourself, aren't you?"

"I used to think I was, before I married. Now I think I am very unlucky indeed."

"Why?"

"Well—never mind! Perhaps I'm not really," she said.

The child looked at her, to see if she meant it. But he saw, by the lines of her mouth, that she was only trying to hide something from him.

"Well, anyhow," he said stoutly, "I'm a lucky person."

"Why?" said his mother, with a sudden laugh.

He stared at her. He didn't even know why he had said it.

"God told me," he asserted, brazening it out.

"I hope He did, dear!" she said, again with a laugh, but rather bitter.

"He did, mother!"

"Excellent!" said the mother, using one of her husband's exclamations.

The boy saw she did not believe him; or, rather, that she paid no attention to his assertion. This angered him somewhat, and made him want to compel her attention.

He went off by himself, vaguely, in a childish way, seeking for the clue to "luck." Absorbed, taking no heed of other people, he went about with a sort of stealth, seeking inwardly for luck. He wanted luck, he wanted it, he wanted it. When the two girls were playing dolls in the nursery, he would sit on his big rocking-horse, charging madly into space, with a frenzy that made the little girls peer at him uneasily. Wildly the horse careered, the waving dark hair of the boy tossed, his eyes had a strange glare in them. The little girls dared not to speak to him.

When he had ridden to the end of his mad little journey, he climbed down and stood in front of his rocking-horse, staring fixedly into its lowered face. Its red mouth was slightly open, its big eye was wide and glassy-bright.

"Now!" he would silently command the snorting steed. "Now, take me to where there is luck! Now take me!"

And he would slash the horse on the neck with the little whip he had asked Uncle Oscar for. He knew the horse could take him to where there was luck, if only he forced it. So he would mount again, and start on his furious ride, hoping at last to get there. He knew he could get there.

"You'll break your horse, Paul!" said the nurse.

"He's always riding like that! I wish he'd leave off!" said his elder sister Joan.

But he only glared down on them in silence. Nurse gave him up. She could make nothing of him. Anyhow he was growing beyond her.

One day his mother and his Uncle Oscar came in when he was on one of his furious rides. He did not speak to them.

"Hallo, you young jockey! Riding a winner?" said his uncle.

"Aren't you growing too big for a rocking-horse? You're not a very little boy any longer, you know," said his mother.

But Paul only gave a blue glare from his big, rather close-set eyes. He would speak to nobody when he was in full tilt. His mother watched him with an anxious expression on her face.

At last he suddenly stopped forcing his horse into the mechanical gallop, and slid down.

"Well, I got there!" he announced fiercely, his blue eyes still flaring, and his sturdy long legs straddling apart.

"Where did you get to?" asked his mother.

"Where I wanted to go," he flared back at her.

"That's right, son!" said Uncle Oscar. "Don't you stop till you get there. What's the horse's name?"

"He doesn't have a name," said the boy.

"Gets on without all right?" asked the uncle.

"Well, he has different names. He was called Sansovino last week."

"Sansovino, eh? Won the Ascot. How did you know his name?"

"He always talks about horse-races with Bassett," said Joan.

The uncle was delighted to find that his small nephew was posted with all the racing news. Bassett, the young gardener, who had been wounded in the left foot in the war and had got his present job through Oscar Cresswell, whose batman he had been, was a perfect blade of the "turf." He lived in the racing events, and the small boy lived with him.

Oscar Cresswell got it all from Bassett.

"Master Paul comes and asks me, so I can't do more than tell him, sir," said Bassett, his face terribly serious, as if he were speaking of religious matters.

"And does he ever put anything on a horse he fancies?"

"Well—I don't want to give him away—he's a young sport, a fine sport, sir. Would you mind asking him yourself? He sort of takes a pleasure in it, and perhaps he'd feel I was giving him away, sir, if you don't mind."

Bassett was serious as a church.

The uncle went back to his nephew, and took him off for a ride in the car.

"Say, Paul, old man, do you ever put anything on a horse?" the uncle asked.

The boy watched the handsome man closely.

"Why, do you think I oughtn't to?" he parried.

"Not a bit of it! I thought perhaps you might give me a tip for the Lincoln."

The car sped on into the country, going down to Uncle Oscar's place in Hampshire.

"Honour bright?" said the nephew.

"Honour bright, son!" said the uncle.

"Well, then, Daffodil."

"Daffodil! I doubt it, sonny. What about Mirza?"

"I only know the winner," said the boy. "That's Daffodil."

"Daffodil, eh?"

There was a pause. Daffodil was an obscure horse comparatively.

"Uncle!"

"Yes, son?"

"You won't let it go any further, will you? I promised Bassett."

"Bassett be damned, old man! What's he got to do with it?"

Nurse = an artifical mother → fob off responsibility

"We're partners. We've been partners from the first. Uncle, he lent me my first five shillings, which I lost. I promised him, honour bright, it was only between me and him; only you gave me that ten-shilling note I started winning with, so I thought you were lucky. You won't let it go any further, will you?"

The boy gazed at his uncle from those big, hot, blue eyes, set rather close together. The uncle stirred and laughed uneasily.

"Right you are, son! I'll keep your tip private. Daffodil, eh? How much are you putting on him?"

"All except twenty pounds," said the boy. "I keep that in reserve."

The uncle thought it a good joke.

"You keep twenty pounds in reserve, do you, you young romancer? What are you betting, then?"

"I'm betting three hundred," said the boy gravely. "But it's between you and me, Uncle Oscar! Honour bright?"

The uncle burst into a roar of laughter.

"It's between you and me all right, you young Nat Gould," he said, laughing. "But where's your three hundred?"

"Bassett keeps it for me. We're partners."

"You are, are you! And what is Bassett putting on Daffodil?"

"He won't go quite as high as I do, I expect. Perhaps he'll go a hundred and fifty."

"What, pennies?" laughed the uncle.

"Pounds," said the child, with a surprised look at his uncle. "Bassett keeps a bigger reserve than I do."

Between wonder and amusement Uncle Oscar was silent. He pursued the matter no further, but he determined to take his nephew with him to the Lincoln races.

"Now, son," he said, "I'm putting twenty on Mirza, and I'll put five for you on any horse you fancy. What's your pick?"

"Daffodil, uncle."

"No, not the fiver on Daffodil!"

"I should if it was my own fiver," said the child.

"Good! Good! Right you are! A fiver for me and a fiver for you on Daffodil."

The child had never been to a race-meeting before, and his eyes were blue fire. He pursed his mouth tight, and watched. A Frenchman just in front had put his money on Lancelot. Wild with excitement, he flayed his arms up and down, yelling "Lancelot! Lancelot!" in his French accent.

comment on marriage, family life, poverty of Rumania

Daffodil came in first, Lancelot second, Mirza third. The child, flushed and with eyes blazing, was curiously serene. His uncle brought him four five-pound notes, four to one.

"What am I to do with these?" he cried, waving them before the boy's eyes.

"I suppose we'll talk to Bassett," said the boy. "I expect I have fifteen hundred now; and twenty in reserve; and this twenty."

His uncle studied him for some moments.

"Look here, son!" he said. "You're not serious about Bassett and that fifteen hundred, are you?"

"Yes, I am. But it's between you and me, uncle. Honour bright!"

"Honour bright all right, son! But I must talk to Bassett."

"If you'd like to be a partner, uncle, with Bassett and me, we could all be partners. Only, you'd have to promise, honour bright, uncle, not to let it go beyond us three. Bassett and I are lucky, and you must be lucky, because it was your ten shillings I started winning with. . . ."

Uncle Oscar took both Bassett and Paul into Richmond Park for an afternoon, and there they talked.

"It's like this, you see, sir," Bassett said. "Master Paul would get me talking about racing events, spinning yarns, you know, sir. And he was always keen on knowing if I'd made or if I'd lost. It's about a year since, now, that I put five shillings on Blush of Dawn for him—and we lost. Then the luck turned, with that ten shillings he had from you, that we put on Singhalese. And since that time, it's been pretty steady, all things considering. What do you say, Master Paul?"

"We're all right when we're sure," said Paul. "It's when were not quite sure that we go down."

"Oh, but we're careful then," said Bassett.

"But when are you sure?" smiled Uncle Oscar.

"It's Master Paul, sir," said Bassett, in a secret, religious voice. "It's as if he had it from heaven. Like Daffodil, now, for the Lincoln. That was as sure as eggs."

"Did you put anything on Daffodil?" asked Oscar Cresswell.

"Yes, sir, I made my bit."

"And my nephew?"

Bassett was obstinately silent, looking at Paul.

"I made twelve hundred, didn't I, Bassett? I told uncle I was putting three hundred on Daffodil."

"That's right," said Bassett, nodding.

"But where's the money?" asked the uncle.

"I keep it safe locked up, sir. Master Paul he can have it any minute he likes to ask for it."

"What, fifteen hundred pounds?"

"And twenty! And forty, that is, with the twenty he made on the course."

"It's amazing!" said the uncle.

"If Master Paul offers you to be partners, sir, I would, if I were you; if you'll excuse me," said Bassett.

Oscar Cresswell thought about it.

"I'll see the money," he said.

They drove home again, and sure enough, Bassett came round to the garden-house with fifteen hundred pounds in notes. The twenty pounds reserve was left with Joe Glee, in the Turf Commission deposit.

"You see, it's all right, uncle, when I'm sure! Then we go strong, for all we're worth. Don't we, Bassett?"

"We do that, Master Paul."

"And when are you sure?" said the uncle, laughing.

"Oh, well, sometimes I'm absolutely sure, like about Daffodil," said the boy; "and sometimes I have an idea; and sometimes I haven't even an idea, have I, Bassett? Then we're careful, because we mostly go down."

"You do, do you! And when you're sure, like about Daffodil, what makes you sure, sonny?"

"Oh, well, I don't know," said the boy uneasily. "I'm sure, you know, uncle; that's all."

"It's as if he had it from heaven, sir," Bassett reiterated.

"I should say so!" said the uncle.

But he became a partner. And when the Leger was coming on, Paul was "sure" about Lively Spark, which was a quite inconsiderable horse. The boy insisted on putting a thousand on the horse, Bassett went for five hundred, and Oscar Cresswell two hundred. Lively Spark came in first, and the betting had been ten to one against him. Paul had made ten thousand.

"You see," he said, "I was absolutely sure of him."

Even Oscar Cresswell had cleared two thousand.

"Look here, son," he said, "this sort of thing makes me nervous."

"It needn't, uncle! Perhaps I shan't be sure again for a long time."

"But what are you going to do with your money?" asked the uncle.

"Of course," said the boy, "I started it for mother. She said she had no luck, because father is unlucky, so I thought if I was lucky, it might stop whispering."

"What might stop whispering?"

"Our house. I hate our house for whispering."

"What does it whisper?"

"Why—why"—the boy fidgeted—"why, I don't know. But it's always short of money, you know, uncle."

"I know it, son, I know it."

"You know people send mother writs, don't you, uncle?"

"I'm afraid I do," said the uncle.

"And then the house whispers, like people laughing at you behind your back. It's awful, that is! I thought if I was lucky . . ."

"You might stop it," added the uncle.

The boy watched him with big blue eyes that had an uncanny cold fire in them, and he said never a word.

"Well, then!" said the uncle. "What are we doing?"

"I shouldn't like mother to know I was lucky," said the boy.

"Why not, son?"

"She'd stop me."

"I don't think she would."

"Oh!"—and the boy writhed in an odd way—"I don't want her to know, uncle."

"All right, son! We'll manage it without her knowing."

They managed it very easily. Paul, at the other's suggestion, handed over five thousand pounds to his uncle, who deposited it with the family lawyer, who was then to inform Paul's mother that a relative had put five thousand pounds into his hands, which sum was to be paid out a thousand pounds at a time, on the mother's birthday, for the next five years.

"So she'll have a birthday present of a thousand pounds for five successive years," said Uncle Oscar. "I hope it won't make it all the harder for her later."

Paul's mother had her birthday in November. The house had been "whispering" worse than ever lately, and, even in spite of his luck, Paul could not bear up against it. He was very anxious to see the effect of the birthday letter, telling his mother about the thousand pounds.

When there were no visitors, Paul now took his meals with his parents, as he was beyond the nursery control. His mother went into town nearly every day. She had discovered that she had an odd knack of sketching furs and dress materials, so she worked secretly in the studio of a friend who was the chief "artist" for the leading drapers. She drew the figures of ladies in furs and ladies in silk and sequins for the newspaper advertisements. This young woman artist earned several thousand pounds a year, but Paul's mother only made several hundreds, and she was again dissatisfied. She so wanted to be first in something, and she did not succeed, even in making sketches for drapery advertisements.

She was down to breakfast on the morning of her birthday. Paul watched her face as she read her letters. He knew the lawyer's letter. As his mother read it, her face hardened and became more expressionless. Then a cold, determined look came on her mouth. She hid the letter under the pile of others, and said not a word about it.

"Didn't you have anything nice in the post for your birthday, mother?" said Paul.

"Quite moderately nice," she said, her voice cold and absent.

She went away to town without saying more.

But in the afternoon Uncle Oscar appeared. He said Paul's mother had had a long interview with the lawyer, asking if the whole five thousand could be advanced at once, as she was in debt.

"What do you think, uncle?" said the boy.

"I leave it to you, son."

"Oh, let her have it, then! We can get some more with the other," said the boy.

"A bird in the hand is worth two in the bush, laddie!" said Uncle Oscar.

"But I'm sure to know for the Grand National; or the Lincolnshire; or else the Derby. I'm sure to know for one of them," said Paul.

So Uncle Oscar signed the agreement, and Paul's mother touched the whole five thousand. Then something very curious happened. The voices in the house suddenly went mad, like a chorus of frogs on a spring evening. There were certain new furnishings, and Paul had a tutor. He was really going to Eton, his father's school, in the following autumn. There were flowers in the winter, and a blossoming of the luxury Paul's mother had been used to. And yet the voices in the house, behind the sprays of mimosa and almond blossom, and from under the piles of iridescent cushions, simply trilled and screamed in a sort of ecstasy: "There must be more money! Oh-h-h, there must be more money. Oh, now, now-w-w! there must be more money!—more than ever! More than ever!"

It frightened Paul terribly. He studied away at his Latin and Greek with his tutors. But his intense hours were spent with Bassett. The Grand National had gone by: he had not "known," and had lost a hundred pounds. Summer was at hand. He was in agony for the Lincoln. But even for the Lincoln he didn't "know" and he lost fifty pounds. He became wild-eyed and strange, as if something were going to explode in him.

"Let it alone, son! Don't you bother about it!" urged Uncle Oscar. But it was as if the boy couldn't really hear what his uncle was saying.

"I've got to know for the Derby! I've got to know for the Derby!" the child reiterated, his big blue eyes blazing with a sort of madness.

His mother noticed how overwrought he was.

"You'd better go to the seaside. Wouldn't you like to go now to the seaside, instead of waiting? I think you'd better," she said, looking down at him anxiously, her heart curiously heavy because of him.

But the child lifted his uncanny blue eyes.

"I couldn't possibly go before the Derby, mother!" he said. "I couldn't possibly!"

"Why not?" she said, her voice becoming heavy when she was opposed. "Why not? You can still go from the seaside to see the Derby with your Uncle Oscar, if that's what you wish. No need for you to wait here. Besides, I think you care too much about these races. It's a bad sign. My family has been a gambling family, and you won't know till you grow up how much damage it has done. But it has done damage. I shall have to send Bassett away, and ask Uncle Oscar not to talk racing to you, unless you promise to be reasonable about it; go away to the seaside and forget it. You're all nerves!"

"I'll do what you like, mother, so long as you don't send me away till after the Derby," the boy said.

"Send you away from where? Just from this house?"

"Yes," he said, gazing at her.

"Why, you curious child, what makes you care about this house so much, suddenly? I never knew you loved it."

He gazed at her without speaking. He had a secret within a secret, something he had not divulged, even to Bassett or to his Uncle Oscar.

But his mother, after standing undecided and a little bit sullen for some moments, said:

"Very well, then! Don't go to the seaside till after the Derby, if you don't wish it. But promise me you won't let your nerves go to pieces. Promise you won't think so much about horseracing and events, as you call them!"

"Oh, no," said the boy casually. "I won't think much about them, mother. You needn't worry. I wouldn't worry, mother, if I were you."

"If you were me and I were you," said his mother, "I wonder what we should do!"

"But you know you needn't worry, mother, don't you?" the boy repeated.

"I should be awfully glad to know it," she said wearily.

"Oh, well, you can, you know. I mean, you ought to know you needn't worry," he insisted.

"Ought I? Then I'll see about it," she said.

Paul's secret of secrets was his wooden horse, that which had no name. Since he was emancipated from a nurse and a nursery-governess, he had had his rocking-horse removed to his own bedroom at the top of the house.

"Surely, you're too big for a rocking-horse!" his mother had remonstrated.

"Well, you see, mother, till I can have a real horse, I like to have some sort of animal about," had been his quaint answer.

"Do you feel he keeps you company?" she laughed.

"Oh, yes! He's very good, he always keeps me company, when I'm there," said Paul.

So the horse, rather shabby, stood in an arrested prance in the boy's bedroom.

The Derby was drawing near, and the boy grew more and more tense. He hardly heard what was spoken to him, he was very frail, and his eyes were really uncanny. His mother had sudden seizures of uneasiness about him. Sometimes, for half-an-hour, she would feel a sudden anxiety about him that was almost anguish. She wanted to rush to him at once, and know he was safe.

Two nights before the Derby, she was at a big party in town, when one of her rushes of anxiety about her boy, her firstborn, gripped her heart till she could hardly speak. She fought with the feeling, might and main, for she believed in common sense. But it was too strong. She had to leave the dance and go downstairs to telephone to the country. The children's nursery-governess was terribly surprised and startled at being rung up in the night.

"Are the children all right, Miss Wilmot?"

"Oh, yes, they are quite all right."

"Master Paul? Is he all right?"

"He went to bed as right as a trivet. Shall I run up and look at him?"

"No," said Paul's mother reluctantly. "No! Don't trouble. It's all right. Don't sit up. We shall be home fairly soon." She did not want her son's privacy intruded upon.

"Very good," said the governess.

It was about one o'clock when Paul's mother and father drove up to their house. All was still. Paul's mother went to her room and slipped off her white fur coat. She had told her maid not to wait up for her. She heard her husband downstairs, mixing a whisky-and-soda.

And then, because of the strange anxiety at her heart, she stole upstairs to her son's room. Noiselessly she went along the upper corridor. Was there a faint noise? What was it?

She stood, with arrested muscles, outside his door, listening. There was a strange, heavy, and yet not loud noise. Her heart stood still. It was a soundless noise, yet rushing and powerful. Something huge, in violent, hushed motion. What was it? What in God's name was it? She ought to know. She felt that she knew the noise. She knew what it was.

Yet she could not place it. She couldn't say what it was. And on and on it went, like a madness.

Softly, frozen with anxiety and fear, she turned the door handle.

The room was dark. Yet in the space near the window, she heard and saw something plunging to and fro. She gazed in fear and amazement.

Then suddenly she switched on the light, and saw her son, in his green pyjamas, madly surging on the rocking-horse. The blaze of light suddenly lit him up, as he urged the wooden horse, and lit her up, as she stood, blonde, in her dress of pale green and crystal, in the doorway.

"Paul!" she cried. "Whatever are you doing?"

"It's Malabar!" he screamed, in a powerful, strange voice. "It's Malabar."

His eyes blazed at her for one strange and senseless second, as he ceased urging his wooden horse. Then he fell with a crash to the ground, and she, all her tormented motherhood flooding upon her, rushed to gather him up.

But he was unconscious, and unconscious he remained, with some brain-fever. He talked and tossed, and his mother sat stonily by his side.

"Malabar! It's Malabar! Bassett, Bassett, I know! It's Malabar!"

So the child cried, trying to get up and urge the rocking-horse that gave him his inspiration.

"What does he mean by Malabar?" asked the heart-frozen mother.

"I don't know," said the father stonily.

"What does he mean by Malabar?" she asked her brother Oscar.

"It's one of the horses running for the Derby," was the answer.

And, in spite of himself, Oscar Cresswell spoke to Bassett, and himself put a thousand on Malabar: at fourteen to one.

The third day of the illness was critical: they were waiting for a change. The boy, with his rather long, curly hair, was tossing ceaselessly on the pillow. He neither slept nor regained consciousness, and his eyes were like blue stones. His mother sat, feeling her heart had gone, turned actually into a stone.

In the evening, Oscar Cresswell did not come, but Bassett sent a message, saying could he come up for one moment, just one moment? Paul's mother was very angry at the intrusion, but on second thought she agreed. The boy was the same. Perhaps Bassett might bring him to consciousness.

The gardener, a shortish fellow with a little brown moustache, and sharp little brown eyes, tiptoed into the room, touched his imaginary cap to Paul's mother, and stole to the bedside, staring with glittering, smallish eyes, at the tossing, dying child.

"Master Paul!" he whispered. "Master Paul! Malabar come in first all right, a clean win. I did as you told me. You've made over seventy thousand pounds, you have; you've got over eighty thousand. Malabar came in all right, Master Paul."

"Malabar! Malabar! Did I say Malabar, mother? Did I say Malabar? Do you think I'm lucky, mother? I knew Malabar, didn't I? Over eighty thousand pounds! I call that lucky, don't you, mother? Over eighty thousand pounds! I knew, didn't I know I knew? Malabar came in all right. If I ride my horse till I'm sure, then I tell you, Bassett, you can go as high as you like. Did you go for all you were worth, Bassett?"

"I went a thousand on it, Master Paul."

"I never told you, mother, that if I can ride my horse, and get there, then I'm absolutely sure—oh, absolutely! Mother, did I ever tell you? I am lucky."

"No, you never did," said the mother.

But the boy died in the night.

And even as he lay dead, his mother heard her brother's voice saying to her: "My God, Hester, you're eighty-odd thousand to the good and a poor devil of a son to the bad. But, poor devil, poor devil, he's best gone out of a life where he rides his rocking-horse to find a winner."

STUDY QUESTIONS:

1. Since this story ends with the death of its most important character, it might be thought of as a tragedy. If so, what is the destructive force which brings about Paul's death?

2. Write a careful character sketch of Paul's mother. Do not overlook the contradictions in her personality which the story points out.

3. On what grounds, if any, could the encouragement of Paul by Bassett and Paul's uncle be justified?

4. Biblical parables often end with specifically stated "morals" or "lessons" to be learned from the narrative. How would you state the "moral" for this story?

mother's insatiable appetite - he tries to satisfy her
greed - compensation for lack of love

mother - pretentious, fake, self-centred, highly strung
irresponsible, heartless, cold, isolated, truely indifferent,
conscious-stricken, loveless, concerned,
guilt complex

Bassett - played horses for $, whole life evolves around
racing
- introduced Paul to racing

BEAT DOWN
FRIGID ROME

ESTHER WAGNER

This unusual short story, which first appeared in *The Atlantic Monthly*, was written by Mrs. Esther Wagner, who was born in Chicago, took a Ph.D. at Bryn Mawr, and now lives in northwestern California. She both writes and teaches. "Beat Down Frigid Rome" was her first published story.

It takes its odd title from a line in a poem by William Butler Yeats, a modern Irish poet greatly interested in ancient civilization. Since the line is discussed in the story, the unusualness of it as a story title is cleared up, though not without the author's leading us on to think of other striking words and phrases which are part of our heritage from the classical past.

Mr. Latimer's bold action in filling out Robert Lang's college admission form as he does is difficult to understand, much less to accept, unless we realize both what Latimer represents and what he is protesting against. Mr. Latimer is a thorough professional in his subject, and in the section in which he catalogs and describes the major practicing classicists in today's universities, we see that he has little respect for any of them. How does this relate to the special excellence which he sees in Robert Lang?

The story raises interesting questions about the problem of profes-

sional integrity in the modern world. Mr. Latimer has very high standards
—of a particular sort. Mr. Merton's standards are, no doubt, equally high,
but they are of an entirely different kind. Is it the fate of the Robert Langs
of today's schools to be caught in between them? Mr. Latimer protests against
the kind of admissions form he is asked to fill out. What kind might have
satisfied him, if any?

Mrs. Wagner combines story and idea in brillian fashion. This had
to be a story of thought and dialog rather than of action. What Latimer is
and what he sees in Robert Lang are all-important. And the touch at the
end is superb, in that the story returns to Merton, and we see another
side of him. Latimer has won and Rome is not beaten down. But
what about Robert Lang?

The bell had just rung for the first period, and old Latimer threw open
the door with one of his long-armed, extravagant, precisely controlled gestures. He stood back to supervise with his cold ancient-looking smile the
entry of his Latin I class from the Gothic marches of the corridors to the
centurion atmosphere of his classroom. He had a trick of fixing his eyes on
the feet of his students as they crossed the doorsill, an elaborately blank
glance which stilled the last flap of every loafer, deadened the last clump
of every ski boot. At the end of this morning's stream of feet came a pair
of unobtrusively foreign-made, cordovan-polished brogues, and old Latimer
shifted his gaze to the unlined pleasant face of his colleague, Mr. Merton,
English teacher and Administrative Assistant to the Dean of Boys.

All the faculty felt rather sorry for Merton, who had to handle the college admissions correspondence and was continually writing hopeful,
covertly pleading letters to the deans of admissions of the great Eastern
colleges. Merton had to give them the hard sell on sons of three generations
of Harvard or Yale or Hurstleigh men who now found themselves doubtful
candidates because they had made a couple of C's in junior year. He resented this, remembering his own easy admission to the most august
of colleges during the depression years, and sometimes thinking almost
savagely of their jowled fathers, survivors of the Cretaceous age[1] of the
gentleman's C. Worst of all, he couldn't even be certain that his sure-fire
candidates would get just where they wanted to go.

---

[1] Cretaceous age. Prehistoric, the age of chalk. Mrs. Wagner means that the day of the
"Gentleman's C" has long since disappeared from Eastern colleges.

He now brought in to old Latimer a sheaf of application papers and a student's dossier in a battered manila folder, from which a wild-eyed photograph unpromisingly slopped over at the top.

"Lang's application for the Hurstleigh scholarship, sir," he muttered, looking warily at the nearest amorphous little countenances staring apprehensively at the assignment on the blackboard or bowed in swift vocabulary review. "Here's their stuff about qualifications, and Lang's paper. The Head would like to have your letter today if it's at all possible."

"Fourth period, or end of third," said old Latimer with the effortless laconic air which marked everything he said and did. He could make long speeches or perform the most complex personal rituals without ever letting go his characteristic effects of concision, condensation, compression. No one ever analyzed these effects or dissected his techniques; the Head never sent student teachers to work under him, though they were always assigned to visit his classes in the capacity of audience. His authority was beyond formulation. The Head was the Head; the Dean was the Little Corporal or the Boss-man; the Old Man was Latimer, who had no administrative position whatever, no connection with the faculty council, was never put on committees or made Sponsor of anything. He was the Old Man of the Mountain, the Old Man of the Sea. The funny thing was that he wasn't even very old: fifty-five at the most, with thick silver-fox hair.

Merton left and the freshmen were silent. The door swung with a click, and there rose behind it the great strange atmosphere of the Latin room, haunting to generations of students, compounded of the smell of Latimer's old beautiful tweeds, the wild fragrance of the ferns in his extravagant window boxes, the stone eyes of the Roman senators in prints on the front wall, the glint of gold letters on the leather bindings ranged on the desk, the complex lines of the small, fiercely exact reproduction of a Roman trireme encased in glass.

Old Latimer's classes always began quietly enough. The students lifted their faces to him, confident, expecting something to happen. Some waited for the great gusts of temper that swept the room rhythmically, periodically, like the rise and fall of some giant breathing chest. Some hoped for a dramatic chastisement, in baritone shout or chill sibilant whisper, of some classmate; some simply wished to escape this. Old Latimer never had any trouble with discipline and never thought about it.

Now he ran rapidly over the vocabulary, asking for meanings of words, principal parts of verbs, suddenly swooping to demand a whole declension, the total conjugation of one of the hard tenses, like the future passive of the -io verbs. For good answers he gave his swift wolfish smile, baring an astonishingly long, sharp left incisor. For a slow one he waited in impassive, gentlemanly patience or in the most ill-concealed ennui, rolling up his eyes, shaking his chalk in his hand. The choice of manner depended on the personality of the student, the past performances, known ability, standing of the student after some scene of the day before, and so on.

Over kitten-like, earnest little Emily Rushmore in the front row, struggling with the forms of the infinitive in her accustomed style of mixed timidity and stubbornness, valor and misgiving, he lingered long, hinting, grinning, exhorting, correcting, suddenly thrusting his large-boned brilliant-eyed countenance within one inch of hers to hiss an ending at her, bowing with a genuine smiling courtesy when she hit happily on a correct form. The little girl's face lit and shadowed, her eyelids drooped or lifted, following this peculiar orchestration. Latimer pressed her on to the fifth declension, new for the day; her maunderings over this caused him suddenly to throw up his hands, throw out his arms, throw back his head, and shout: "Emily Rushmore! Emily Rushmore!" Out came the rush of eloquence all knew would come, this time untinged with violence, just ringing with passion, elevated, sincere. In the great hills of North Dakota, he informed her, where the Sioux thought there abided forever the spirits of the dead, there was a great slab of mountain which bore her name. He called to her mind the images of great men hewn there by tremendous effort. Even so, he told her, he had hewn into the great slabs of her blank child's mind the forms of the four great Latin declensions, "complete, Emily, with mutations and characteristic variations from the norm—the -i of the ablative of *mare, insigne, animal, exemplar.*" The low beautiful baritone rose to a deep shout as he showered on her the epithets of Slab, Granite Hillside, Erstwhile Smooth Expanse. "And now you boggle at the second -i in *diei*," he added, suddenly in a normal, conversational voice, and smiled.

Emily began to relax; a delicate little giggle escaped her and a deep chortle spread through the class.

"Now, the translation," said old Latimer, smothering a yawn. "It's a simplified little anecdote taken from the *Aeneid,* which you —*some* of you, I mean—will be reading late next year." He piloted them through the short story of Aeneas' landing on the coast near Carthage, Dido's reception of him, the banquet, and the beginning of the tale. He excoriated someone for making a passive active, praised someone for making the historical present a past, explained neatly and lucidly the Roman attitude towards the order of words, reminded everyone that some ablatives of manner take *cum* and some do not take *cum*, assigned a lesson dealing with the comparison of irregular adjectives, pointed out to everyone that the translation for that lesson described the love of Dido for Aeneas and incarnated the idea of romantic love which most appealed to the ancient world, "not *exactly* a valentine affair! June and moon were not its symbols, but chains and fire and destroying disease; naked force and terrible pain. Here is great Virgil telling about Dido wandering through the city, burned with it, pierced with it, sick with it . . ." and the deep beautiful voice rolled over the classroom in a tide of unintelligible sound, as strongly marked by rhythm as any music they had ever heard:

> Heu vatum ignarae mentes! quid vota furentem,
> quid delubra iuvant? Est mollis flamma medullas
> interea, et tacitum vivit sub pectore volnus.
> Uritur infelix Dido . . .[2]

Over the faces of two or three, the incantation seekers, who would never forget this face or room, this sound, so long as they lived, came the drop-jawed, feeble-minded look of total acceptance they habitually wore at these moments. The bell rang; old Latimer seemed suddenly to forget the whole thing, smiled his briskest smile, said, "All right, now *watch those irregulars*," and flung open his door.

In every school there is one teacher concerning whom a rumor circulates that he has a large personal fortune and teaches not for money but from some obscure disinterested motive. In Latimer's school this role fell naturally to him, and each generation increased the collection of wild stories about his personal life and background. The man's clothes, bearing, accent, all suggested some world of personal autonomy and distinction totally foreign to their own world of hard-working, commuting, cocktail-drinking, sense-talking older men, with their ordinary expensive suits, their speech full of flat *a*'s, slurred consonants, dulled vowels *(guv'munt)*, and familiar well-understood words.

---

[2] To give a translation here would be to cheat on Mrs. Wagner's story, since Mr. Latimer makes so much of reading the selection in the original. An excellent translation can be found in *The Aeneid of Virgil*. Tr. by C. Day Lewis. Doubleday Anchor A 20; the entire section referred to by Mr. Latimer covers pp. 98–102.

He seemed also a fortuitous ambassador from some world quite different from that represented by their other teachers. All this was augmented by the fact that nobody really did know anything much about Latimer. The students all knew that he was an accomplished athlete; he played an almost embarrassingly good game of tennis for one so old, was seen with his wife on golf links and on the bridle paths. He skated on the school pond once or twice a year, with great competence, using a fine pair of Austrian skates. But he coached no teams, never talked of sports or went to football games.

The faculty knew with a fair degree of certainty that he had taught in several Eastern colleges and in at least one of the great prep schools, and that there was some quite exciting story about his marriage to the mother of one of his pupils. The tall dashing-looking woman whom everybody knew only as Mrs. Latimer certainly was not a very representative faculty wife. She was more than merely civil, really friendly in a fast-talking, brilliantly smiling way. She gave a large cocktail party once a year for all the faculty and served very good food and drinks. She wore dark red or dark green or purple tweeds in the daytime and black silk in the evening. It was thought that she had many friends "in town"—not in the suburb where the school was located—and that these were not suburban types. Nobody ever saw her in the summer. She and her husband simply disappeared off the Middle Western map, to return always just in time for the opening reception given by the Head, coming into it as though they had never been away, hard and precise in physical outline, clipped of speech, vague and uninformative in conversation.

Parents and other teachers quite often felt that Latimer did not take as much personal interest in the students as was the prevailing mode at the school. Certainly he spent little time on his inept and failing students. But no one dared reproach him with this, in view of the long fanatical hours he devoted to helping the middle range of his students, lavishing upon them his burning gaze, his infinite powers of dramatization, his gifts of lucid explanation and varied repetition, in an impassioned effort to bring them out of their uncertainties and into that state of life where they could translate with confidence, decline and conjugate with aplomb, recognize without hesitation the landmarks of early Latin studies, indirect discourse, purpose clauses, and the like. He never spoke to these students or to any others about their outside life, never allowed them to speak of their family routines or their home atmospheres. They could not feel that he was interested in them as human beings; it seemed unlikely that he ever thought of them as such,

and probable that he did not consider them people as they had been taught
to expect that their teachers would.

Not one of them resented this. Indeed, it seemed to relieve them, a
cool, sharp, stinging astringent applied to the irritations of their adolescence. And for all his lack of interest in their personal existences, when
he turned that deep brilliant glance upon them to see what they knew about
the passive periphrastic or whether they had studied the vocabulary, they
felt *noticed* as in few other departments of their lives.

Old Latimer cared no more for himself as a human being than he did
for them. His mad histrionics and Dionysian[3] outbursts were not designed
to compel their admiration nor to impose upon them a sense of his autoc-
racy and difference. They were teaching devices. For all his personal
complexities and the baroque, even rococo fabric of his individual being,
he was the one person of power in their lives who wished and demanded of
them something really simple and clear in outline. He wanted them
to learn Latin.

He now looked down at the little mess of papers on his desk. The face
of his best student, Robert Lang, looked wildly up at him from the photograph, denuded of its habitual steel-rimmed glasses. He picked up the
Hurstleigh folder on the classical scholarship, prepared by a man he knew
well and coldly disliked, a representative at classical meetings and archae-
ological congresses of the billboard world of Rotarianism, adjustment,
genial cooperation, and general group dynamics. Latimer narrowed his eyes
and tossed the folder aside. Next he picked up the general statement
of Hurstleigh's Dean of Admissions on the college's admission policies.
His eye fell on the phrase "breadth of extracurricular interests" and,
further on, "ability to function effectively in the group," and a savage scowl
twisted the upper part of his face. It disappeared as he looked up to see
Lang entering the room and quietly closing the door behind him.

The exotic airs generated in the classroom during the freshman class
were dissipated in an instant as Latimer's senior student took his seat
immediately opposite the master's chair and smiled his thin smile. Anything less "all-round" than the appearance and personal atmosphere of
Robert Lang would be difficult to imagine. From head to foot of his
physical being the general stigma of unattractive adolescence were sur-
charged by the presence of an imposing array of particularities. Behind a
fierce hedge of skin disorders and scattered bristle, under a layer of

[3] Dionysian. Frenzied, as suggested by ceremonies in honor of the god Dionysos.

impermanent childish flesh, slept a fine regular profile and a nobly sculp-
tured jawbone. But the boy's pale eyes shone with the fanaticisms of the
early-blooming specialist; his encrusted shirt collar, bedraggled Fair Isle
sweater, smudged shoes spoke of the sacrifice of one order of fastidiousness
to another.

Latimer always sat at his desk during his conferences with Lang. He
spoke in even, courteous tones, both friendly and remote, as one gentleman
addressing another slightly younger. "What is it today, Bob?" he asked
quietly, taking up his green Cicero and leafing through its opening pages.

"The peroration from the *Pro Cluentio,* sir," said Lang, and began to
translate from his little student's edition. The flowery and passionate appeal
for the life of an upright man unjustly charged with a low murder,
the crown of the great lawyer's defense against a prosecution which had
moved almost exclusively in the territories of political and class prejudice,
took shape in effortless English. Here and there Lang paused for a moment
to comment on a series of gerundives, to mention the names of less familiar
grammatical constructions, to guess at the reason for a curious ordering of
phrases.

Latimer listened in silence, inclining his head, turning the pages,
catching the boy's eye from time to time over the top of his book and communicating assent. At the end he nodded gravely and said, "All right. Now
read a bit of the Latin, Bob, and remember the trouble we had last time
with the long *i*'s." Lang looked up from his page and did not look back at
it as he recited the last section from memory, his eyes plunged deep into
Latimer's. *"Orat vos Habitus, indices, et flens obsecrat"*—his voice sank
and deepened at the end of the clause, in imitation not of Latimer but of
his own notion of Cicero's tones at this melodramatic moment. Latimer permitted himself a discreet smile.

"Well, Bob?" he asked, as the dying fall faded away. Lang's smile, as
discreet as his own, commented restrainedly on the last measures of the
speech.

"Well, sir . . . of course you can't miss the Old Silvertongue in it, the
Clarence Darrow[4] touch; naturally he had to overdo it, with that jury, and
all the emotion hung over from the other trial, eight years before. But you
can't help admiring his judgment. He brings it out about old Sassia being
an unnatural mother and rubs it in about her coming up for the trial, such
a terrible old bitch that nobody could miss it, even in the country towns.

4 Clarence Darrow. (1857–1938) a brilliant American defense lawyer.

Then he pulls out the stops about Cluentius 'weeping, begs you to restore him
to his life, his kinsmen' and the rest of it, and then to bring up the
old prejudice from the other trial when Cluentius bribed the jury—that
really took nerve. Nobody else would have dared; they would have ended
with the boo-hoo stuff. I think he's great. The trouble is, you can feel him
thinking it, too. And you can tell he despised the jury and the court and
the whole system. But it's good. You feel he knows his business. It's the
thing you really can like about him in these straight law cases where he's
just *being* a lawyer, the best in Rome, and forgetting the rest of it."

"The rest of it?"

"Yes, being the great philosopher and the father of his country and
all that stuff that spoils him later on. The pleasures of old age part,
the hysterical old woman part, all that."

"Bob," said Latimer in a soft idle voice, twirling a gold pencil, "what
do you want at Hurstleigh with that scholarship? What are you going to do
in college?"

"I don't know exactly, sir," said Lang, surprised. "Just learn Greek,
I guess. Read the other Latin stuff. Try archaeology and history. Just be a
classicist—learn to be one, I mean."

"Is that what you want? Just to *be* a classicist?"

"Well . . . I don't know yet what part of it I can go in for permanently. I've got to find that out."

"What, do you suppose," inquired the Old Man, a sharp, flinty note
edging into his voice, "is the role of the classicist in our present society?"
Bob Lang caught and held his eyes in another of those long, profoundly
calm gazes. He shrugged, without impertinence. "I don't know much about
it. I only know about a couple: Professor Hanley, I guess, and Ladislaw."

"Hanley! Yes, Hanley lives like a duke at what passes for a great university. He has his cigarettes and his jackets made for him in London, and
he makes a large thing out of teaching the boys the names of the wines they
ought to like. He does give good parties, that I'll say for him, and he keeps
his invitation cards piled up on his mantel, and they *do* pile up. Everybody
asks him to write introductions for their new little translation or their new
little historical novel. But that, my dear Lang, is not a classicist. That is
the Master of Hixon House. That is—uh, let's say, a personality."

Lang looked slightly alarmed, not so much at this novel portrait of an
august figure, hitherto a name on a title page and in a catalogue, as at the
sudden crackling tone in the Old Man's voice. Since he had been taken out

of the regular Latin class in the middle of his second year, two years ago, he had not seen any of Latimer's famous histrionics. There was a code drawn silently between the two. It was understood that this sort of thing was not necessary.

"Ladislaw!" continued the Old Man, his voice picking up speed, though still low-pitched. "You are probably unaware, Lang, that Ladislaw reaches the age of retirement next year. Last year he had performed on himself a brain operation known as a frontal lobotomy, calculated to remove from the sufferer all traces of the anxieties and tensions which have been disordering his personality, and with them all sense of responsibility and involvement in the knottier questions of life. I understand the result has been quite striking. Both Ladislaw and his administration can envisage the next year with fortitude, if not exactly with equanimity. Equanimity is, I am afraid, quite out of the question in the Ladislaw affair. But at any rate, the enrollment in classical studies at his university has for the past decade been such that it will not be necessary to replace him."

A violent silence fell. He resumed, speaking now with great weariness, "My friend, the poet Raphael Stein, maintains a very good position at Essex Academy. His students graduate with distinction, are joyously accepted everywhere simply on his say-so, and go on to major in government, history, economics, journalism—on his advice. The knowledge of Greek and Roman letters with which he has equipped them often stays with them, as a sort of interior decoration of the mind, for quite a while before it is relegated to the mental attic where, in most of their cases, one can only admit that it belongs. But Stein is not a classicist; he is a poet, who has found an agreeable, even quite sympathetic means of support.

"Throckmorton instructs young ladies in the number of half a dozen or so annually; he retires this year, and they are replacing him with a Scotchman who will devote most of his energies to the teaching of theology. Interest in religion and anthropology grows; the classics departments are, my boy, becoming more and more interdepartmental. It may perhaps be possible for you to make use of these bodies of knowledge as stalking horses, or as ritual masks, behind which you may carry on undisturbed your classicist's freakish endeavors."

"What about the department at Hurstleigh, sir?" asked Lang in the manner of one who more or less changes the subject. There was no answer. Latimer snapped off the point of his gold pencil, looked out the window, and let the matter drop. Feeling the need to get the conference back on that impersonal level which had for years now been the scene of his most profoundly enjoyable experiences, Lang introduced another theme.

"I was reading a poem of Yeats's last night," he said cautiously, feeling his way a bit. "It goes at the end: *Whence had they come, The hand and lash that beat down frigid Rome?* I couldn't quite make it out. Why 'frigid'?"

"Oh, just to suggest something cold and resistant, not easily beaten down, I imagine," said the Old Man in the same low weary tone. "Good question, that *Whence had they come?* He has a poem about Whiggery, too: *All's Whiggery now . . .*"

"Can't get what he's trying to bring out with that 'Whiggery,' either," said Lang. "Mr. Fletcher told us what the Whigs were, and all, but it doesn't help much."

"The man himself tells you, boy! 'A leveling, rancorous, rational sort of mind.' You read a lot, don't you? Tell me what you see in Latin! What's *in* it for you?"

At it again, thought Lang. But with perfect aplomb he began to look round for something true to tell the Old Man. "Well, at first I thought it was the language itself, the constructions and all that. I like the syntax, and thinking about the forms. Take that motto, for instance, they're always using in the Renaissance: *Nec spe nec metu.* You see it in the corner of old maps all the time. Well, if it's an ablative of manner it would mean 'with neither hope nor fear,' and just bring out a kind of stoicism, a stiff-upper-lip attitude, ready to take the rough with the smooth. But it shouldn't be an ablative of manner: no *cum,* and no adjective to let them off the *cum.* Some exceptions, like *dolo*—but not many. So if it's an ablative of cause, it changes the whole thing: 'Neither because of hope nor because of fear,' and it means the man's doing whatever he's doing not because he wants to get something out of it, not because he's afraid of what will happen if he doesn't, but just because he wants to. Probably because of the thing itself. That sort of thing is interesting to think about; interesting to me, anyway. But this year, and last year with Virgil, there's a lot more to it. You start to get an idea of what it was like, with them. I guess I just *like* the Romans. They're my type, I mean." He grinned suddenly and added, "*Romani nil me alienum puto,* you could say."

Latimer grinned back at him over the pun. The bell rang. Lang snapped out of it, gathered up his books and papers, looked curiously at his folder on Latimer's desk, snuffled a bit, and lurched out of the room.

The Old Man stared after him, then turned his glance to the pile of papers. He took up the recommendation blank, unscrewed his fine gold fountain pen, and began to write rapidly.

Gentlemen:

I am requested to write in support of the application of my student Robert Lang for admission to your freshman class as Wroxbury Scholar. As I read your statements concerning your freshman class and concerning this scholarship, I find myself rather at a loss. It seems unlikely to me that Robert Lang will satisfy your most important requirements. It is with regret that I write this, but I feel that candor is in order.

The boy is the most brilliant scholar I have ever prepared. There is small doubt that his performance on the College Board will be as near perfect as the circumstances of the examination allow. His mastery of the language is complete, or nearly so; his acquaintance with Roman civilization of the late republican and early imperial period is broad and his understanding of it sensitive. He can compose sensible and elegant Latin sentences. His translations are unexceptionable both in accuracy and in grace. In short, it is difficult to imagine him as a member of your first-year Latin class under Professor Speidel.

Furthermore, it would be idle to pretend that he has profited from or enjoyed his experience as manager of the basketball squad here this winter. The duties of the position demanded nothing but a little correspondence, and attendance at the games; when Lang had fulfilled these obligations, which he found tedious but not difficult, he considered that he had done what was required. His participation in the group emotions and satisfactions made available to him through this experience was, in fact, minimal.

The truth is that Lang's extracurricular interests are not broad in the sense you intend. His grasp of three languages, Latin, French, *and* English, and his continually expanding acquaintance with the literature and histories, ancient and modern, preserved in these languages, have made it somewhat difficult for him to "function effectively in the group," if I may be forgiven for borrowing a phrase of yours. In fact, Lang's group considers him very odd indeed, and rightly so.

His complexion falls far short of the Hurstleigh ideal, and I fear his posture is inelegant. Should you wish me to supply you with any further relevant information, and should this information be in my possession, I shall of course be happy to furnish you with more details.

Very truly yours.

As the Old Man signed this letter, the door opened to admit Mr. Merton, hands full of folders and papers as usual. The young man smiled with satisfaction as he saw that the recommendation was complete and ready for the Head. Remembering with pleasure that Lang had made the highest score on record in the entire country on the junior College Board in Latin the last year, and permitting himself to hope for at least one easy admission, he stretched out his hand for the paper and let his eye run quickly over it. His expression changed rapidly as he took in the sense of the clear fine writing. Amusement and irritation gave way to a real indignation as he suddenly imagined himself showing this thing to the Head. He scowled and drew in his breath to launch his protest; then his eyes fell on Latimer, staring up at him, a muscle fluttering wildly near the temple, perspiration standing coldly at the hairline. The passion in the clawed old face was appalling.

Merton's voice stopped in his throat, and for a moment he heard nothing but the bumping, plunging of his heart. Horrified, he watched tears gather in Latimer's eyes. Silent, he left the room, clutching the sheet of paper with his others. As the bell screamed through the hall he darted on an impulse into the boys' washroom, happily empty, and leaned against the wall for a moment. He was quite young, an English teacher of the new school, full of ideas about communication; but he was not stupid, not unread, and above all not insensitive. He simply felt that it wasn't normal to be invaded by this kind of thing at ten thirty in the morning. He waited passively, unresentfully, for the harsh grip of pity and terror to relax, before he should plunge again into the whirling, clattering corridor of the last period before Morning Exercise.

STUDY QUESTIONS:

1. Mr. Latimer, obviously a very able scholar, seems somewhat out of place at this school. The author gives us some explanation of why he is there, but in what other ways might you account for his situation?

2. What specifically in Robert Lang does Mr. Latimer value? The boy is obviously a very good student, but what one quality in him stands out above all others to his teacher?

3. How does the title apply to the story?

4. Can you think of any other ways in which Mr. Latimer might have registered his protest against the college form without damaging Robert Lang's chances for a scholarship?

5. Why is it appropriate that the story end with Mr. Merton?

6. What do you think Mr. Latimer would now advise Robert Lang to do about college?

THE PORTABLE PHONOGRAPH

WALTER VAN TILBURG CLARK

Imaginative wonder about the end of the world has long been exercised by men. The theme goes back to the ancient Greeks, many of whom thought time goes around in a cycle of destruction and re-birth; and the Book of Revelations, the Latin hymr used in the mass for the dead ("Dies irae, dies illa"), Byron's poem "Darkness," Thomas Hood's "The Last Man," and the end of H.G.Wells' powerful novel, *The Time Machine*, are all treatments of this great theme. But no version is more poignant than "The Portable Phonograph" by Walter Van Tilburg Clark. Mr. Clark was born in Maine in 1909, received a B.A. degree from the University of Nevada, and teaches at San Francisco State College. Among his books *The Ox Bow Incident* (1940), a story of the West, has become classic. After publication in the *Yale Review* "The Portable Phonograph" was collected into *The Watchful Gods and Other Stories* (1950).

The first task of anyone who writes about the extinction of mankind on this planet is, possibly, to give the reader a sense of what a desolate earth would be like. This Mr. Clark accomplishes with skill and compression in his opening paragraphs. Then, since it would be difficult to tell a story about the last man (or the last men) without having any, his second task is to present the survivors of the human race as they attempt to keep alive amid the ruins of civilization. Mr. Clark has done this by generalizing, so to speak, a war landscape and by centering his story upon a cell dug in the bank of a stream, where the incidents happen. His characters are nameless save one, a device that adds to the dreary desolation.

Nothing especially dramatic takes place. Four men listen reverently to the playing of an old phonograph record as they have listened to a reading of *The Tempest*. Three go away. Dr. Jenkins elaborately conceals the phonograph and the records. But can anything be more eloquent of the hunger of men for culture when they no longer have it and cannot possibly revive it?

The red sunset, with narrow black cloud strips like threads across it, lay on the curved horizon of the prairie. The air was still and cold, and in it settled the mute darkness and greater cold of night. High in the air there was wind, for through the veil of the dusk the clouds could be seen gliding rapidly south and changing shapes. A queer sensation of torment, of two-sided, unpredictable nature, arose from the stillness of the earth air beneath the violence of the upper air. Out of the sunset, through the dead, matted grass and isolated weed stalks of the prairie, crept the narrow and deeply rutted remains of a road. In the road, in places, there were crusts of shallow, brittle ice. There were little islands of an old oiled pavement in the road too, but most of it was mud, now frozen rigid. The frozen mud still bore the toothed impress of great tanks, and a wanderer on the neighboring undulations might have stumbled, in this light, into large, partially filled-in and weed-grown cavities, their banks channeled and beginning to spread into badlands. These pits were such as might have been made by falling meteors, but they were not. They were the scars of gigantic bombs, their rawness already made a little natural by rain, seed, and time. Along the road there were rakish remnants of fence. There was also, just visible, one portion of tangled and multiple barbed wire still erect, behind which was a shelving ditch with small caves, now very quiet and empty, at intervals in its back wall. Otherwise there was no structure or remnant of a structure visible over the dome of the darkling earth, but only, in sheltered hollows, the darker shadows of young trees trying again.

Under the wuthering arch of the high wind a V of wild geese fled south. The rush of their pinions sounded briefly, and the faint, plaintive notes of their expeditionary talk. Then they left a still greater vacancy.

There was the smell and expectation of snow, as there is likely to be when the wild geese fly south. From the remote distance, towards the red sky, came faintly the protracted howl and quick yap-yap of a prairie wolf.

North of the road, perhaps a hundred yards, lay the parallel and deeply intrenched course of a small creek, lined with leafless alders and willows. The creek was already silent under ice. Into the bank above it was dug a sort of cell, with a single opening, like the mouth of a mine tunnel. Within the cell there was a little red of fire, which showed dully through the opening, like a reflection or a deception of the imagination. The light came from the chary burning of four blocks of poorly aged peat, which gave off a petty warmth and much acrid smoke. But the precious remnants of wood, old fenceposts and timbers from the long-deserted dugouts, had to be saved for the real cold, for the time when a man's breath blew white, the moisture in his nostrils stiffened at once when he stepped out, and the expansive blizzards paraded for days over the vast open, swirling and settling and thickening, till the dawn of the cleared day when the sky was thin blue-green and the terrible cold, in which a man could not live for three hours unwarmed, lay over the uniformly drifted swell of the plain.

Around the smoldering peat four men were seated crosslegged. Behind them, traversed by their shadows, was the earth bench, with two old and dirty army blankets, where the owner of the cell slept. In a niche in the opposite wall were a few tin utensils which caught the glint of the coals. The host was rewrapping in a piece of daubed burlap four fine, leather-bound books. He worked slowly and very carefully and at last tied the bundle securely with a piece of grass-woven cord. The other three looked intently upon the process, as if a great significance lay in it. As the host tied the cord he spoke. He was an old man, his long, matted beard and hair gray to nearly white. The shadows made his brows and cheekbones appear gnarled, his eyes and cheeks deeply sunken. His big hands, rough with frost and swollen by rheumatism, were awkward but gentle at their task. He was like a prehistoric priest performing a fateful ceremonial rite. Also his voice had in it a suitable quality of deep, reverent despair, yet perhaps at the moment a sharpness of selfish satisfaction.

"When I perceived what was happening," he said, "I told myself, 'It is the end. I cannot take much; I will take these.' "

"Perhaps I was impractical," he continued. "But for myself, I do not regret, and what do we know of those who will come after us? We are the doddering remnant of a race of mechanical fools. I have saved what I love;

the soul of what was good in us is here; perhaps the new ones will make a strong enough beginning not to fall behind when they become clever."

He rose with slow pain and placed the wrapped volumes in the niche with his utensils. The others watched him with the same ritualistic gaze.

"Shakespeare, the Bible, *Moby Dick,* the *Divine Comedy*," one of them said softly. "You might have done worse, much worse."

"You will have a little soul left until you die," said another harshly. "That is more than is true of us. My brain becomes thick, like my hands." He held the big, battered hands, with their black nails, in the glow to be seen.

"I want paper to write on," he said. "And there is none."

The fourth man said nothing. He sat in the shadow farthest from the fire, and sometimes his body jerked in its rags from the cold. Although he was still young, he was sick and coughed often. Writing implied a greater future than he now felt able to consider.

The old man seated himself laboriously and reached out, groaning at the movement, to put another block of peat on the fire. With bowed heads and averted eyes his three guests acknowledged his magnanimity.

"We thank you, Dr. Jenkins, for the reading," said the man who had named the books.

They seemed then to be waiting for something. Dr. Jenkins understood but was loath to comply. In an ordinary moment he would have said nothing. But the words of *The Tempest,* which he had been reading, and the religious attention of the three made this an unusual occasion.

"You wish to hear the phonograph," he said grudgingly.

The two middle-aged men stared into the fire, unable to formulate and expose the enormity of their desire.

The young man, however, said anxiously, between suppressed coughs, "Oh, please," like an excited child.

The old man rose again in his difficult way and went to the back of the cell. He returned and placed tenderly upon the packed floor, where the firelight might fall upon it, an old portable phonograph in a black case. He smoothed the top with his hands and then opened it. The lovely green-felt-covered disk became visible.

"I have been using thorns as needles," he said. "But tonight, because we have a musician among us"—he bent his head to the young man, almost invisible in the shadow—"I will use a steel needle. There are only three left."

The two middle-aged men stared at him in speechless adoration. The one with the big hands, who wanted to write, moved his lips, but the whisper was not audible.

"Oh, don't!" cried the young man, as if he were hurt. "The thorns will do beautifully."

"No," the old man said. "I have become accustomed to the thorns, but they are not really good. For you, my young friend, we will have good music tonight."

"After all," he added generously, and beginning to wind the phonograph, which creaked, "they can't last forever."

"No, nor we," the man who needed to write said harshly. "The needle, by all means."

"Oh, thanks," said the young man. "Thanks," he said again in a low, excited voice, and then stifled his coughing with a bowed head.

"The records, though," said the old man when he had finished winding, "are a different matter. Already they are very worn. I do not play them more than once a week. One, once a week, that is what I allow myself.

"More than a week I cannot stand it; not to hear them," he apologized.

"No, how could you?" cried the young man. "And with them here like this."

"A man can stand anything," said the man who wanted to write, in his harsh, antagonistic voice.

"Please, the music," said the young man.

"Only the one," said the old man. "In the long run, we will remember more that way."

He had a dozen records with luxuriant gold and red seals. Even in that light the others could see that the threads of the records were becoming worn. Slowly he read out the titles and the tremendous, dead names of the composers and the artists and the orchestras. The three worked upon the names in their minds, carefully. It was difficult to select from such a wealth what they would at once most like to remember. Finally the man who wanted to write named Gershwin's "New York."

"Oh, no!" cried the sick young man, and then could say nothing more because he had to cough. The others understood him, and the harsh man withdrew his selection and waited for the musician to choose.

The musician begged Dr. Jenkins to read the titles again, very slowly, so that he could remember the sounds. While they were read he lay back against the wall, his eyes closed, his thin, horny hand pulling at his light beard, and listened to the voices and the orchestras and the single instruments in his mind.

When the reading was done he spoke despairingly. "I have forgotten," he complained. "I cannot hear them clearly.

"There are things missing," he explained.

"I know," said Dr. Jenkins. "I thought that I knew all of Shelley by heart. I should have brought Shelley."

"That's more soul than we can use," said the harsh man. "*Moby Dick* is better.

"By God, we can understand that," he emphasized.

The Doctor nodded.

"Still," said the man who had admired the books, "we need the absolute if we are to keep a grasp on anything.

"Anything but these sticks and peat clods and rabbit snares," he said bitterly.

"Shelley desired an ultimate absolute," said the harsh man. "It's too much," he said. "It's no good; no earthly good."

The musician selected a Debussy[1] nocturne. The others considered and approved. They rose to their knees to watch the Doctor prepare for the playing, so that they appeared to be actually in an attitude of worship. The peat glow showed the thinness of their bearded faces, and the deep lines in them, and revealed the condition of their garments. The other two continued to kneel as the old man carefully lowered the needle onto the spinning disk, but the musician suddenly drew back against the wall again, with his knees up, and buried his face in his hands.

At the first notes of the piano the listeners were startled. They stared at each other. Even the musician lifted his head in amazement but then quickly bowed it again, strainingly, as if he were suffering from a pain he might not be able to endure. They were all listening deeply, without movement. The wet, blue-green notes tinkled forth from the old machine and were individual, delectable presences in the cell. The individual, delectable presences swept into a sudden tide of unbearably beautiful dissonance and then continued fully the swelling and ebbing of that tide, the dissonant inpourings, and the resolutions, and the diminishments, and the little, quiet wavelets of interlude lapping between. Every sound was piercing and singularly sweet. In all the men except the musician there occurred rapid

[1] Claude Debussy, (1862–1918). French impressionist composer.

sequences of tragically heightened recollection. He heard nothing but what
was there. At the final, whispering disappearance, but moving quietly so
that the others would not hear him and look at him, he let his head
fall back in agony, as if it were drawn there by the hair, and clenched the
fingers of one hand over his teeth. He sat that way while the others were
silent and until they began to breathe again normally. His drawn-up legs
were trembling violently.

Quickly Dr. Jenkins lifted the needle off, to save it and not to spoil
the recollection with scraping. When he had stopped the whirling of the sacred disk he courteously left the phonograph open and by the fire, in sight.

The others, however, understood. The musician rose last, but then
abruptly, and went quickly out at the door without saying anything.
The others stopped at the door and gave their thanks in low voices. The
Doctor nodded magnificently.

"Come again," he invited, "in a week. We will have the 'New York.'"

When the two had gone together, out towards the rimed road, he stood
in the entrance, peering and listening. At first there was only the resonant
boom of the wind overhead, and then far over the dome of the dead, dark
plain the wolf cry lamenting. In the rifts of clouds the Doctor saw four stars
flying. It impressed the Doctor that one of them had just been obscured by
the beginning of a flying cloud at the very moment he heard what he had
been listening for, a sound of suppressed coughing. It was not near
by, however. He believed that down against the pale alders he could see
the moving shadow.

With nervous hands he lowered the piece of canvas which served as
his door and pegged it at the bottom. Then quickly and quietly, looking at
the piece of canvas frequently, he slipped the records into the case, snapped the lid shut, and carried the phonograph to his couch. There, pausing
often to stare at the canvas and listen, he dug earth from the wall and disclosed a piece of board. Behind this there was a deep hole in the wall, into
which he put the phonograph. After a moment's consideration he went over
and reached down his bundle of books and inserted it also. Then, guard-
edly, he once more sealed up the hole with the board and the earth. He
also changed his blankets and the grass-stuffed sack which served as a
pillow, so that he could lie facing the entrance. After carefully placing two
more blocks of peat upon the fire he stood for a long time watching
the stretched canvas, but it seemed to billow naturally with the first gusts
of a lowering wind. At last he prayed, and got in under his blankets, and

closed his smoke-smarting eyes. On the inside of the bed, next the wall, he could feel with his hand the comfortable piece of lead pipe.

STUDY QUESTIONS:

1. Do you know enough about music to suggest why a Debussy nocturne is appropriate for the story? Even if you do not, the text offers its suggestions. And why *The Tempest?*

2. Why is Dr. Jenkins described as "a prehistoric priest performing a fateful ceremonial rite" (every word, one guesses, has been carefully chosen)?

3. What connection is there between the statement: "I want paper to write on, and there is none," and the behavior of the musician when the record ends?

4. What are the moral implications of Dr. Jenkin's care to conceal the phonograph and the records?

5. Clark says nothing about why the world came to an end. Is there any hint given? In what way might the phonograph be an ironic commentary about the hint?

A VISIT
OF CHARITY

EUDORA WELTY

    Eudora Welty (1909–   ), who has done most of her work in the short story, belongs to that group of modern Southern writers who have preferred to emphasize the exceptional and grotesque characteristics of modern life, particularly as they are to be found in the South. She was born in Jackson, Mississippi, attended Mississippi State College for Women and, later, Columbia University. She worked for a while in New York but then returned to Mississippi, where she has resided since, giving all of her time to writing. For an author who takes unlimited pains with her stories, she has been surprisingly prolific. Her published volumes of stories include *A Curtain of Green* (1941), *The Wide Net* (1943), and *The Golden Apples* (1949). Three of her novels are *The Robber Bridegroom* (1942), a delightful fantasy written in the manner of an old ballad; *Delta Wedding* (1946), and *The Ponder Heart* (1954). The critical acclaim her work has received can be determined from the fact that she has received four O. Henry Memorial story prizes, two Guggenheim awards, and a $1,000 award from the American Academy of Arts and Letters in 1944 "in recognition of her skill in the short story."

    Regularly in her stories we are led into positions where an expected result turns out quite differently from what we at first thought might happen. Such is the case in "A Visit of Charity." All of us are encouraged by our religious and civic organizations to perform acts of kindness for others, especially for those who are underprivileged, handicapped, or in any way deprived of the fullness of life. Most of us accept the obligation of charity without question, but we accept it also, for the most part, without reference to the specific individual to whom the charity is to be extended, or to the set of circumstances which may have produced the situation that seems to call for the charity.

Some of us, furthermore, often perform the act of charity for quite selfish reasons. We want to think better of ourselves; the act of charity makes us feel good. We behave like the Pharisee of the Biblical parable of the Pharisee and the Publican. When the recipient of the charity does not appreciate our act as we expect him to, we are angered and hurt.

These are a few of the ideas raised by Miss Welty's story, but there are others as well. The great gap between youth and age is made clear. Can the girl and the old ladies really communicate? Then, too, the reader is asked to consider the drabness of institutional life and of what it may do to the human spirit—of how it may take away all impulses to generosity and the sharing of one's possessions with others. When one has little, one tends to hold on desperately to every new acquisition and particularly to those which come as one is reduced to the humiliation of charity.

Miss Welty's story does not reject the beautiful prescriptions of the Sermon on the Mount. It asks the reader instead to consider how the full dignity of both giver and receiver should be served when a visit of charity takes place.

It was mid-morning—a very cold, bright day. Holding a potted plant before her, a girl of fourteen jumped off the bus in front of the Old Ladies' Home, on the outskirts of town. She wore a red coat, and her straight yellow hair was hanging down loose from the pointed white cap all the little girls were wearing that year. She stopped for a moment beside one of the prickly dark shrubs with which the city had beautified the Home, and then proceeded slowly toward the building, which was of whitewashed brick and reflected the winter sunlight like a block of ice. As she walked vaguely up the steps she shifted the small pot from hand to hand; then she had to set it down and remove her mittens before she could open the heavy door.

"I'm a Campfire Girl. . . . I have to pay a visit to some old lady," she told the nurse at the desk. This was a woman in a white uniform who looked as if she were cold; she had closecut hair which stood up on the very top of her head exactly like a sea wave. Marian, the little girl, did not tell her that this visit would give her a minimum of only three points in her score.

"Acquainted with any of our residents?" asked the nurse. She lifted one eyebrow and spoke like a man.

"With any old ladies? No—but—that is, any of them will do," Marian stammered. With her free hand she pushed her hair behind her ears, as she did when it was time to study Science.

The nurse shrugged and rose. "You have a nice *multiflora cineraria*[1] there," she remarked as she walked ahead down the hall of closed doors to pick out an old lady.

There was loose, bulging linoleum on the floor. Marian felt as if she were walking on the waves, but the nurse paid no attention to it. There was a smell in the hall like the interior of a clock. Everything was silent until, behind one of the doors, an old lady of some kind cleared her throat like a sheep bleating. This decided the nurse. Stopping in her tracks, she first extended her arm, bent her elbow, and leaned forward from the hips—all to examine the watch strapped to her wrist; then she gave a loud double-rap on the door.

"There are two in each room," the nurse remarked over her shoulder.

"Two what?" asked Marian without thinking. The sound like a sheep's bleating almost made her turn around and run back.

One old woman was pulling the door open in short, gradual jerks, and when she saw the nurse a strange smile forced her old face dangerously awry. Marian, suddenly propelled by the strong, impatient arm of the nurse, saw next the side-face of another old woman, even older, who was lying flat in bed with a cap on and a counterpane drawn up to her chin.

"Visitor," said the nurse, and after one more shove she was off up the hall.

Marian stood tongue-tied; both hands held the potted plant. The old woman, still with that terrible, square smile (which was a smile of welcome) stamped on her bony face, was waiting. . . . Perhaps she said something. The old woman in bed said nothing at all, and she did not look around.

Suddenly Marian saw a hand, quick as a bird claw, reach up in the air and pluck the white cap off her head. At the same time, another claw

[1] Multiflora cineraria. The botanical name for the plant Marian is carrying.

to match drew her all the way into the room, and the next moment the door closed behind her.

"My, my, my," said the old lady at her side.

Marian stood enclosed by a bed, a washstand and a chair; the tiny room had altogether too much furniture. Everything smelled wet— even the bare floor. She held onto the back of the chair, which was wicker and felt soft and damp. Her heart beat more and more slowly, her hands got colder and colder, and she could not hear whether the old women were saying anything or not. She could not see them very clearly. How dark it was! The window shade was down, and the only door was shut. Marian looked at the ceiling. . . . It was like being caught in a robber's cave, just before one was murdered.

"Did you come to be our little girl for a while?" the first robber asked.

Then something was snatched from Marian's hand—the little potted plant.

"Flowers!" screamed the old woman. She stood holding the pot in an undecided way. "Pretty flowers," she added.

Then the old woman in bed cleared her throat and spoke. "They are not pretty," she said, still without looking around, but very distinctly.

Marian suddenly pitched against the chair and sat down in it.

"Pretty flowers," the first old woman insisted. "Pretty—pretty. . . ."

Marian wished she had the little pot back for just a moment—she had forgotten to look at the plant herself before giving it away. What did it look like?

"Stinkweeds," said the other old woman sharply. She had a bunchy white forehead and red eyes like a sheep. Now she turned toward Marian. The fogginess seemed to rise in her throat again, and she bleated, "Who—are—you?"

To her surprise, Marian could not remember her name. "I'm a Campfire Girl," she said finally.

"Watch out for the germs," said the old woman like a sheep, not addressing anyone.

"One came out last month to see us," said the first old woman.

A sheep or a germ? wondered Marian dreamily, holding onto the chair.

"Did not!" cried the other old woman.

"Did so! Read to us out of the Bible, and we enjoyed it!" screamed the first.

"Who enjoyed it!" said the woman in bed. Her mouth was unexpectedly small and sorrowful, like a pet's.

"We enjoyed it," insisted the other. "You enjoyed it—I enjoyed it."

"We all enjoyed it," said Marian, without realizing that she had said a word.

The first old woman had just finished putting the potted plant high, high on the top of the wardrobe, where it could hardly be seen from below. Marian wondered how she had ever succeeded in placing it there, how she could ever have reached so high.

"You mustn't pay any attention to old Addie," she now said to the little girl. "She's ailing today."

"Will you shut your mouth?" said the woman in bed. "I am not."

"You're a story."

"I can't stay but a minute—really, I can't," said Marian suddenly. She looked down at the wet floor and thought that if she were sick in here they would have to let her go.

With much to-do the first old woman sat down in a rocking chair—still another piece of furniture!—and began to rock. With the fingers of one hand she touched a very dirty cameo pin on her chest. "What do you do at school?" she asked.

"I don't know . . ." said Marian. She tried to think but she could not.

"Oh, but the flowers are beautiful," the old woman whispered. She seemed to rock faster and faster; Marian did not see how anyone could rock so fast.

"Ugly," said the woman in bed.

"If we bring flowers—" Marian began, and then fell silent. She had almost said that if Campfire Girls brought flowers to the Old Ladies' Home, the visit would count one extra point, and if they took a Bible with them on the bus and read it to the old ladies, it counted double. But the old woman had not listened, anyway; she was rocking and watching the other one, who watched back from the bed.

"Poor Addie is ailing. She has to take medicine—see?" she said, pointing a horny finger at a row of bottles on the table, and rocking so high that her black comfort shoes lifted off the floor like a little child's.

"I am no more sick than you are," said the woman in bed.

"Oh yes you are!"

"I just got more sense than you have, that's all," said the other old woman, nodding her head.

"That's only the contrary way she talks when *you all* come," said the first old lady with sudden intimacy. She stopped the rocker with a neat pat of her feet and leaned toward Marian. Her hand reached over—it felt like a petunia leaf, clinging and just a little sticky.

"Will you hush! Will you hush!" cried the other one.

Marian leaned back rigidly in her chair.

"When I was a little girl like you, I went to school and all," said the old woman in the same intimate, menacing voice. "Not here—another town. . . ."

"Hush!" said the sick woman. "You never went to school. You never came and you never went. You never were anywhere—only here. You never were born! You don't know anything. Your head is empty, your heart and hands and your old black purse are all empty, even that little old box that you brought with you you brought empty—you showed it to me. And yet you talk, talk, talk, talk, talk all the time until I think I'm losing my mind. Who are you? You're a stranger—a perfect stranger! Don't you know you're a stranger? Is it possible that they have actually done a thing like this to anyone—sent them in a stranger to talk, and rock, and tell away her whole long rigmarole? Do they seriously suppose that I'll be able to keep it up, day in, day out, night in, night out, living in the same room with a terrible old woman—forever?"

Marian saw the old woman's eyes grow bright and turn toward her. This old woman was looking at her with despair and calculation in her face. Her small lips suddenly dropped apart, and exposed a half circle of false teeth with tan gums.

"Come here, I want to tell you something," she whispered. "Come here!"

Marian was trembling, and her heart nearly stopped beating altogether for a moment.

"Now, now, Addie," said the first old woman. "That's not polite. Do you know what's really the matter with old Addie today?" She, too, looked at Marion; one of her eyelids drooped low.

"The matter?" the child repeated stupidly. "What's the matter with her?"

"Why, she's mad because it's her birthday!" said the first old woman, beginning to rock again and giving a little crow as though she had answered her own riddle.

"It is not, it is not!" screamed the old woman in bed. "It is not my birthday, no one knows when that is but myself, and will you please be quiet and say nothing more, or I'll go straight out of my mind!" She turned her eyes toward Marian again, and presently she said in a soft, foggy voice, "When the worst comes to the worst, I ring this bell, and the nurse comes." One of her hands was drawn out from under the patched counterpane—a thin little hand with enormous black freckles. With a finger which would not hold still she pointed to a little bell on the table among the bottles.

"How old are you?" Marian breathed. Now she could see the old woman in bed very closely and plainly, and very abruptly, from all sides, as in dreams. She wondered about her—she wondered for a moment as though there was nothing else in the world to wonder about. It was the first time such a thing had happened to Marian.

"I won't tell!"

The old face on the pillow, where Marian was bending over it, slowly gathered and collapsed. Soft whimpers came out of the small open mouth. It was a sheep that she sounded like—a little lamb. Marian's face drew very close, the yellow hair hung forward.

"She's crying!" She turned a bright, burning face up to the first old woman.

"That's Addie for you," the old woman said spitefully.

Marian jumped up and moved toward the door. For the second time, the claw almost touched her hair, but it was not quick enough. The little girl put her cap on.

"Well, it was a real visit," said the old woman, following Marian through the doorway and all the way out into the hall. Then from behind she suddenly clutched the child with her sharp little fingers. In an affected, high-pitched whine she cried, "Oh, little girl, have you a penny to spare for a poor old woman that's not got anything of her own? We don't have a thing in the world—not a penny for candy—not a thing! Little girl, just a nickle—a penny—"

Marian pulled violently against the old hands for a moment before she was free. Then she ran down the hall, without looking behind her and without looking at the nurse, who was reading *Field & Stream* at her desk. The nurse, after another triple motion to consult her wrist watch, asked automatically the question put to visitors in all institutions: "Won't you stay and have dinner with *us?*"

Marian never replied. She pushed the heavy door open into the cold air and ran down the steps.

Under the prickly shrub she stopped and quickly, without being seen retrieved a red apple she had hidden there.

Her yellow hair under the white cap, her scarlet coat, her bare knees all flashed in the sunlight as she ran to meet the big bus rocketing through the street.

"Wait for me!" she shouted. As though at an imperial command, the bus ground to a stop.

She jumped on and took a big bite out of the apple.

STUDY QUESTIONS:

1. How do you account for the difference in the two old women? What would cause Addie to be always bitter and antagonistic?

2. The atmosphere of this story becomes truly frightening? How does Miss Welty bring this about?

3. Is the failure of the visit due in any way to Marian herself? Can you imagine a way in which the visit might have been successful?

4. The story begins and ends with the nurse. What function does she serve in the story? Why her strange invitation at the end, "Won't you stay and have dinner with us?"

THE LAST DAY
IN THE FIELD

CAROLINE GORDON

Caroline Gordon writes mostly about the South, particularly about the traditions and intricate relationships of old Southern families. As in the novels of William Faulkner, the reader keeps re-encountering her characters or their descendants from book to book. Miss Gordon was born in Kentucky of a family which had lived formerly in Virginia. She knows the people and the countryside of these areas well. One of the delights of "The Last Day in the Field" is the care with which she presents the appearance and the *feeling* of autumn in the country. The figures of speech which describe trees, bushes and shrubs are both fresh and accurate.

Miss Gordon once said of her work, "I write, of course, about people of my own time and place. In order to get to know them well enough to write about them I first had to write about their fathers and grandfathers." In short, in her stories, the reader always sees the continuity of life, the way in which one generation replaces another. "The Last Day in the Field," though a wonderful story about hunting (quite a feat for a woman writer!), is actually more than just that. It is the story of an older man passing on to a younger man the skill he values most. It is a skill to which he has given a life-long dedication, and he can't let it go easily. He sees

414

the ineptness of the younger man, but he has confidence in him, too, and before the day is over the younger man has gone far toward becoming the kind of hunter the older man has been. The story, therefore, is also one of a young man's initiation.

A note of elegy hangs over the entire story, not only of farewell to hunting on the older man's part, but also as if the author were saying farewell to a way of life in which such simple and unqualified dedication can take place. For many men, sports, and particularly hunting, can become a kind of ritual, and the conclusion of a season always has a note of sadness. Most sports stories are crowded with action and suspense, and "The Last Day in the Field" is not deficient in either of these, but Miss Gordon demonstrates that it is possible also to write with reverence about sports.

That was the fall when the leaves stayed green so long. We had a drouth in August and the ponds everywhere were dry and the watercourse shrunken. Then in September heavy rains came. Things greened up. It looked like winter was never coming.

"You aren't going to hunt this year, Aleck," Molly said. "Remember how you stayed awake nights last fall with that pain in your leg."

In October light frosts came. In the afternoons when I sat on the back porch going over my fishing tackle I marked their progress on the elderberry bushes that were left standing against the stable fence. The lower, spreading branches had turned yellow and were already sinking to the ground but the leaves in the top clusters still stood up stiff and straight.

"Ah-h, it'll get you yet!" I said, thinking how frost creeps higher and higher out of the ground each night of fall.

The dogs next door felt it and would thrust their noses through the wire fence scenting the wind from the north. When I walked in the back yard they would bound twice their height and whine, for meat scraps Molly said, but it was because they smelled blood on my old hunting coat.

They were almost matched liver-and-white pointers. The big dog had a beautiful, square muzzle and was deep-chested and rangy. The bitch, Judy, had a smaller head and not so good a muzzle but she was springy loined too and had one of the merriest tails I've ever watched.

When Joe Thomas, the boy that owned them, came home from the hardware store he would change his clothes and then come down the back way into the wired enclosure and we would stand there watching the dogs and wondering how they would work. Joe said they were keen as mustard. He was going to take them out the first good Saturday and wanted me to come along.

"I can't make it," I said, "my leg's worse this year than it was last."

The fifteenth of November was clear and so warm that we sat out on the porch till nine o'clock. It was still warm when we went to bed towards eleven. The change must have come in the middle of the night. I woke once, hearing the clock strike two, and felt the air on my face and thought before I went back to sleep that the weather had broken at last. When I woke again at dawn the cold air was slapping my face hard. I came wide awake, turned over in bed and looked out the window.

There was a scaly-bark hickory tree growing on the east side of the house. You could see its upper branches from the bedroom window. The leaves had turned yellow a week ago. But yesterday evening when I walked out there in the yard they had still been flat with green streaks showing in them. Now they were curled up tight and a lot of leaves had fallen on to the ground.

I got out of bed quietly so as not to wake Molly, dressed and went down the back way over to the Thomas house. There was no one stirring but I knew which room Joe's was. The window was open and I could hear him snoring. I went up and stuck my head in.

"Hey," I said, "killing frost."

He opened his eyes and looked at me and then his eyes went shut. I reached my arm through the window and shook him. "Get up," I said, "we got to start right away."

He was awake now and out on the floor stretching. I told him to dress and be over at the house as quick as he could. I'd have breakfast ready for us both.

Aunt Martha had a way of leaving fire in the kitchen stove at night. There were red embers there now. I poked the ashes out and piled kindling on top of them. When the flames came up I put some heavier wood on, filled the coffee pot, and put some grease on in a skillet. By the time Joe got there I had coffee ready and some hoe cakes to go with our fried eggs. Joe had brought a thermos bottle. We put the rest of the coffee in it and I found a ham in the pantry and made some sandwiches.

While I was fixing the lunch Joe went down to the lot to hitch up. He was just driving Old Dick out of the stable when I came down the back steps. The dogs knew what was up, all right. They were whining and surging against the fence and Bob, the big dog, thrust his paw through and into the pocket of my hunting coat as I passed. While Joe was snapping on the leashes I got a few handfuls of straw from the rack and put it in the foot of the buggy. It was twelve miles where we were going; the dogs would need to ride warm coming back late.

Joe said he would drive. We got in the buggy and started out, up Seventh Street and on over to College and out through Scufftown. When we got into the negro section we could see what a killing frost it had been. A light shimmer over all the ground still and the weeds around the cabins dark and matted the way they are when the frost hits them hard and twists them.

We drove on over the Red River bridge and up into the open country. At Jim Gill's place the cows had come up and were standing waiting to be milked but nobody was stirring yet from the house. I looked back from the top of the hill and saw that the frost mists still hung heavy in the bottom and thought it was a good sign. A day like this when the earth is warmer than the air currents is good for the hunter. Scent particles are borne on the warm air and birds will forage far on such a day.

It took us over an hour to get from Gloversville to Spring Creek. Joe wanted to get out as soon as we hit the big bottom there but I held him down and we drove on to the top of the ridge. We got out there, unhitched Old Dick and turned him into one of Rob Fayerlee's pastures—I thought how surprised Rob would be when he saw him grazing there—put our guns together, and started out, the dogs still on leash.

It was rough, broken ground, scrub oak, with a few gum trees and lots of buckberry bushes. One place a patch of corn ran clear up to the top of the ridge. As we passed along between the rows I could see the frost glistening on the north side of the stalks. I knew it was going to be a good day.

I walked over to the brow of the hill. From here you can see off over the whole valley—I've hunted every foot of it in my time—tobacco land, mostly. One or two patches of corn there on the side of the ridge. I thought we might start there and then I knew that wouldn't do. Quail will linger on the roost a cold day and feed in shelter during the morning. It is only in the afternoon that they will work out to the open.

The dogs were whining. Joe bent down and was about to slip their leashes. "Hey, boy," I said, "don't do that."

I turned around and looked down the other side of the ridge. It was better that way. The corn land of the bottoms ran high up on to the hill in several places there and where the corn stopped there were big patches of ironweed and buckberry. I knocked my pipe out on a stump.

"Let's go that way," I said.

Joe was looking at my old buckhorn whistle that I had slung around my neck. "I forgot to bring mine."

"All right," I said, "I'll handle 'em."

He unfastened their collars and cast off. They broke away, racing for the first hundred yards and barking, then suddenly swerved. The big dog took off to the right along the hillside. The bitch, Judy, skirted a belt of corn along the upper bottomlands. I kept my eye on the big dog. A dog that has bird sense will know cover when he sees it. This big Bob was an independent hunter, all right, I could see him moving fast through the scrub oaks, working his way down toward a patch of ironweed. He caught first scent just on the edge of the weed patch and froze with every indication of class, head up, nose stuck out, and tail straight in air. Judy, meanwhile, had been following the line of the corn field. A hundred yards away she caught sight of Bob's point and backed him.

We went up and flushed the birds. They got up in two bunches. I heard Joe's shot while I was in the act of raising my gun and I saw his bird fall not thirty paces from where I stood. I had covered the middle bird of the larger bunch—that's the one led by the boss cock—the way I usually do. He fell, whirling head over heels, driven a little forward by the impact. A well-centered shot. I could tell by the way the feathers fluffed as he tumbled.

The dogs were off through the grass. They had retrieved both birds. Joe stuck his in his pocket. He laughed. "I thought there for a minute you were going to let him get away."

I looked at him but I didn't say anything. It's a wonderful thing to be twenty years old.

The majority of the singles had flown straight ahead to settle in the rank grass that jutted out from the bottomland. Judy got down to work at once but the big dog broke off to the left, wanting to get footloose to find another covey. I thought of how Trecho, the best dog I ever had—the best dog any man ever had—used always to be wanting to do the same thing and I laughed.

"Naw, you don't," I said, "come back here, you scoundrel, and hunt these singles."

He stopped on the edge of a briar patch, looked at me and heeled up promptly. I clucked him out again. He gave me another look. I thought we were beginning to understand each other better. We got some nice points among those singles but we followed that valley along the creek bed and through two or three more corn fields without finding another covey. Joe was disappointed but I wasn't beginning to worry yet; you always make your bag in the afternoon.

It was twelve o'clock by this time, no sign of frost anywhere and the sun beating down steady on the curled-up leaves.

"Come on," I said, "let's go up to Buck's spring and eat."

We walked up the ravine whose bed was still moist with the fall rains and came out at the head of the hollow. They had cleared out some of the trees on the side of the ravine but the spring itself was the same: a deep pool welling up between the roots of an old sycamore. I unwrapped the sandwiches and the piece of cake and laid them on a stump. Joe got the thermos bottle out of his pocket. Something had gone wrong with it and the coffee was stone cold. We were about to drink it that way when Joe saw a good tin can flung down beside the spring. He made a trash fire and we put the coffee in the can and heated it to boiling.

It was warm in the ravine, sheltered from the wind, with the little fire burning. I turned my game leg so that the heat fell full on my knee. Joe had finished his last sandwich and was reaching for the cake.

"Good ham," he said.

"It's John Ferguson's," I told him.

He had got up and was standing over the spring. "Wonder how long this wood'll last, under water this way."

I looked at the sycamore root, green and slick where the thin stream of water poured over it, then my eyes went back to the dogs. They were tired, all right. Judy had gone off to lie down in a cool place at the side of the spring, but the big dog, Bob, lay there, his forepaws stretched out in front of him, never taking his eyes off our faces. I looked at him and thought how different he was from his mate and like some dogs I had known—and men too—who lived only for hunting and could never get enough no matter how long the day. There was something about his head and his markings that reminded one of another dog I used to hunt with a long time ago and I asked the boy who had trained him. He said the old fellow he bought the dogs from had been killed last spring, over in Trigg —Charley Morrison.

Charley Morrison! I remembered how he died, out hunting by himself and the gun had gone off, accidentally they said. Charley had called his dog to him, got blood over him and sent him home. The dog went, all right, but when they got there Charley was dead. Two years ago that was and now I was hunting the last dogs he'd ever trained. . . .

Joe lifted the thermos bottle. "Another cup?"

I held my cup out and he filled it. The coffee was still good and hot. I drank it, standing up, running my eye over the country in front of us. Afternoon is different from morning, more exciting. It isn't only as I say that you'll make your bag in the afternoon, but it takes more figuring. They're fed and rested and when they start out again they'll work in the open and over a wider range.

Joe was stamping out his cigarette: "Let's go."

The dogs were already out of sight but I could see the sedge grass ahead moving and I knew they'd be making for the same thing that took my eye: a spearhead of thicket that ran far out into this open field. We came up over a little rise. There they were, Bob on a point and Judy backing him not fifty feet from the thicket. I saw it was going to be tough shooting. No way to tell whether the birds were between the dog and the thicket or in the thicket itself. Then I saw that the cover was more open along the side of the thicket and I thought that that was the way they'd go if they were in the thicket. But Joe had already broken away to the left. He got too far to the side. The birds flushed to the right and left him standing, flat-footed, without a shot.

He looked sort of foolish and grinned.

I thought I wouldn't say anything and then I found myself speaking: "Trouble with you, you try to out-think the dog."

There was nothing to do about it, though. The chances were that the singles had pitched in the trees below. We went down there. It was hard hunting. The woods were open, the ground everywhere heavily carpeted with leaves. Dead leaves make a tremendous rustle when the dogs surge through them. It takes a good nose to cut scent keenly in such noisy cover. I kept my eye on Bob. He never faltered, getting over the ground in big, springy strides but combing every inch of it. We came to an open place in the woods. Nothing but hickory trees and bramble thickets overhung with trailing vines. Bob passed the first thicket and came to a beautiful point. We went up. He stood perfectly steady but the bird flushed out fifteen or twenty steps ahead of him. I saw it swing to the right, gaining altitude very quickly—woods birds will always cut back to known territory—and it came to me how it would be.

I called to Joe: "Don't shoot yet."

He nodded and raised his gun, following the bird with the barrel. It was directly over the treetops when I gave the word and he shot, scoring a clean kill.

He laughed excitedly as he stuck the bird in his pocket. "My God, man, I didn't know you could take that much time!"

We went on through the open woods. I was thinking about a day I'd had years ago in the woods at Grassdale, with my uncle, James Morris, and his son, Julian. Uncle James had given Julian and me hell for missing just such a shot. I can see him now standing up against a big pine tree, his face red from liquor and his gray hair ruffling in the wind: *"Let him alone! Let him alone!* And establish your lead as he climbs."

Joe was still talking about the shot he'd made. "Lord, I wish I could get another one like that."

"You won't," I said, "we're getting out of the woods now."

We struck a path that led due west and followed it for half a mile. My leg was stiff from the hip down now and every time I brought it over, the pain would start in my knee, Zing! and travel up and settle in the small of my back. I walked with my head down, watching the light catch on the ridges of Joe's brown corduroy trousers and then shift and catch again. Sometimes he would get on ahead and then there would be nothing but the black tree trunks coming up out of the dead leaves.

Joe was talking about some wild land up on the Cumberland. We could get up there on an early train. Have a good day. Might even spend the night. When I didn't answer he turned around: "Man, you're sweating."

I pulled my handkerchief out and wiped my face. "Hot work," I said.

He had stopped and was looking about him. "Used to be a spring somewhere around here."

He had found the path and was off. I sat down on a stump and mopped my face some more. The sun was halfway down through the trees now, the whole west woods ablaze with the light. I sat there and thought that in another hour it would be good and dark and I wished that the day could go on and not end so soon and yet I didn't see how I could make it much farther with my leg the way it was.

Joe was coming up the path with his folding cup full of water. I hadn't thought I was thirsty but the cold water tasted good. We sat there awhile and smoked, then Joe said that we ought to be starting back, that we must be a good piece from the rig by this time.

We set out, working north through the edge of the woods. It was rough going and I was thinking that it would be all I could do to make it back to the rig when we climbed a fence and came out at one end of a long field that sloped down to a wooded ravine. Broken ground, badly gullied and covered with sedge everywhere except where sumac thickets had

sprung up—as birdy a place as ever I saw. I looked it over and knew I had
to hunt it, leg or no leg, but it would be close work, for me and the dogs too.

I blew them in a bit and we stood there watching them cut up
the cover. The sun was down now; there was just enough light left to see
the dogs work. The big dog circled the far wall of the basin and came up
wind just off the drain, then stiffened to a point. We walked down to it. The
birds had obviously run a bit into the scraggly sumac stalks that bordered
the ditch. My mind was so much on the dogs I forgot Joe. He took one step
too many. The fullest blown bevy of the day roared up through the tangle.
It had to be fast work. I raised my gun and scored with the only barrel I
had time to peg. Joe shouted; I knew he had got one too.

We stood there trying to figure out which way the singles had gone
but they had fanned out too quick for us, excited as we were, and
after beating around awhile we gave up and went on.

We came to the rim of the swale, eased over it, crossed the dry creek
bed that was drifted thick with leaves, and started up the other side. I had
blown in the dogs, thinking there was no use for them to run their heads
off now we'd started home, but they didn't come. I walked on a little farther, then I looked back and saw Bob's white shoulders through a tangle
of cinnamon vine.

Joe had turned around too. "They've pinned a single out of that last
covey," he said.

I looked over at him quick. "Your shot."

He shook his head. "No, you take it."

I limped back and flushed the bird. It went skimming along the buckberry bushes that covered that side of the swale. In the fading light I could
hardly make it out and I shot too quick. It swerved over the thicket and I
let go with the second barrel. It staggered, then zoomed up. Up, up, up, over
the rim of the hill and above the tallest hickories. It hung there for a second, its wings black against the gold light, before, wings still spread,
it came whirling down, like an autumn leaf, like the leaves that were everywhere about us, all over the ground.

STUDY QUESTIONS:

1. This is a story of initiation. Aleck, knowing that his hunting days are
over, wants to be sure that the traditions of hunting are carried on by young Joe.

Where in the story do you find examples of Aleck's careful instruction?

2. Miss Gordon has a superb eye for scenic detail. Notice how shrubs, trees, and bushes are specifically named and described. What are the advantages in a story of this kind of such scenic exactness?

3. What indications are there that Joe has learned his lessons well and that he will become quite as dedicated a hunter as Aleck?

4. How would the story differ if it were told from Joe's point of view?

5. The occasion for Aleck is a very sad one, and the reader feels his sadness, yet there is no emotionalism in the story. How does Miss Gordon manage to convey the tone of sadness and farewell?

SREDNI VASHTAR

H. H. MUNRO

H. H. Munro (1870–1916), better known as "Saki," a name he took
over from the *Rubaiyat* of Omar Khayyam, was born in Burma when it
was a British possession, brought to England like the children of other
"colonials" to be educated, went back to Burma, where he entered the
police service for a time, and then returned again to England. There he became a newspaper correspondent. He also served in World War I. As early
as 1904 in a collection called *Reginald* he had displayed his peculiar power
in the "short" short story, his characteristic form. The present tale comes
from a later collection, *The Chronicles of Clovis* (1912).

Library catalogues often put Saki under "humor," but this humor is
a special sort. Originally it appealed only to the smart set among the
younger intellectuals; today his audience has widened, but his appeal is
still to the few rather than the many. His audience will never be anything like
that of, say, Mark Twain. His tales are more like those of the great French
satirist of the eighteenth century, Voltaire, who stripped a story to its
bones and then (to change the figure) aimed it neatly at the center of the
target, which was always some form of human folly. "Sredni Vashtar" is
this kind of tale with a moral, but it is more complex.

424

It is of course an indirect but powerful plea for a better understanding of children by the adult world. It is, even more obviously, a rather gruesome anecdote. It is, in the third place, a modern fairy tale about the appropriate end of a wicked witch. But it is also one of the oldest of fables, that of the wishes-come-true-in-the-wrong-way. A worshipper's prayer is answered but not in the fashion he anticipated. In one sense Mrs. de Ropp may perhaps be said to get what she deserves; in another sense the little boy's prayer lets loose horror beyond his comprehending. Whether the story is comedy, or fantasy, or irony, or tragedy, or a fable for our time is something every reader will have to decide for himself.

Conradin was ten years old, and the doctor had pronounced his professional opinion that the boy would not live another five years. The doctor was silky and effete, and counted for little, but his opinion was endorsed by Mrs. De Ropp, who counted for nearly everything. Mrs. De Ropp was Conradin's cousin and guardian, and in his eyes she represented those three-fifths of the world that are necessary and disagreeable and real; the other two-fifths, in perpetual antagonism to the foregoing, were summed up in himself and his imagination. One of these days Conradin supposed he would succumb to the mastering pressure of wearisome necessary things—such as illnesses and coddling restrictions and drawn-out dullness. Without his imagination, which was rampant under the spur of loneliness, he would have succumbed long ago.

Mrs. De Ropp would never, in her honestest moments, have confessed to herself that she disliked Conradin, though she might have been dimly aware that thwarting him "for his good" was a duty which she did not find particularly irksome. Conradin hated her with a desperate sincerity which he was perfectly able to mask. Such few pleasures as he could contrive for himself gained an added relish from the likelihood that they would be displeasing to his guardian, and from the realm of his imagination she was locked out—an unclean thing, which should find no entrance.

In the dull, cheerless garden, overlooked by so many windows that were ready to open with a message not to do this or that, or a reminder that medicines were due, he found little attraction. The few fruit-trees that it contained were set jealously apart from his plucking, as though they were rare specimens of their kind blooming in an arid waste; it would probably have been difficult to find a market-gardener who would have offered ten shillings for their entire yearly produce. In a forgotten corner, however,

almost hidden behind a dismal shrubbery, was a disused tool-shed of respectable proportions, and within its walls Conradin found a haven, something that took on the varying aspects of a playroom and a cathedral. He
had peopled it with a legion of familiar phantoms, evoked partly from
fragments of history and partly from his own brain, but it also boasted two
inmates of flesh and blood. In one corner lived a ragged-plumaged Houdan
hen, on which the boy lavished an affection that had scarcely another out-
let. Further back in the gloom stood a large hutch, divided into two
compartments, one of which was fronted with close iron bars. This was the
abode of a large polecat-ferret, which a friendly butcher-boy had once
smuggled, cage and all, into its present quarters, in exchange for a long-
secreted hoard of small silver. Conradin was dreadfully afraid of the lithe,
sharp-fanged beast, but it was his most treasured possession. Its very
presence in the tool-shed was a secret and fearful joy, to be kept scrupulously from the knowledge of the Woman, as he privately dubbed his cousin.
And one day, out of Heaven knows what material, he spun the beast
a wonderful name, and from that moment it grew into a god and a religion.
The Woman indulged in religion once a week at a church near by, and took
Conradin with her, but to him the church service was an alien rite in the
House of Rimmon.[1] Every Thursday, in the dim and musty silence of the
tool-shed, he worshipped with mystic and elaborate ceremonial before the
wooden hutch where dwelt Sredni Vashtar, the great ferret. Red flowers in
their season and scarlet berries in the winter-time were offered at his
shrine, for he was a god who laid some special stress on the fierce impatient side of things, as opposed to the Woman's religion, which, as far as
Conradin could observe, went to great lengths in the contrary direction.
And on great festivals powdered nutmeg was strewn in front of his hutch,
an important feature of the offering being that the nutmeg had to be stolen.
These festivals were of irregular occurrence, and were chiefly appointed to
celebrate some passing event. On one occasion, when Mrs. De Ropp
suffered from acute toothache for three days, Conradin kept up the festival
during the entire three days, and almost succeeded in persuading himself
that Sredni Vashtar was personally responsible for the toothache. If the
malady had lasted for another day the supply of nutmeg would have
given out.

The Houdan hen was never drawn into the cult of Sredni Vashtar.

[1] House of Rimmon. In II Kings, 5:18 in The Old Testament Naaman obtains Elisha's
permission to accompany his master when he worships the god Rimmon, even though Naaman
is not an idolator.

she goes to church ritually,

Conradin had long ago settled that she was an Anabaptist. He did not pretend to have the remotest knowledge as to what an Anabaptist was, but he privately hoped that it was dashing and not very respectable. Mrs. De Ropp was the ground plan on which he based and detested all respectability.

After a while Conradin's absorption in the tool-shed began to attract the notice of his guardian. "It is not good for him to be pottering down there in all weathers," she promptly decided, and at breakfast one morning she announced that the Houdan hen had been sold and taken away overnight. With her short-sighted eyes she peered at Conradin, waiting for an outbreak of rage and sorrow, which she was ready to rebuke with a flow of excellent precepts and reasoning. But Conradin said nothing: there was nothing to be said. Something perhaps in his white set face gave her a momentary qualm, for at tea that afternoon there was toast on the table, a delicacy which she usually banned on the ground that it was bad for him; also because the making of it "gave trouble," a deadly offence in the middle-class feminine eye.

"I thought you liked toast," she exclaimed, with an injured air, observing that he did not touch it.

"Sometimes," said Conradin.

In the shed that evening there was an innovation in the worship of the hutch-god. Conradin had been wont to chant his praises, tonight he asked a boon.

"Do one thing for me, Sredni Vashtar."

The thing was not specified. As Sredni Vashtar was a god he must be supposed to know. And choking back a sob as he looked at that other empty corner, Conradin went back to the world he so hated.

And every night, in the welcome darkness of his bedroom, and every evening in the dusk of the tool-shed, Conradin's bitter litany went up: "Do one thing for me, Sredni Vashtar."

Mrs. De Ropp noticed that the visits to the shed did not cease, and one day she made a further journey of inspection.

"What are you keeping in that locked hutch?" she asked. "I believe it's guinea-pigs. I'll have them all cleared away."

Conradin shut his lips tight, but the Woman ransacked his bedroom till she found the carefully hidden key, and forthwith marched down to the shed to complete her discovery. It was a cold afternoon, and Conradin had been bidden to keep to the house. From the furthest window of the dining-room the door of the shed could just be seen beyond the corner of the shrubbery, and there Conradin stationed himself. He saw the Woman

enter, and then he imagined her opening the door of the sacred hutch and
peering down with her short-sighted eyes into the thick straw bed where his
god lay hidden. Perhaps she would prod at the straw in her clumsy impatience. And Conradin fervently breathed his prayer for the last time. But he
knew as he prayed that he did not believe. He knew that the Woman would
come out presently with that pursed smile he loathed so well on her face,
and that in an hour or two the gardener would carry away his wonderful
god, a god no longer, but a simple brown ferret in a hutch. And he knew
that the Woman would triumph always as she triumphed now, and that he
would grow ever more sickly under her pestering and domineering and
superior wisdom, till one day nothing would matter much more with him,
and the doctor would be proved right. And in the sting and misery of his
defeat, he began to chant loudly and defiantly the hymn of his threat-
ened idol:

> Sredni Vashtar went forth,
> His thoughts were red thoughts and his teeth were white.
> His enemies called for peace, but he brought them death.
> Sredni Vashtar the Beautiful.

And then of a sudden he stopped his chanting and drew closer to the
window-pane. The door of the shed still stood ajar as it had been left, and
the minutes were slipping by. They were long minutes, but they slipped by
nevertheless. He watched the starlings running and flying in little parties
across the lawn; he counted them over and over again, with one eye always
on that swinging door. A sour-faced maid came in to lay the table for tea,
and still Conradin stood and waited and watched. Hope had crept by inches
into his heart, and now a look of triumph began to blaze in his eyes that
had only known the wistful patience of defeat. Under his breath, with a
furtive exultation, he began once again the pæan of victory and devastation.
And presently his eyes were rewarded: out through that doorway came a
long, low, yellow-and-brown beast, with eyes a-blink at the waning daylight,
and dark wet stains around the fur of jaws and throat. Conradin dropped
on his knees. The great polecat-ferret made its way down to a small brook
at the foot of the garden, drank for a moment, then crossed a little plank
bridge and was lost to sight in the bushes. Such was the passing of
Sredni Vashtar.

"Tea is ready," said the sour-faced maid; "where is the mistress?"

"She went down to the shed some time ago," said Conradin.

And while the maid went to summon her mistress to tea, Conradin fished a toasting-fork out of the sideboard drawer and proceeded to toast himself a piece of bread. And during the toasting of it and the buttering of it with much butter and the slow enjoyment of eating it, Conradin listened to the noises and silences which fell in quick spasms beyond the dining-room door. The loud foolish screaming of the maid, the answering chorus of wondering ejaculations from the kitchen region, the scuttering footsteps and hurried embassies for outside help, and then, after a lull, the scared sobbings and the shuffling tread of those who bore a heavy burden into the house.

"Whoever will break it to the poor child? I couldn't for the life of me!" exclaimed a shrill voice. And while they debated the matter among themselves, Conradin made himself another piece of toast.

STUDY QUESTIONS:

1. What does calling the polecat-ferret by an Oriental name add to the credibility of the event?

2. What is the purpose of the final statement?

3. Discuss whether or not this story represents a conflict between pagan nature and respectability, giving your reasons.

4. Do you regard Mrs. de Ropp's supposed motives in "thwarting him 'for his good' " sufficient reason for the manner of her death? Discuss.

5. If the whole story were to be called a fantasy which nevertheless reveals a profound adult sympathy with a child's mind, how would you describe the author's attitude toward the boy?

Mrs De Ropp is responsible for releasing his hatred and the ferret

Sredi Vashtar is right god because he worship Power and violence.

MAMMON
AND THE ARCHER

O. HENRY

William Sidney Porter (O. Henry) has probably been the most popular writer of the American short story. Indeed, there was a time when the terms "short story" and "O. Henry" were virtually synonymous. Much of his popularity has diminished; modern readers find many of the stories dated in both subject and form. Still, there will no doubt always be an audience for a number of his tales, and because of its theme, love versus money, "Mammon and the Archer" would seem to be one of these.

O. Henry was born in Greensboro, North Carolina, in 1862 and died in New York City in 1910. He came to writing late and in a very unusual manner. Convicted of having embezzled funds from an Austin, Texas, bank, where he had worked as teller, he was sentenced to five years' imprisonment in a Federal penitentiary in Columbus, Ohio. He was a model prisoner, determined on rehabiliation and making up for the unfortunate blunder of his life. He was released after little more than three years, but during his incarceration he had begun writing stories and submitting them to magazines. His reason for doing this was, quite honestly, that he wanted to earn money in order to take care of his wife, who was ill. The stories caught on with the public. When he left prison he went immediately to employment with a New York newspaper, for which he produced about a story a week between 1902 and 1910.

In the short story form O. Henry's particular contribution is what critics have come to call the "surprise ending." Nearly all of the stories end in a peculiar twist, somewhat unanticipated by the reader. When the reader who knows O. Henry's work picks up an unfamiliar story, he is prepared for something unexpected at the conclusion. Generally these conclusions are an ironic comment on life, and, as such, they sometimes violate the sense of reality. Life, says the reader, is not quite so full of trickery. Furthermore, O. Henry's style often makes the reader impatient. There are, perhaps, too many "punch lines"; the author occasionally seems to be straining for cleverness. Nevertheless, his work must be known to the student of American fiction, and there is no doubt that he has left a permanent mark on the history of the American short story. Even without being aware of it, many writers still follow the basic formula of his tales, particularly if they write for commercial T.V., the movies, or mass-circulation magazines.

"Mammon and the Archer" raises an interesting and fundamental question for young people in America to consider: which is the more powerful, love or money? Can the possession of money influence the course of love, and, if so, how much? The story is not altogether a serious one, and the characters are really not people at all, yet there is enough semblance of life here to make the reader chuckle at its ending and to ponder the meaning after he puts the story down. O. Henry never intended to be anything but a popular writer; consequently his stories are not in any sense "deep" or philosophic. But there may be more to "Mammon and the Archer" than meets the eye.

Old Anthony Rockwall, retired manufacturer and proprietor of Rockwall's Eureka Soap, looked out the library window of his Fifth Avenue mansion and grinned. His neighbor to the right—the aristocratic clubman, G. Van Schuylight Suffold-Jones—came out to his waiting motor-car, wrinkling a contumelious[1] nostril, as usual, at the Italian renaissance sculpture of the soap palace's front elevation.

"Stuck-up old statuette of nothing doing!" commented the ex-Soap King. "The Eden Musée'll[2] get that old frozen Nesselrode yet if he don't

---

[1] Contumelious (Con·tyoo·MEE·lee·us): insulting or humiliating.

[2] Eden Musée: a collection of wax figures of celebrated persons, opened in 1884 and later moved to Coney Island.

watch out. I'll have this house painted red, white, and blue next summer and see if that'll make his Dutch nose turn up any higher."

And then Anthony Rockwall, who never cared for bells, went to the door of his library and shouted "Mike!" in the same voice that had once chipped off pieces of the welkin[3] on the Kansas prairies.

"Tell my son," said Anthony to the answering menial, "to come in here before he leaves the house."

When young Rockwall entered the library the old man laid aside his newspaper, looked at him with a kindly grimness on his big, smooth, ruddy countenance, rumpled his mop of white hair with one hand and rattled the keys in his pocket with the other.

"Richard," said Anthony Rockwall, "what do you pay for the soap that you use?"

Richard, only six months home from college, was startled a little. He had not yet taken the measure of this sire of his, who was as full of unexpectednesses as a girl at her first party.

"Six dollars a dozen, I think, dad."

"And your clothes?"

"I suppose about sixty dollars, as a rule."

"You're a gentleman," said Anthony, decidedly. "I've heard of these young bloods spending twenty-four dollars a dozen for soap, and going over the hundred mark for clothes. You've got as much money to waste as any of 'em, and yet you stick to what's decent and moderate. Now I use the old Eureka—not only for sentiment, but it's the purest soap made. Whenever you pay more than ten cents a cake for soap you buy bad perfumes and labels. But fifty cents is doing very well for a young man in your generation, position and condition. As I said, you're a gentleman. They say it takes three generations to make one. They're off. Money'll do it as slick as soap grease. It's made you one. By hokey! it's almost made one of me. I'm nearly as impolite and disagreeable and ill-mannered as these two old Knickerbocker gents on each side of me that can't sleep of nights because I bought in between 'em."

"There are some things that money can't accomplish," remarked young Rockwall, rather gloomily.

"Now, don't say that," said old Anthony, shocked. "I bet my money on money every time. I've been through the encyclopaedia down to Y looking for something you can't buy with it; and I expect to have to take up the

[3] Welkin: sky.

appendix next week. I'm for money against the field. Tell me something money won't buy."

"For one thing," answered Richard rankling a little, "it won't buy one into the exclusive circles of society."

"Oho! won't it?" thundered the champion of the root of evil. "You tell me where your exclusive circles would be if the first Astor hadn't had the money to pay for his steerage passage over?"

Richard sighed.

"And that's what I was coming to," said the old man, less boisterously. "That's why I asked you to come in. There's something going wrong with you, boy. I've been noticing it for two weeks. Out with it. I guess I could lay my hands on eleven millions within twenty-four hours, besides the real estate. If it's your liver, there's the *Rambler* down in the bay, coaled, and ready to steam down to the Bahamas in two days."

"Not a bad guess, dad; you haven't missed it far."

"Ah," said Anthony, keenly; "what's her name?"

Richard began to walk up and down the library floor. There was enough comradeship and sympathy in this crude old father of his to draw his confidence.

"Why don't you ask her?" demanded old Anthony. "She'll jump at you. You've got the money and the looks, and you're a decent boy. Your hands are clean. You've got no Eureka soap on 'em. You've been to college, but she'll overlook that."

"I haven't had a chance," said Richard.

"Make one," said Anthony. "Take her for a walk in the park, or a straw ride, or walk home with her from church. Chance! Pshaw!"

"You don't know the social mill, dad. She's part of the stream that turns it. Every hour and minute of her time is arranged for days in advance. I must have that girl, dad, or this town is a blackjack swamp forevermore. And I can't write it—I can't do that."

"Tut!" said the old man. "Do you mean to tell me that with all the money I've got you can't get an hour or two of a girl's time for yourself?"

"I've put it off too late. She's going to sail for Europe at noonday after tomorrow for a two years' stay. I'm to see her alone tomorrow evening for a few minutes. She's at Larchmont now at her aunt's. I can't go there. But I'm allowed to meet her with a cab at the Grand Central Station tomorrow evening at the 8:30 train. We drive down Broadway to Wallack's at a gallop, where her mother and a box party will be waiting for us in the lobby.

Do you think she would listen to a declaration from me during the six or eight minutes under those circumstances? No. And what chance would I have in the theater or afterward? None. No, dad, this is one tangle that your money can't unravel. We can't buy one minute of time with cash; if we could, rich people would live longer. There's no hope of getting a talk with Miss Lantry before she sails."

"All right, Richard, my boy," said old Anthony, cheerfully. "You may run along down to your club now. I'm glad it isn't your liver. But don't forget to burn a few punk sticks in the joss house to the great god Mazuma[4] from time to time. You say money won't buy time? Well, of course, you can't order eternity wrapped up and delivered at your residence for a price, but I've seen Father Time get pretty bad stone bruises on his heels when he walked through the gold diggings."

That night came Aunt Ellen, gentle, sentimental, wrinkled, sighing, oppressed by wealth, in to brother Anthony at his evening paper, and began discourse on the subject of lovers' woes.

"He told me all about it," said brother Anthony, yawning. "I told him my bank account was at his service. And then he began to knock money. Said money couldn't help. Said the rules of society couldn't be bucked for a yard by a team of ten-millionaires."

"Oh, Anthony," sighed Aunt Ellen, "I wish you would not think so much of money. Wealth is nothing where a true affection is concerned. Love is all-powerful. If he only had spoken earlier! She could not have refused our Richard. But now I fear it is too late. He will have no opportunity to address her. All your gold cannot bring happiness to your son."

At eight o'clock the next evening Aunt Ellen took a quaint old gold ring from a moth-eaten case and gave it to Richard.

"Wear it tonight, nephew," she begged. "Your mother gave it to me. Good luck in love she said it brought. She asked me to give it to you when you had found the one you loved."

Young Rockwall took the ring reverently and tried it on his smallest finger. It slipped as far as the second joint and stopped. He took it off and stuffed it into his vest pocket, after the manner of man. And then he phoned for his cab.

At the station he captured Miss Lantry out of the gabbing mob at eight thirty-two.

"We mustn't keep mamma and the others waiting," she said.

---

[4] Punk sticks . . . the great god Mazuma: Mr. Rockwall is really saying "don't forget to burn incense in the temple to the great god 'money.'"

"To Wallack's Theater as fast as you can drive!" said Richard loyally.

They whirled up Forty-second to Broadway, and then down the white-starred lane that leads from the soft meadows of sunset to the rocky hills of morning.

At Thirty-fourth Street young Richard quickly thrust up the trap and ordered the cabman to stop.

"I've dropped a ring," he apologized, as he climbed out. "It was my mother's, and I'd hate to lose it. I won't detain you a minute—I saw where it fell."

In less than a minute he was back in the cab with the ring.

But within that minute a crosstown car had stopped directly in front of the cab. The cabman tried to pass to the left, but a heavy express wagon cut him off. He tried the right, and had to back away from a furniture van that had no business to be there. He tried to back out, but dropped his reins and swore dutifully. He was blockaded in a tangled mess of vehicles and horses.

One of those street blockades had occurred that sometimes tie up commerce and movement quite suddenly in the big city.

"Why don't you drive on?" said Miss Lantry, impatiently. "We'll be late."

Richard stood up in the cab and looked around. He saw a congested flood of wagons, trucks, cabs, vans and streetcars filling the vast space where Broadway, Sixth Avenue and Thirty-fourth Street cross one another as a twenty-six inch maiden fills her twenty-two inch girdle. And still from all the cross streets they were hurrying and rattling toward the converging point at full speed, and hurling themselves into the struggled mass, locking wheels and adding their drivers' imprecations to the clamor. The entire traffic of Manhattan seemed to have jammed itself around them. The oldest New Yorker among the thousands of spectators that lined the sidewalks had not witnessed a street blockade of the proportions of this one.

"I'm very sorry," said Richard, as he resumed his seat, "but it looks as if we are stuck. They won't get this jumble loosened up in an hour. It was my fault. If I hadn't dropped the ring we—"

"Let me see the ring," said Miss Lantry. "Now that it can't be helped, I don't care. I think theaters are stupid anyway."

At eleven o'clock that night somebody tapped lightly on Anthony Rockwall's door.

"Come in," shouted Anthony, who was in a red dressing-gown, reading a book of piratical adventures.

Somebody was Aunt Ellen, looking like a gray-haired angel that had been left on earth by mistake.

"They're engaged, Anthony," she said, softly. "She has promised to marry our Richard. On their way to the theater there was a street blockade, and it was two hours before their cab could get out of it.

"And oh, brother Anthony, don't ever boast of the power of money again. A little emblem of true love—a little ring that symbolized unending and unmercenary affection—was the cause of our Richard finding his happiness. He dropped it in the street, and got out to recover it. And before they could continue the blockade occurred. He spoke to his love and won her there while the cab was hemmed in. Money is dross compared with true love, Anthony."

"All right," said old Anthony. "I'm glad the boy has got what he wanted. I told him I wouldn't spare any expense in the matter if—"

"But, brother Anthony, what good could your money have done?"

"Sister," said Anthony Rockwall. "I've got my pirate in a devil of a scrape. His ship has just been scuttled, and he's too good a judge of the value of money to let drown. I wish you would let me go on with this chapter."

The story should end here. I wish it would as heartily as you who read it wish it did. But we must go to the bottom of the well for truth.

The next day a person with red hands and a blue polka-dot necktie, who called himself Kelly, called at Anthony Rockwall's house, and was at once received in the library.

"Well," said Anthony, reaching for his checkbook, "it was a good bilin' of soap. Let's see—you had $5,000 in cash."

"I paid out $300 more of my own," said Kelly. "I had to go a little above the estimate. I got the express wagons and cabs mostly for $5; but the trucks and two-horse teams mostly raised me to $10. The motormen wanted $10 and some of the loaded teams $20. The cops struck me hardest —$50 I paid two, and the rest $20 and $25. But didn't it work beautiful, Mr. Rockwall? I'm glad William A. Brady[5] wasn't onto that little outdoor vehicle mob scene. I wouldn't want William to break his heart with jealousy. And never a rehearsal, either! It was two hours before a snake could get below Greeley's statue."

"Thirteen hundred—there you are, Kelly," said Anthony, tearing off

[5] William A. Brady: noted theatrical manager and producer.

a check. "Your thousand, and the $300 you were out. You don't despise money, do you, Kelly?"

"Me?" said Kelly. "I can lick the man that invented poverty."

Anthony called Kelly when he was at the door.

"You didn't notice," said he, "anywhere in the tie-up, a kind of a fat boy without any clothes on shooting arrows around with a bow, did you?"

"Why, no," said Kelly, mystified. "I didn't. If he was like you say, maybe the cops pinched him before I got there."

"I thought the little rascal wouldn't be on hand," chuckled Anthony. "Good-by, Kelly."

STUDY QUESTIONS:

1. What does the title of this story mean?

2. Anthony Rockwall (notice his name) is a rather crude character, judged by most standards of taste and good manners. What are his redeeming features? Are you sympathetic with him at all? Does he seem true-to-life or is he a mere caricature of the self-made successful business man?

3. In what terms does Anthony assess his son's character? Is the reader willing to accept Anthony's judgment that Richard is a "gentleman"?

4. Like the Damon Runyon story, this one pretends to be tough-minded, and yet there is a good deal of sentimentality. Point out examples of both these characteristics.

5. The technique of narration in this story is unusual. It cannot rightly be called a first-person story, and yet the author or some kind of narrator seems very close to the reader. How would you describe O. Henry's method?

6. Do you approve the "surprise ending" of this story? Why or why not? Did you see it coming?